A collecti...
the worl...

International bestselling author

DIANA PALMER

has appeared on the New York Times *and* USA Today *bestseller lists, has written more than 130 books and sold more than 30 million copies of her novels.*

"Diana Palmer's storytelling shines."
—*Romantic Times*

"Ms Palmer brings Texas vibrantly alive through a memorable pair of lovers and a sizzling passionate intensity."
—*Romantic Times*

Available in the

Queens of Romance

collection

17th March 2006

7th April 2006

21st April 2006

5th May 2006

Collect all 4 superb books!

DIANA PALMER

Tycoon Lovers

Containing

Maggie's Dad
Matt Caldwell: Texas Tycoon

DID YOU PURCHASE THIS BOOK WITHOUT A COVER?
If you did, you should be aware it is **stolen property** as it was
reported *unsold and destroyed* by a retailer. Neither the author nor
the publisher has received any payment for this book.

All the characters in this book have no existence outside the
imagination of the author, and have no relation whatsoever to anyone
bearing the same name or names. They are not even distantly inspired
by any individual known or unknown to the author, and all the
incidents are pure invention.

All Rights Reserved including the right of reproduction in whole or
in part in any form. This edition is published by arrangement with
Harlequin Enterprises II B.V. The text of this publication or any part
thereof may not be reproduced or transmitted in any form or by any
means, electronic or mechanical, including photocopying, recording,
storage in an information retrieval system, or otherwise, without the
written permission of the publisher.

This book is sold subject to the condition that it shall not, by way of
trade or otherwise, be lent, resold, hired out or otherwise circulated
without the prior consent of the publisher in any form of binding or
cover other than that in which it is published and without a similar
condition including this condition being imposed on the subsequent
purchaser.

M&B™ and M&B™ with the Rose Device
are trademarks of the publisher.
Harlequin Mills & Boon Limited, Eton House,
18-24 Paradise Road,
Richmond, Surrey TW9 1SR

Tycoon Lovers © by Harlequin Books S.A. 2006

Matt Caldwell: Texas Tycoon and *Maggie's Dad* were
first published in Great Britain by Harlequin Mills & Boon
Limited in separate, single volumes.

Matt Caldwell: Texas Tycoon © Diana Palmer 2000
Maggie's Dad © Diana Palmer 1995

ISBN 0 263 85040 4

062-0506

Printed and bound in Spain
by Litografia Rosés S.A., Barcelona

Maggie's Dad

DIANA PALMER

Diana Palmer got her start in writing as a newspaper reporter and columnist, where she acquired many of her writing skills during her 16-year tenure. Once she wrote her first novel for Silhouette® Books in 1982, however, she never looked back. Diana has a gift for telling the most sensual tales with charm and humour. With over 40 million copies of her books in print, she is one of North America's most beloved authors and considered one of the top ten romance writers in America. Diana's hobbies include gardening, archaeology, anthropology, iguanas, astronomy and music. She has been married to James Kyle since 1972, and they have one son, Blayne Edward.

Diana Palmer has a fabulous new novel available in October 2006. Look for *Boss Man* in Silhouette Desire®.

Prologue

Rain was peppering down on the roof of the small house where Antonia Hayes's parents lived. It was a cold rain, and Antonia thought absently that she was very glad it was summer, because by early autumn that soft rain would turn to sleet or snow. Bighorn, a small town in northwestern Wyoming, was not an easy town to leave once it was covered in ice. It was rural and despite having three thousand inhabitants, it was too small to offer the transportation choices of a larger town. There wasn't even an airport; only a bus station. The railroad ran through it, too, but the trains were spaced too far apart to do Antonia much good.

She was about to begin her sophomore year in college, at the University of Arizona in Tucson, and

snow was fairly rare in that area in winter, except up
in the mountains. The desert floor had light dustings,
but not enough to inconvenience anyone. Besides,
Antonia—having just finished her first year there—
had been much too busy trying to pass her core
courses and heal a broken heart to notice the weather.
She did notice the summer heat now, though, she
mused, and thanked God for air-conditioning.

The clock sounded and Antonia turned, her short,
blond hair perky and her gray eyes full of sadness at
having to leave. But fall semester started in less than
a week, and she had to get back into her dorm room
and set up some sort of schedule. The only comforting
thing about going back was that George Rutherford's
stepdaughter, Barrie Bell, was her dorm roommate,
and they got along very well indeed.

"It's been lovely having you home for a whole
week," her mother, Jessica, said warmly. "I do wish
you could have stayed the whole summer...."

Her voice trailed off. She knew, as did Antonia and
Ben, her husband, why Antonia couldn't stay in Bighorn very long. It was a source of great sadness to all
of them, but they didn't discuss it. It still hurt too
much, and the gossip hadn't quite died down even
now, almost a year after the fact. George Rutherford's
abrupt move to France a few months after Antonia's
departure had quelled the remaining gossip.

Despite what had happened, George had remained
a good, true friend to Antonia and her family. Her
college education was his gift to her. She would pay

him back every penny, but right now the money was a godsend. Her parents were well regarded in the community, but lacked the resources to swing her tuition. George had been determined to help, and his kindness had cost them both so much.

But George's son, Dawson, and his stepdaughter, Barrie, had rallied around Antonia, defending her against the talk.

It was comforting to know that the two people closest to George didn't believe he was Antonia's sugar daddy. And of course, it helped that Dawson and Powell Long were rivals for a strip of land that separated their respective Bighorn ranch holdings. George had lived on his Bighorn ranch until the scandal. Then he went back to the family home he shared with Dawson in Sheridan, hoping to stem the gossip. It hadn't happened. So he'd moved to France, leaving more bitterness between Dawson and Powell Long. There was no love lost there.

But even with George out of the country, and despite the support of friends and family, Sally Long had done so much damage to Antonia's reputation that she was sure she would never be able to come home again.

Her mind came back to the remark her mother had just made. "I took classes this summer," she murmured absently. "I'm really sorry, but I thought I'd better, and some of my new friends went, too. It was nice, although I do miss being home. I miss both of you."

Jessica hugged her warmly. "And we miss you."

"That damn fool Sally Long," Ben muttered as he also hugged his daughter. "Spreading lies so that she could take Powell away from you. And that damn fool Powell Long, believing them, marrying her, and that baby born just seven months later…!"

Antonia's face went pale, but she smiled gamely. "Now, Dad," she said gently. "It's all over," she added with what she hoped was a reassuring smile, "they're married and they have a daughter now. I hope he's happy."

"Happy! After the way he treated you?"

Antonia closed her eyes. The memories were still painful. Powell had been the center of her life. She'd never imagined she could feel a love so sweeping, so powerful. He'd never said he loved her, but she'd been so sure that he did. Looking back now, though, she knew that he'd never really loved her. He *wanted* her, of course, but he had always drawn back. *We'll wait for marriage,* he'd said.

And waiting had been a good thing, considering how it had all turned out.

At the time, Antonia had wanted him desperately, but she'd put him off. Even now, over a year later, she could still see his black eyes and dark hair and thin, wide mouth. That image lived in her heart despite the fact that he'd canceled their wedding the day before it was to take place. People who hadn't been notified in time were sitting in the church, waiting. She shuddered faintly, remembering her humiliation.

Ben was still muttering about Sally.

"That's enough, Ben." Jessica laid a hand on her husband's arm. "It's water under the bridge," she said firmly. Her voice was so tranquil that it was hard for Antonia to believe that the scandal had caused her mother to have heart problems. She'd done very well, and Antonia had done everything possible to avoid the subject so that her mother wouldn't be upset.

"I wouldn't say Powell was happy," Ben continued, unabashed. "He's never home, and we never see him out with Sally in public. In fact, we never see Sally much at all. If she's happy, she doesn't let it show." He studied his daughter's pale, rigid face. "She called here one day before Easter and asked for your address. Did she write to you?"

"She wrote me."

"Well?" he prompted, curious.

"I returned the letter without opening it," Antonia said tightly, even paler now. She looked down at her shoes. "It's ancient history."

"She might have wanted to apologize," Jessica ventured.

Antonia sighed. "Some things go beyond apologies," she said quietly. "I loved him, you know," she added with a faint smile. "But he never loved me. If he did, he didn't say so in all the time we went together. He believed everything Sally told him. He just told me what he thought of me, called off the wedding and walked away. I had to leave. It hurt too much to stay." She could picture in her mind that long, straight back, the rigid set of his dark head. The pain had been terrible. It still was.

"As if George was that sort of man," Jessica said wearily. "He's the kindest man in the world, and he adores you."

"Not the sort to play around with young girls," Ben agreed. "Idiots, people who could believe that about him. I know that's why he moved out of the country, to spare us any more gossip."

"Since he and I are both gone, there's not much to gossip about," Antonia said pointedly. She smiled. "I'm working hard on my grades. I want George to be proud of me."

"He will be. And we already are," Jessica said warmly.

"Well, it serves Powell Long right that he ended up with that selfish little madam," Ben persisted irritably. "He thinks he's going to get rich by building up that cattle ranch, but he's just a dreamer," Ben scoffed. "His father was a gambler, and his mother was a doormat. Imagine him thinking he's got enough sense to make money with cattle!"

"He does seem to be making strides," his wife said gently. "He just bought a late-model truck, and they say a string of ranches up in Montana have given him a contract to supply them with seed bulls. You remember, Ben, when his big purebred Angus bull was in the paper, it won some national award."

"One bull doesn't make an empire," Ben scoffed.

Antonia felt the words all the way to her heart.

Powell had told her his dreams, and they'd planned that ranch together, discussed having the best Angus bulls in the territory...

"Could we not...talk about him, please?" Antonia asked finally. She forced a smile. "It still stings a little."

"Of course it does. We're sorry," Jessica said, her voice soft now. "Can you come home for Christmas?"

"I'll try. I really will."

She had one small suitcase. She carried it out to the car and hugged her mother one last time before she climbed in beside her father for the short ride to the bus depot downtown.

It was morning, but still sweltering hot. She got out of the car and picked up her suitcase as she waited on the sidewalk for her father to get her ticket from the office inside the little grocery store. There was a line. She'd just turned her attention back to the street when her eyes froze on an approaching pedestrian; a cold, quiet ghost from the past.

He was just as lean and dark as she remembered him. The suit was better than the ones he'd worn when they were dating, and he looked thinner. But it was the same Powell Long.

She'd lost everything to him except her pride. She still had it, and she forced her gray eyes up to his as he walked down the sidewalk with that slow, elegant stride that was particularly his own. She wouldn't let him see how badly his distrust had hurt her, even now.

His expression gave away nothing that he was feeling. He paused when he reached her, glancing at the suitcase.

"Well, well," he drawled, watching her face. "I heard you were here. The chicken came home to roost, did she?"

"I'm not here to stay," she replied coolly. "I've been to visit my parents. I'm on my way to Arizona, back to college."

"By bus?" he taunted. "Couldn't your sugar daddy afford a plane ticket? Or did he leave you high and dry when he hightailed it to France?"

She kicked him right in the shin. It wasn't premeditated, and he looked as shocked as she did when he bent to rub the painful spot where her shoe had landed.

"I wish I'd been wearing steel-toed combat boots like one of the girls in my dorm," she said hotly. "And if you ever so much as speak to me again, Powell Long, I'll break your leg the next time!"

She brushed past him and went into the depot.

Her father had just paid for the ticket when his attention was captured by the scene outside the depot. He started outside, but Antonia pushed him back into the building.

"We can wait for the bus in here, Dad," she said, her face still red and hot with anger.

He glanced past her to where Powell had straightened to send a speaking look toward the depot.

"Well, he seems to have learned to control that hot temper, at least. A year ago, he'd have been in here, right through the window," Ben Hayes remarked coldly. "I hope you crippled him."

She managed a wan smile. "No such luck. You can't wound something that ornery."

Powell had started back down the street, his back stiff with outrage.

"I hope Sally asks him how he hurt his leg," Antonia said under her breath.

"Here, girl, the bus is coming." He shepherded her outside, grateful that the ticket agent hadn't been paying attention and that none of the other passengers seemed interested in the byplay out the window. All they needed was some more gossip.

Antonia hugged her father before she climbed aboard. She wanted to look down the street, to see if Powell was limping. But even though the windows were dark, she wouldn't risk having him catch her watching him. She closed her eyes as the bus pulled away from the depot and spent the rest of the journey trying to forget the pain of seeing Powell Long again.

Chapter One

"That's very good, Martin, but you've left out something, haven't you?" Antonia prompted gently. She smiled, too, because Martin was very shy even for a nine-year-old and she didn't want to embarrass him in front of her other fourth graders. "The secret weapon the Greeks used in battle...a military formation?"

"Secret weapon," he murmured to himself. Then his dark eyes lit up and he grinned. "The phalanx!" he said at once.

"Yes," she replied. "Very good!"

He beamed, glancing smugly at his worst enemy in the second row over, who was hoping Martin would miss the question and looked very depressed indeed that he hadn't.

Antonia glanced at her watch. It was almost time to dismiss class for the day, and the week. Odd, she thought, how loose that watch was on her wrist.

"It's time to start putting things away," she told her students. "Jack, will you erase the board for me, please? And, Mary, please close the windows."

They rushed to obey, because they liked Miss Hayes. Mary glanced at her with a smile. Miss Hayes smiled back. She wasn't as pretty as Miss Bell down the hall, and she dressed in a very backward sort of way, always wearing suits or pantsuits, not miniskirts and frilly blouses. She had pretty long blond hair, though, when she took it out of that awful bun, and her gray eyes were like the December sky. It would be Christmas soon, and in a week they could all go home for the holidays. Mary wondered what Miss Hayes would do. She never went anywhere exciting for holidays. She never talked about her family, either. Maybe she didn't have one.

The bell rang and Antonia smiled and waved as her students marched out to waiting buses and cars. She tidied her desk with steady hands and wondered if her father would come for Christmas this year. It was very lonely for both of them since her mother's death last year. It had been hard, coping with the loss. It had been harder having to go home for the funeral. *He* was there. He, and his daughter. Antonia shivered just remembering the look on his dark, hard face. Powell hadn't softened even then, even when her mother was being buried. He still hated Antonia after nine years. She'd barely glanced at the sullen, dark-haired little girl by his side. The child was like a knife through her heart, a reminder that Powell had been sleeping with Sally even while he and Antonia were engaged to be married; because the little girl had been born only seven months after Powell married Sally. Antonia had glanced at them once, only once, to meet Powell's hateful stare. She hadn't looked toward the pew where they sat again.

Incredible how he could hate Antonia after marriage and a child, when everyone must have told him the truth ten times over in the years between. He was rich now. He had money and power and a fine home. His wife had died only three years after their wedding, and he hadn't remarried. Antonia imagined it was because he missed Sally so much. She didn't. She hated even the memory of her one-time best friend. Sally had cost her everything she loved, even her home, and she'd done it with deliberate lies. Of course, Powell had believed the lies. That was what had hurt most.

Antonia was over it now. It had been nine years. It hardly hurt at all, in fact, to remember him.

She blinked as someone knocked at the door, interrupting her train of thought. It was Barrie, her good friend and the Miss Bell of the miniskirt who taught math, grinning at her. Barrie was gorgeous. She was slender and had beautiful long legs. Her hair was almost black, like a wavy curtain down her back. She had green eyes with mischief in them, and a ready smile.

"You could stay with me at Christmas," Barrie invited merrily, her green eyes twinkling.

"In Sheridan?" she asked idly, because that was where Barrie's stepfather's home was, where George Rutherford and her stepbrother Dawson Rutherford, and Barrie and her late mother had lived before she left home and began teaching with Antonia in Tucson.

"No," Barrie said tightly. "Not ever there. In my apartment here in Tucson," she added, forcing a smile to her face. "I have four boyfriends. We can split them, two each. We'll have a merry whirl!"

Antonia only smiled. "I'm twenty-seven, too old for merry whirls, and my father will probably come here for Christmas. But thanks anyway."

"Honestly, Annie, you're not old, even if you do dress like someone's maiden aunt!" she said explosively. "Look at you!" she added, sweeping her hand toward the gray suit and white blouse that was indicative of the kind of clothes Antonia favored. "And your hair in that infernal bun…you look like a hold-over from the Victorians! You need to loose that glorious blond hair and put on a miniskirt and some makeup and look for a man before you get too old! And you need to eat! You're so thin that you're beginning to look like skin and bones."

Antonia knew that. She'd lost ten pounds in the past month or so and she'd finally gotten worried enough to make an appointment with her doctor. It was probably nothing, she thought, but it wouldn't hurt to check. Her iron might be low. She said as much to Barrie.

"That's true. You've had a hard year, what with losing your mother and then that awful scare with the student who brought his dad's pistol to school and held everybody at bay for an hour last month."

"Teaching is becoming the world's most danger-ous profession," Antonia agreed. She smiled sadly at Barrie. "Perhaps if we advertised it that way, we'd attract more brave souls to boost our numbers."

"That's an idea," came the dry agreement. "Want adventure? Try teaching! I can see the slogan now—"

"I'm going home," Antonia interrupted her.

"Ah, well, I suppose I will, too. I have a date to-night."

"Who is it this time?"

"Bob. He's nice and we get along well. But some-times I think I'm not cut out for a conventional sort of man. I need a wild-eyed artist or a composer or a drag racer."

Antonia chuckled. "I hope you find one."

"If I did, he'd probably have two wives hidden in another country or something. I do have the worst luck with men."

"It's your liberated image," Antonia said in a con-spiratorial tone. "You're devil-may-care and outra-geous. You scare off the most secure bachelors."

"Bunkum. If they were secure enough, they'd rush

to my door,'' Barrie informed her. ''I'm sure there's a man like that somewhere, just waiting for me.''

''I'm sure there is, too,'' her friend said kindly, and didn't for a minute let on that she thought there was already one waiting in Sheridan.

Beneath Barrie's outrageous persona, there was a sad and rather lonely woman. Barrie wasn't at all what she seemed. Barrie basically was afraid of men—especially her stepbrother, Dawson. He was George's blood son. Dear George, the elderly man who'd been another unfortunate victim of Sally Long's lies. The tales hadn't fazed Dawson, though, who not only knew better, but who was one of the coldest and most intimidating men Antonia had ever met where women were concerned. Barrie never mentioned Dawson, never talked about him. And if his name was mentioned, she changed the subject. It was common knowledge that they didn't get along. But secretly, Antonia thought there was something in their past, something that Barrie didn't talk about.

She never had, and now that poor George was dead and Dawson had inherited his estate, there was a bigger rift between them because a large interest in the cattle empire that Dawson inherited had been willed to Barrie.

''I've got to phone Dad and see what his plans are,'' Antonia murmured, dragging herself back from her memories.

''If he can't come down here, will you go home for Christmas?''

She shook her head. "I don't go home."

"Why not?" She grimaced. "Oh. Yes. I forget from time to time, because you never talk about him. I'm sorry. But it's been nine years. Surely he couldn't hold a grudge for that long? After all, he's the one who called off the wedding and married your best friend less than a month later. And she caused the scandal in the first place!"

"Yes, I know," Antonia replied.

"She must have loved him a lot to take such a risk. But he did eventually find out the truth," she added, tugging absently on a strand of her long, wavy black hair.

Antonia sighed. "Did he? I suppose someone told him, eventually. I don't imagine he believed it, though. Powell likes to see me as a villain."

"He loved you…"

"He wanted me," Antonia said bitterly. "At least that's what he said. I had no illusions about why he was marrying me. My father's name carried some weight in town, even though we were not rich. Powell needed the respectability. The love was all on my side. As it worked out, he got rich and had one child and a wife who was besotted with him. But from what I heard, he didn't love her either. Poor Sally," she added on a cold laugh, "all that plotting and lying, and when she got what she wanted, she was miserable."

"Good enough for her," Barrie said curtly. "She ruined your reputation and your parents'."

"And your stepfather's," she added, sadly. "He was very fond of my mother once."

Barrie smiled gently. "He was very fond of her up until the end. It was a blessing that he liked your father, and that they were friends. He was a good loser when she married your father. But he still cared for her, and that's why he did so much to help you."

"Right down to paying for my college education. That was the thing that led to all the trouble. Powell didn't like George at all. His father lost a lot of land to George—in fact, Dawson is still at odds with Powell over that land, even today, you know. He may live in Sheridan, but his ranch covers hundreds of acres right up against Powell's ranch, and I understand from Dad that he gives him fits at any opportunity."

"Dawson has never forgotten or forgiven the lies that Sally told about George," came the quiet reply. "He spoke to Sally, you know. He cornered her in town and gave her hell, with Powell standing right beside her."

"You never told me that," Antonia said on a quick breath.

"I didn't know how to," Barrie replied. "It hurts you just to have Powell's name mentioned."

"I suppose Powell stood up for her," she said, fishing.

"Even Powell is careful about how he deals with Dawson," Barrie reminded her. "Besides, what could he say? Sally told a lie and she was caught, red-handed. Too late to do you any good, they were already married by then."

"You mean, Powell's known the truth for nine years?" Antonia asked, aghast.

"I didn't say he *believed* Dawson," the other woman replied gently, averting her eyes.

"Oh. Yes. Well." Antonia fought for composure. How ridiculous, to think Powell would have accepted the word of his enemy. He and Dawson never had gotten along. She said it aloud even as she thought it.

"Is it likely that they would? My stepfather beat old man Long out of everything he owned in a poker game when they were both young men. The feud has gone on from there. Dawson's land borders Powell's, and they're both bent on empire building. If a tract comes up for sale, you can bet both men will be standing on the Realtor's doorstep trying to get first dibs on it. In fact, that's what they're butting heads about right now, that strip of land that separates their ranches that the widow Holton owns."

"They own the world between them," Antonia said pointedly.

"And they only want what joins theirs." Barrie chuckled. "Ah, well, it's no concern of ours. Not now. The less I see of my stepbrother, the happier I am."

Antonia, who'd only once seen the two of them together, had to agree. When Dawson was anywhere nearby, Barrie became another person, withdrawn and tense and almost comically clumsy.

"Well, if you change your mind about the holidays, my door is open," Barrie reminded her.

Antonia smiled warmly. "I'll remember. If Dad can't come down for the holidays, you could come home with me," she added.

Barrie shivered. "No, thanks! Bighorn is too close to Dawson for my taste."

"Dawson lives in Sheridan."

"Not all the time. Occasionally he stays at the ranch in Bighorn. He spends more and more time there these days." Her face went taut. "They say the widow Holton is the big attraction. Her husband had lots of land, and she hasn't decided who she'll sell it to."

A widow with land. Barrie had mentioned that Powell was also in competition with Dawson for the land. Or was it the widow? He was a widower, too, and a long-standing one. The thought made her sad.

"You need to eat more," Barrie remarked, concerned by her friend's appearance. "You're getting so thin, Annie, although it does give you a more fragile appearance. You have lovely bone structure. High cheekbones and good skin."

"I inherited the high cheekbones from a Cheyenne grandmother," she said, remembering sadly that Powell had called her Cheyenne as a nickname—actually meant as a corruption of "shy Ann," which she had been when they first started dating.

"Good blood," Barrie mused. "My ancestry is black Irish—from the Spanish armada that was blown off course to the coast of Ireland. Legend has it that one of my ancestors was a Spanish nobleman, who ended up married to a stepsister of an Irish lord.''

"What a story."

"Isn't it, though? I must pursue historical fiction one day—in between stuffing mathematical formulae into the heads of innocents.'' She glanced at her watch. "Heavens, I'll be late for my date with Bob! Gotta run. See you Monday!''

"Have fun."

"I always have fun. I wish you did, once in a while." She waved from the door, leaving behind a faint scent of perfume.

Antonia loaded her attaché case with papers to grade and her lesson plan for the following week, which badly needed updating. When her desk was cleared, she sent a last look around the classroom and went out the door.

Her small apartment overlooked "A" mountain in Tucson, so-called because of the giant letter "A" which was painted at its peak and was repainted year after year by University of Arizona students. The city was flat and only a small scattering of tall buildings located downtown made it seem like a city at all. It was widespread, sprawling, sandy and hot. Nothing like Bighorn, Wyoming, where Antonia's family had lived for three generations.

She remembered going back for her mother's funeral less than a year ago. Townspeople had come by the house to bring food for every meal, and to pay their respects. Antonia's mother had been well-loved in the community. Friends sent cartloads of the flowers she'd loved so much.

The day of the funeral had dawned bright and sunny, making silver lights in the light snow covering, and Antonia thought how her mother had loved spring. She wouldn't see another one now. Her heart, always fragile, had finally given out. At least, it had been a quick death. She'd died at the stove, in the very act of putting a cake into the oven.

The service was brief but poignant, and afterward Antonia and her father had gone home. The house was empty. Dawson Rutherford had stopped to offer George's sympathy, because George had been desperately ill, far too ill to fly across the ocean from France for the funeral. In fact, George had died less than two weeks later.

Dawson had volunteered to drive Barrie out to the airport to catch her plane back to Arizona, because Barrie had come to the funeral, of course. Antonia had noted even in her grief how it affected Barrie just to have to ride that short distance with her stepbrother.

Later, Antonia's father had gone to the bank and Antonia had been halfheartedly sorting her mother's unneeded clothes and putting them away when Mrs. Harper, who lived next door and was helping with the household chores, announced that Powell Long was at the door and wished to speak with her.

Having just suffered the three worst days of her life, she was in no condition to face him now.

"Tell Mr. Long that we have nothing to say to each other," Antonia had replied with cold pride.

"Guess he knows how it feels to lose somebody, since he lost Sally a few years back," Mrs. Harper reminded her, and then watched to see how the news would be received.

Antonia had known about Sally's death. She hadn't sent flowers or a card because it had happened only three years after Antonia had fled Bighorn, and the bitterness had still been eating at her.

"I'm sure he understands grief," was all Antonia said, and waited without saying another word until Mrs. Harper got the message and left.

She was back five minutes later with a card. "Said to give you this," she murmured, handing the business card to Antonia, "and said you should call him if you needed any sort of help."

Help. She took the card and, without even looking at it, deliberately tore it into eight equal parts. She handed them back to Mrs. Harper and turned again to her clothes sorting.

Mrs. Harper looked at the pieces of paper in her hand. "Enough said," she murmured, and left.

It was the last contact Antonia had had with Powell Long since her mother's death. She knew that he'd built up his purebred Angus ranch and made a success of it. But she didn't ask for personal information about him after that, despite the fact that he remained a bachelor. The past, as far as she was concerned, was truly dead. Now, she wondered vaguely why Powell had come to see her that day. Guilt, perhaps? Or something more? She'd never know.

She found a message on her answering machine and played it. Her father, as she'd feared, was suffering his usual bout of winter bronchitis and his doctor wouldn't let him go on an airplane for fear of what it would do to his sick lungs. And he didn't feel at all like a bus or train trip, so Antonia would have to come home for Christmas, he said, or they'd each have to spend it alone.

She sat down heavily on the floral couch she'd purchased at a local furniture store and sighed. She didn't want to go home. If she could have found a reasonable excuse, she wouldn't have, either. But it would be impossible to leave her father sick and alone on the holidays. With resolution, she picked up the telephone and booked a seat on the next commuter flight to Billings, where the nearest airport to Bighorn was located.

Because Wyoming was so sparsely populated, it was lacking in airports. Powell Long, now wealthy and able to afford all the advantages, had an airstrip on his ranch. But there was nowhere in Bighorn that a commercial aircraft, even a commuter one, could land. She knew that Barrie's stepbrother had a Learjet and that he had a landing strip near Bighorn on his

own ranch, but she would never have presumed on
Barrie's good nature to ask for that sort of favor. Besides, she admitted to herself, she was as intimidated
by Dawson Rutherford as Barrie was. He, like Powell,
was high-powered and aggressively masculine. Antonia felt much safer seated on an impersonal commuter plane.

She rented a car at the airport in Billings and, with
the easy acceptance of long distances on the road
from her time in Arizona, she set out for Bighorn.

The countryside was lovely. There were scattered
patches of snow, something she hadn't thought about
until it was too late and she'd already rented the car.
There was snow on the ground in Billings, quite a lot
of it, and although the roads were mostly clear, she
was afraid of icy patches. She'd get out, somehow,
she told herself. But she did wish that she'd had the
forethought to ask her father about the local weather
when she'd phoned to say she was leaving Tucson on
an early-morning flight. But he was hoarse and she
hadn't wanted to stress his voice too much. He knew
when she was due to arrive, though, and if she was
too long overdue, she was certain that he'd send
someone to meet her.

She gazed lovingly at the snow-covered mountains,
thinking of how she'd missed this country that was
home to her, home to generations of her family. There
was so much of her history locked into these sweeping mountain ranges and valleys, where lodgepole
pines stood like sentinels over shallow, wide blue

streams. The forests were green and majestic, looking much as they must have when mountain men plied their trade here. Arizona had her own forests, too, and mountains. But Wyoming was another world. It was home.

The going got rough the closer to home she went. It was just outside Bighorn that her car slipped on a wide patch of ice and almost went into a ditch. She knew all too well that if she had, there would have been no way she could get the vehicle out, because the slope was too deep.

With a prayer of thanks, she made it into the small town of Bighorn, past the Methodist Church and the post office and the meat locker building to her father's big Victorian house on a wide street off the main thoroughfare. She parked in the driveway under a huge cottonwood tree. How wonderful to be home for Christmas!

There was a decorated tree in the window, all aglow with the lights and ornaments that had been painstakingly purchased over a period of years. She looked at one, a crystal deer, and remembered painfully that Powell had given it to her the Christmas they'd become engaged. She'd thought of smashing it after his desertion, but she couldn't bring herself to do it. The tiny thing was so beautiful, so fragile; like their destroyed relationship. So long ago.

Her father came to the door in a bathrobe and pajamas, sniffling.

He hugged her warmly. "I'm so glad you came,

girl," he said hoarsely, and coughed a little. "I'm much better, but the damn doctor wouldn't let me fly!"

"And rightly so," she replied. "You don't need pneumonia!"

He grinned at her. "I reckon not. Can you stay until New Year's?"

She shook her head. "I'm sorry. I have to go back the day after Christmas." She didn't mention her upcoming doctor's appointment. There was no need to worry him.

"Well, you'll be here for a week, anyway. We won't get to go out much, I'm afraid, but we can keep each other company, can't we?"

"Yes, we can."

"Dawson said he might come by one evening," he added surprisingly. "He's just back from Europe, some convention or other he said he couldn't miss."

"At least he never believed the gossip about George and me," she said wistfully.

"Why, he knew his father too well," he replied simply.

"George was a wonderful man. No wonder you and he were friends for so long."

"I miss him. I miss your mother, too, God rest her soul. She was the most important person in my life, next to you."

"You're the most important person in mine," she agreed, smiling. "It's good to be home!"

"Still enjoy teaching?"

"More than ever," she told him warmly.

"There's some good schools here," he remarked. "They're always short of teachers. And two of them are expecting babies any day. They'll have problems getting supply teachers in for that short little period." He eyed her. "You wouldn't consider…?"

"I like Tucson," she said firmly.

"The hell you do," he muttered. "It's Powell, isn't it? Damn fool, listening to that scatterbrained woman in the first place! Well, he paid for it. She made his life hell."

"Would you like some coffee?" she asked, changing the subject.

"Oh, I suppose so. And some soup. There's some canned that Mrs. Harper made for me."

"Does she still live next door?"

"She does," he murmured with a wicked smile, "and she's a widow herself. No need to ask why she brought the soup, is there?"

"I like Mrs. Harper," she said with a grin. "She and mother were good friends, and she's like family already. Just in case you wondered what I thought," she added.

"It's only been a year, girl," he said, and his eyes were sad.

"Mother loved you too much to want you to go through life alone," she said. "She wouldn't want you to grieve forever."

He shrugged. "I'll grieve as long as I please."

"Suit yourself. I'll change clothes and then I'll see about the soup and coffee."

"How's Barrie?" her father asked when Antonia came out of her bedroom dressed in jeans and a white sweatshirt with golden sequined bells and red ribbon on it.

"She's just fine. Spunky as ever."

"Why didn't you bring her with you?"

"Because she's juggling four boyfriends," she said, chuckling as she went about warming soup.

"Dawson won't wait forever."

She glanced at him. "Is that what you think, too? She won't talk about him."

"He won't talk about her, either."

"What's this rumor about him and the widow Holton?"

He sat down in a chair at the table with a painful breath. "The widow Holton is redheaded and vivacious and a man-killer," he said. "She's after Dawson. And Powell Long. And any other man with money and a passable face."

"I see."

"You don't remember her, do you? Came here before you went off to college, but she and her husband traveled a lot. She was some sort of actress. She's been home more since he died."

"What does she do?"

"For a living, you mean?" He chuckled and had

to fight back a cough. "She's living on her inheritance. Doesn't have to do anything, lucky girl."

"I wouldn't want to do nothing," Antonia remarked thoughtfully. "I like teaching. It's more than just a job."

"Some women aren't made for purposeful employment."

"I guess not."

She finished heating the soup and poured the coffee she'd made. They ate in silence.

"I wish your mother was here," he said.

She smiled sadly. "So do I."

"Well, we'll make the most of what we have and thank God for it."

She nodded. "We have more than some people do."

He smiled, seeing her mother's face in her own. "And a lot more than most," he added. "I'm glad you came home for Christmas."

"So am I. Eat your soup." She poured him some more, and thought that she was going to make this Christmas as happy for him as she could.

Chapter Two

Dawson Rutherford was tall, lean and drop-dead gorgeous with blond, wavy hair and eyes that seemed to pierce skin. Even if he hadn't been so handsome, his physical presence was more than enough to make him attractive, added to a deep voice that had the smoothness of velvet, even in anger. But he was as icy a man as she'd ever known, especially with women. At his father's funeral, she'd actually seen him back away from a beautiful woman to avoid being touched. Odd, that, when she knew for a fact that he'd been quite a rounder with women in his checkered past.

If Antonia hadn't given her heart to Powell Long so many years before, she wouldn't have minded setting her cap at Dawson, intimidating though he was. But he was plainly meant for another type of woman altogether. Barrie, perhaps.

It was Christmas Eve, and he'd stopped by with a pipe for her father. Antonia walked him out a few minutes later.

"Shame on you," she muttered, pausing on the porch.

Dawson's green eyes twinkled. "He'll get over the bronchitis. Besides, you know he won't quit smoking, whether or not I give him a new pipe. You've tried and I've tried for years to break him. The best we can do is make him smoke it outdoors."

"I know that," she agreed, and smiled. "Well, it was a nice gesture."

"Want to see what he gave me?" he asked, and produced a smooth silver lighter with inlaid turquoise.

"I didn't know you smoked," she observed.

"I don't."

Her eyes widened.

"I did, just briefly, smoke cigars." He corrected himself. "I gave it up months ago. He doesn't know, so don't tell him."

"I won't. But good for you!" she said approvingly.

He shrugged. "I don't know any smokers who don't want to quit." His eyes narrowed, and he watched her without blinking. "Except one, maybe."

She knew he was talking about Powell, who always had smoked cigars, and presumably still did. Her face began to close up. "Don't say it."

"I won't. You look tortured."

"It was nine years ago."

"Somebody should have shot him for the way he treated you," he replied. "I've never liked him, but that didn't win him any points with me. I loved my father. It was a low thing, for Sally to make him out a foolish old man with a lust for young girls."

"She wanted Powell."

His eyes narrowed. "She got him. But he made her pay for it, let me tell you. She took to alcohol because he left her alone so much, and from all accounts, he hated their daughter."

"But why?" Antonia asked, shocked. "Powell loved children, surely…!"

"Sally trapped him with the child," he replied. "Except for that, he'd have left her. Don't you think he knew what a stupid thing he'd done? He knew the truth, almost from the day he married Sally."

"But he stayed with her."

"He had to. He was trying to build a ranch out of nothing, and this is a small town. How would it look for a man to walk out on a pregnant woman, or on his own newborn daughter?" He pursed his lips. "He hates you, you know," he added surprisingly. "He hates you for not making him listen, for running. He blames his misery on you."

"He's your worst enemy, so how do you know so much?" she retorted.

"I have spies." He sighed. "He can't admit that the worst mistake was his own, that he wouldn't believe Sally capable of such underhanded lies. It wasn't until he married her that he realized how she'd conned him.'' He shrugged. ''She wasn't a bad woman, really. She was in love and she couldn't bear losing him, even to you. Love does crazy things to people.''

''She destroyed my reputation, and your father's, and made it impossible for me to live here,'' Antonia said without pity. ''She was my enemy, and he still is. Don't think I'm harboring any tender feelings for him. I'd cut his throat given the slightest opportunity.''

His eyebrows levered up. Antonia was a gentle soul herself for the most part, despite an occasional outburst of temper and a keen wit that surprised people. She hadn't ever seemed vindictive, but she harbored a long-standing grudge against her former best friend, Sally. He couldn't really blame her.

He fingered the lighter her father had given him. ''How's Barrie?'' he asked with deliberate carelessness.

''Fending off suitors,'' she said with a grin, her soft gray eyes twinkling. ''She was juggling four of them when I left.''

He laughed coldly. ''Why doesn't that surprise me? One man was never enough for her, even when she was a teenager.''

She was curious about his antagonism toward Barrie. It seemed out of place. ''Why do you hate her so?'' she asked bluntly.

He looked surprised. "I don't…hate her," he said. "I'm disappointed at the way she behaves, that's all."

"She isn't promiscuous," she said, defending her colleague. "She may act that way, but it's only an act. Don't you know that?"

He looked at the lighter, frowning slightly. "Maybe I know more than you think," he said curtly. His eyes came up. "Maybe you're the one wearing blinders."

"Maybe you're seeing what you want to see," she replied gently.

He pocketed the lighter with a curt gesture. "I'd better go. I've got a deal cooking. I don't want the client to get cold feet."

"Thanks for coming to see Dad. You cheered him up."

"He's my friend." He smiled. "So are you, even when you stick your nose in where you shouldn't."

"Barrie's my friend."

"Well, she's not mine," he said flatly. "Merry Christmas, Annie."

"You, too," she replied with a warm smile. He was kind, in his way. She liked him, but she felt sorry for Barrie. He was a heartbreaker. And unless she missed her guess, Barrie was in love with him. His feelings were much less readable.

After he left, she went back to join her father in the kitchen, where he was fixing hot chocolate in a double boiler. He glanced over his shoulder.

"Did he leave?"

"Yes. Can I help?"

He shook his head. He poured hot chocolate into two mugs and nodded for her to take one while he put the boiler in water to soak.

"He gave me a pipe," he told her when they were seated at the small kitchen table, sipping the hot liquid. He grinned. "Didn't have the heart to tell him that I've finally given it up."

"Dad!" She reached across and patted his hand. "Oh, that's great news!"

He chuckled. "Figured you'd like it. Maybe I won't have so much trouble with my lungs from now on."

"Speaking of lungs," she said, "you gave Dawson a lighter. Guess what he's just given up, and didn't have the heart to tell you?"

He burst out laughing. "Well, maybe he can use it to light fires under his beef cattle when he throws barbecues out on the Rutherford spread."

"What a good idea! I'll suggest it to him the next time we see him."

"I wouldn't hold my breath," he replied. "He travels a lot these days. I hardly ever see him." He lifted his eyes to hers. "Powell came by last week."

Her heart fluttered, but her face was very composed. "Did he? Why?"

"Heard I was sick and came to check on me. Wanted to know where you were."

Her frozen expression grew darker. "Did he?"

"I told him you didn't know about the bronchitis and that he should mind his own business."

"I see."

He sipped hot chocolate and put the mug down with a thud. "Had his daughter with him. Quiet, sullen little thing. She never moved a muscle the whole time, just sat and glared. She's her mother all over."

Antonia was dying inside. She stared into her hot chocolate. That woman's child, here, in her home! She could hardly bear the thought. It was like a violation to have Powell come here with that child.

"You're upset," he said ruefully. "I guessed you would be, but I thought you'd better know. He said he'd be back to check on me after Christmas. Wouldn't want him to just show up without my telling you he was expected sooner or later. Not that I invited him," he added curtly. "Surprised me, too, that he'd come to see about me. Of course, he was fond of your mother. It hurt him that the scandal upset her so much and caused her to have that first heart attack. Anyway, he's taken it upon himself to be my guardian angel. Even sent the doctor when I first got sick, conspired with Mrs. Harper next door to look after me." He sounded disgusted, but he smiled, too.

"That was nice of him," she said, although Powell's actions surprised her. "But thanks for warning me." She forced a smile to her lips. "I'll arrange to do something in the kitchen if he turns up."

"It's been nine years," he reminded her.

"And you think I should have forgotten." She nodded. "You forgive people, Dad. I used to, before all this. Perhaps I should be more charitable, but I can't be. He and Sally made my life hell." She stopped, dragging in a long breath.

"No other suitors, in all that time," he remarked. "No social life, no dating. Girl, you're going to die an old maid, with no kids of your own, no husband, no real security."

"I enjoy my own company," she said lightly. "And I don't want a child." That was a lie, but only a partial one. The children she had wanted were Powell's, no one else's.

Christmas Day passed uneventfully, except for the meager gifts she and her father exchanged and their shared memories of her late mother to keep them company.

The next day, she was packed and dressed for travel in a rose knit suit, her hair carefully coiffed, her long legs in hose and low-heeled shoes on her feet. Her burgundy velvet, full-length coat was slung over one arm, its dark lining gleaming in the overhead light, as she put her suitcase down and went to find her father to say goodbye.

Voices from the living room caught her attention and she moved in that direction. But at the doorway, she froze in place, and in time. That deep, gravelly voice was as familiar as her own, despite the many years since she'd last heard it. And then a tall, lean man turned, and cast narrow black eyes on her face. *Powell!*

She lifted her face slowly, not allowing a hint of emotion to show either in her posture or her eyes. She simply looked at him, reconciling this man in his thirties with the man who'd wanted to marry her. The memories were unfavorable, because he was definitely showing his age, in the new lines beside his mouth and eyes, in the silver that showed at his temples.

He was doing his share of looking, too. The girl he'd jilted was no longer visible in this quiet, conservatively dressed woman with her hair in a bun. She looked schoolmarmish, and he was surprised that the sight of her was still like a knife through the heart, after all these years. He'd been curious about her. He'd wanted to see her again, God knew why. Maybe because she refused to see him at her mother's funeral. Now here she was, and he wasn't sure he was glad. The sight of her touched something sensitive that he'd buried inside himself.

Antonia was the first to look away. The intensity of his gaze had left her shaking inside, but that reaction was quickly hidden. It would never do to show any weakness to him. "Sorry," she told her father. "I didn't realize you had company. If you'll come and see me off, I'll be on my way."

Her father looked uncomfortable. "Powell came by to see how I was doing."

"You're leaving so soon?" Powell asked, addressing her directly for the first time in so many long years.

"I have to report back to work earlier than the students," she said, pleased that her voice was steady and cool.

"Oh, yes. You teach, don't you?"

She couldn't quite meet his eyes. Her gaze fell somewhere between his aggressive chin and his thin but sensuous mouth, below that straight, arrogant nose and the high cheekbones of his lean face. He wasn't handsome, but five minutes after they met him, most women were enchanted with him. He had an intangible something, authority perhaps, in the sureness of his movements, even in the way he held his head. He was overwhelming.

"I teach," she agreed. Her eyes hadn't quite met his. She turned to her father. "Dad?"

He excused himself and came forward to hug her. "Be careful. Phone when you get there, to let me know that you made it all right, will you? It's been snowing again."

"I'll be fine. I have a phone in the car, if I get stuck."

"You're driving to Arizona, in this weather?" Powell interrupted.

"I've been driving in this weather most of my adult life," she informed him.

"You were terrified of slick roads when you were in your teens," he recalled solemnly.

She smiled coldly at him. "I'm not a teenager now."

The way she looked at him spoke volumes about her feelings. He didn't avert his gaze, but his eyes were dark and quiet, full of secrets and seething accusation.

"Sally left a letter for you," he said unexpectedly. "I never got around to posting it. Over the years, I'd forgotten about it."

Her chest rose in a quick, angry breath. It reminded her of the letter that Sally had sent soon after Antonia had left town, the one she'd returned unopened. "Another one?" she asked in a frozen tone. "Well, I want nothing from your late wife, not even a letter."

He bristled. "She was your friend once," he reminded her curtly.

"She was my enemy." She corrected him. "She ruined my reputation and all but killed my mother! Do you really believe I'd want any reminder of what she did?"

He didn't seem to move for a minute. His face hardened. "She did nothing to hurt you deliberately," he said tersely.

"Really? Will her good intentions bring back George Rutherford or my mother?" she demanded hotly, because George himself had died so soon after her mother had. "Will it erase all the gossip?"

He turned away and bent his head to light a cigar, apparently unconcerned. Antonia fought for control.

Her hands were icy cold as she picked up her suitcase and winced at her father's worried expression.

"I'll phone you, Dad. Please take care of yourself," she added.

"You're upset," he said distractedly. "Wait a bit…"

"I won't…I can't…" Her voice choked on the words and she averted her eyes from the long back of the man who was turned away from her. "Bye, Dad!"

She was out the door in a flash, and within two minutes she'd loaded her cases into the trunk and opened the door. But before she could get in, Powell was towering over her.

"Get a grip on yourself," he said curtly, forcing her to look at him. "You won't do your father any favors by landing in a ditch in the middle of nowhere!"

She shivered at the nearness of him and deliberately backed away, her gray eyes wide, accusing.

"You look so fragile," he said, as if the words were torn from him. "Don't you eat?"

"I eat enough." She steadied herself on the door. "Goodbye."

His big hand settled beside hers on the top of the door. "Why was Dawson Rutherford here a couple of nights ago?"

The question was totally unexpected. "Is that your business?" she asked coldly.

He smiled mockingly. "It could be. Rutherford's

father ruined mine, or didn't you remember? I don't
intend to let his son ruin me.''

"My father and George Rutherford were friends.''

"And you and George were lovers.''

She didn't say a word. She only looked at him.
"You know the truth,'' she said wearily. "You just
don't want to believe it.''

"George paid your way through college,'' he reminded her.

"Yes, he did,'' she agreed, smiling. "And I rewarded him by graduating with honors, second in my
graduating class. He was a philanthropist and the best
friend my family ever had. I miss him.''

"He was a rich old man with designs on you,
whether you'll admit it or not!''

She searched his deep-set black eyes. They never
smiled. He was a hard man, and the passing years had
only added to his sarcastic, harsh demeanor. He'd
grown up dirt poor, looked down on in the community
because of his parents. He'd struggled to get where
he was, and she knew how difficult it had been. But
his hard life had warped his perception of people. He
looked for the worst, always. She'd known that,
somehow, even when they were first engaged. And
now, he was the sum of all the tragedies of his life.
She'd loved him so much, she'd tried to make up to
him for the love he'd never had, the life his circumstances had denied him. But even while he was courting her, he'd loved Sally most. He'd told Antonia so,

when he broke their engagement and called her a streetwalker with a price tag....

"You're staring," he said irritably, ramming his hands into the pockets of his dark slacks.

"I was remembering the way you used to be, Powell," she said simply. "You haven't changed. You're still the loner who never trusted anyone, who always expected people to do their worst."

"I believed in you," he replied solemnly.

She smiled. "No, you didn't. If you had, you wouldn't have swallowed Sally's lies without—"

"Damn you!"

He had her by both shoulders, his cigar suddenly lying in the snow at their feet. He practically shook her, and she winced, because she was willow thin and he had the grip of a horseman, developed after long years of back-breaking ranch work long before he ever made any money at it.

She looked up into blazing eyes and wondered dimly why she wasn't afraid of him. He looked intimidating with his black eyes flashing and his straight black hair falling down over his thick eyebrows.

"Sally didn't lie!" he reiterated. "That's the hell of it, Antonia! She was gentle and kind and she never lied to me. She cried when you had to leave town over what happened. She cried for weeks and weeks, because she hadn't wanted to tell me what she knew about you and George! She couldn't bear to see you two-timing me!"

She pulled away from him with a strength she

didn't know she had. "She deserved to cry!" she said through her teeth.

He called her a name that made her flush. She only smiled.

"Sticks and stones, Powell," she said in a steady, if husky, tone. "But if you say that again, you'll get the same thing I gave you the summer after I started college."

He remembered very well the feel of her shoe on his shin. Even through his anger, he had to stifle a mental smile at the memory. Antonia had always had spirit. But he remembered other things, too; like her refusal to talk to him after her mother's death, when he'd offered help. Sally had been long dead by then, but Antonia wouldn't let him close enough to see if she still felt anything for him. She wouldn't even now, and it caused him to lose his temper when he'd never meant to. She wouldn't let go of the past. She wouldn't give him a chance to find out if there was anything left of what they'd felt for each other. She didn't care.

The knowledge infuriated him.

"Now, if you're quite through insulting me, I have to go home," she added firmly.

"I could have helped, when your mother died," he said curtly. "You wouldn't even see me!"

He sounded as if her refusal to speak to him had hurt. What a joke *that* would be. She didn't look at him again. "I had nothing to say to you, and Dad and

I didn't want your help. One way or another, you had enough help from us to build your fortune."

He scowled. "What the hell do you mean by that?"

She did look up, then, with a mocking little smile. "Have you forgotten already? Now if you'll excuse me…?"

He didn't move. His big fists clenched by his sides as she just walked around him to get into the car.

She started it, put it into reverse, and pointedly didn't look at him again, not even when she was driving off down the street toward the main highway. And if her hands shook, he couldn't see them.

He stood watching, his boots absorbing the freezing cold of the snow around them, snowflakes touching the wide brim of his creamy Stetson. He had no idea what she'd meant with that last crack. It made him furious that he couldn't even get her to talk to him. Nine years. He'd smoldered for nine years with seething outrage and anger, and he couldn't get the chance to air it. He wanted a knock-down, drag-out argument with her, he wanted to get everything in the open. He wanted…second chances.

"Do you want some hot chocolate?" Ben Hayes called from the front door.

Powell didn't answer him for a minute. "No," he said in a subdued tone. "Thanks, but I'll pass."

Ben pulled his housecoat closer around him. "You can damn her until you die," he remarked quietly. "But it won't change one thing."

Powell turned and faced him with an expression that wasn't easily read. "Sally didn't lie," he said stubbornly. "I don't care what anyone says about it. Innocent people don't run, and they both did!"

Ben studied the tormented eyes in that lean face for a long moment. "You have to keep believing that, don't you," he asked coldly. "Because if you don't, you've got nothing at all to show for the past nine years. The hatred you've saved up for Antonia is all that's left of your life!"

Powell didn't say another word. He strode angrily back to his four-wheel-drive vehicle and climbed in under the wheel.

Chapter Three

Antonia made it back to Tucson without a hitch, although there had been one or two places along the snow-covered roads that gave her real problems. She was shaken, but it never affected her driving. Powell Long had destroyed enough of her life. She wasn't going to give him possession of one more minute of it, not even through hatred.

She kept busy for the remainder of her vacation and spent New Year's Eve by herself, with only a brief telephone call to her father for company. They didn't mention Powell.

Barrie stopped by on New Year's Day, wearing jeans and a sweatshirt and trying not to look interested in Dawson's visit to Antonia's father's house.

It was always the same, though. Whenever Antonia went to Wyoming, Barrie would wait patiently until her friend said something about Dawson. Then she pretended that she wasn't interested and changed the subject.

But this time, she didn't. She searched Antonia's eyes. "Does he...look well?" she asked.

"He's fine," Antonia replied honestly. "He's quit smoking, so that's good news."

"Did he mention the widow?"

Antonia smiled sympathetically and shook her head. "He doesn't have much to do with women, Barrie. In fact, Dad says they call him "the iceman" around Bighorn. They're still looking for a woman who can thaw him out."

"Dawson?" Barrie burst out. "But he's always had women hanging on him...!"

"Not these days. Apparently all he's interested in is making money."

Barrie looked shocked. "Since when?"

"I don't know. For the past few years at least," Antonia replied, frowning. "He's your stepbrother. You'd know more about that than I would. Wouldn't you?"

Barrie averted her eyes. "I don't see him. I don't go home."

"Yes, I know, but you must hear about him...."

"Only from you," the other woman said stiffly. "I don't...we don't have any mutual friends."

"Doesn't he ever come to see you?"

Barrie went pale. "He wouldn't." She bit off the words and forced a smile to her face. "We're poison to each other, didn't you know?" She looked at her watch. "I'm going to a dance. Want to come?"

Antonia shook her head. "Not me. I'm too tired. I'll see you back at work."

"Sure. You look worse than you did when you left. Did you see Powell?"

Antonia flinched.

"Sorry," came the instant reply. "Listen, don't tell me anything about Dawson even if I beg, and I swear I won't mention Powell again, okay? I'm really sorry. I suppose we both have wounds too raw to expose. See you!"

Barrie left, and Antonia quickly found something to do, so that she wouldn't have to think any more about Powell.

But, oh, it was hard. He'd literally jilted her the day before the wedding. The invitations had been sent out, the church booked, the minister ready to officiate at the ceremony. Antonia had a dress from Neiman Marcus, a heavenly creation that George had helped her buy—which had become part of the fiasco when she admitted it to Powell. And then, out of the blue, Sally had dropped her bombshell. She'd told Powell that George Rutherford was Antonia's sugar daddy and he was paying for her body. Everyone in Bighorn knew it. They probably did, Sally had worked hard enough spreading the rumor. The gossip alone was enough to send Powell crazy. He'd turned on Antonia in a rage and canceled the wedding. She didn't like remembering the things he'd said to her.

Some of the guests didn't get notified in time and came to the church, expecting a wedding. Antonia had had to face them and tell them the sad news. She had been publicly humiliated, and then there was the scandal that involved poor George. He'd had to move back to Sheridan, to the headquarters ranch of the Rutherford chain. It had been a shame, because the Rutherford Bighorn Ranch had been his favorite. He'd escaped a lot of the censure and spared Antonia some of it, especially when he exiled himself to France. But Antonia and her father and mother got the whole measure of local outrage. Denial did no good, because how could she defend herself against knowing glances and haughty treatment? The gossip had hurt her mother most, leaving her virtually isolated from most of the people who knew her. She'd had a mild heart attack from the treatment of her only child as a social outcast. Ironically that had seemed to bring some people to their senses, and the pressure had been eased a bit. But Antonia had left town very quickly, to spare her mother any more torment, taking her broken heart with her.

Perhaps if Powell had thought it through, if the wedding hadn't been so near, the ending might have been different. He'd always been quick-tempered and impulsive. He hated being talked about. Antonia knew that at least three people had talked to him about the rumors, and one of them was the very minister who was to marry them. Later, Antonia had discovered that they were all friends of Sally and her family.

To be fair to Powell, he'd had more than his share of public scandal. His father had been a hopeless gambler who lost everything his mother slaved at housekeeping jobs to provide. In the end he'd killed himself when he incurred a debt he knew he'd never be able to repay. Powell had watched his mother be torn apart by the gossip, and eventually her heart wore out and she simply didn't wake up one morning.

Antonia had comforted Powell. She'd gone to the funeral home with him and held his hand all through the ordeal of giving up the mother he'd loved. Perhaps grief had challenged his reason, because although he'd hidden it well, the loss had destroyed something in him. He'd never quite recovered from it, and Sally had been behind the scenes, offering even more comfort when Antonia wasn't around. Susceptible to her soft voice, perhaps he'd listened when he shouldn't have. But in the end, he'd believed Sally, and he'd married her. He'd never said he loved Antonia, and it had been just after they'd become engaged that Powell had managed several loans, on the strength of her father's excellent references, to get the property he'd inherited out of hock. He was just beginning to make it pay when he'd called off the wedding.

The pain was like a knife. She'd loved Powell more than her own life. She'd been devastated by his de-

fection. The only consolation she'd had was that
she'd put him off physically until after the wedding.
Perhaps that had hurt him most, thinking that she was
sleeping with poor old George when she wouldn't go
to bed with him. Who knew? She couldn't go back
and do things differently. She could only go forward.
But the future looked much more bleak than the past.

She went back to work in the new year, apparently
rested and unworried. But the doctor's appointment
was still looming at the end of her first week after
she started teaching.

She didn't expect them to find anything. She was
run-down and tired all the time, and she'd lost a lot
of weight. Probably she needed vitamins or iron tab-
lets or something. When the doctor ordered a blood
test, a complete blood count, she went along to the
lab and sat patiently while they worked her in and
took blood for testing. Then she went home with no
particular intuition about what was about to happen.

It was early Monday morning when she had a call
at work from the doctor's office. They asked her to
come in immediately.

She was too frightened to ask why. She left her
class to the sympathetic vice principal and went right
over to Dr. Claridge's office.

They didn't make her wait, either. She was hustled
right in, no appointment, no nothing.

He got up when she entered his office and shook
hands. ''Sit down, Antonia. I've got the lab results

from your blood test. We have to make some quick decisions.''

''Quick…?'' Her heart was beating wildly. She could barely breathe. She was aware of her cold hands gripping her purse like a life raft. ''What sort of decisions?''

He leaned forward, his forearms on his legs. ''Antonia, we've known each other for several years. This isn't an easy thing to tell someone.'' He grimaced. ''My dear, you've got leukemia.''

She stared at him without comprehension. *Leukemia.* Wasn't that cancer? Wasn't it…fatal?

Her breath suspended in midair. ''I'm…going to die?'' she asked in a hoarse whisper.

''No,'' he replied. ''Your condition is treatable. You can undergo a program of chemotherapy and radiation, which will probably keep it in remission for some years.''

Remission. Probably. Radiation. Chemotherapy. Her aunt had died of cancer when Antonia was a little girl. She remembered with terror the therapy's effects on her aunt. Headaches, nausea…

She stood up. ''I can't think.''

Dr. Claridge stood up, too. He took her hands in his. ''Antonia, it isn't necessarily a death sentence. We can start treatment right away. We can buy time for you.''

She swallowed, closing her eyes. She'd been worried about her argument with Powell, about the anguish of the past, about Sally's cruelty and her own torment. And now she was going to die, and what did any of that matter?

She was going to die!

"I want...to think about it," she said huskily.

"Of course you do. But don't take too long, Antonia," he said gently. "All right?"

She managed to nod. She thanked him, followed the nurse out to reception, paid her bill, smiled at the girl and walked out. She didn't remember doing any of it. She drove back to her apartment, closed the door and collapsed right there on the floor in tears.

Leukemia. She had a deadly disease. She'd expected a future, and now, instead, there was going to be an ending. There would be no more Christmases with her father. She wouldn't marry and have children. It was all...over.

When the first of the shock passed, and she'd exhausted herself crying, she got up and made herself a cup of coffee. It was a mundane, ordinary thing to do. But now, even such a simple act had a poignancy. How many more cups would she have time to drink in what was left of her life?

She smiled at her own self-pity. That wasn't going to do her any good. She had to decide what to do. Did she want to prolong the agony, as her aunt had, until every penny of her medical insurance ran out, until she bankrupted herself and her father, put herself and him through the long drawn-out treatments when she might still lose the battle? What quality of life would she have if she suffered as her aunt had?

She had to think not what was best for her, but what was best for her father. She wasn't going to rush into treatment until she was certain that she had a chance of surviving. If she was only going to be able to keep it at bay for a few painful months, then she had some difficult decisions to make. If only she could think clearly! She was too shocked to be rational. She needed time. She needed peace.

Suddenly, she wanted to go home. She wanted to be with her father, at her home. She'd spent her life running away. Now, when things were so dire, it was time to face the past, to reconcile herself with it, and with the community that had unjustly judged her. There would be time left for that, to tie up all the loose ends, to come to grips with her own past.

Her old family doctor, Dr. Harris, was still in Bighorn. She'd get Dr. Claridge to send him her medical files and she'd go from there. Perhaps Dr. Harris might have some different ideas about how she could face the ordeal. If nothing could be done, then at least she could spend her remaining time with the only family she had left.

Once the decision was made, she acted on it at once. She turned in her resignation and told Barrie that her father needed her at home.

"You didn't say that when you first came back," Barrie said suspiciously.

"Because I was thinking about it," she lied. She smiled. "Barrie, he's so alone. And it's time I went back and faced my dragons. I've been running too long already.''

"But what will you do?" Barrie asked.

"I'll get a job as a relief teacher. Dad said that two of the elementary school teachers were expecting and they didn't know what they'd do for replacements. Bighorn isn't exactly Tucson, you know. It's not that easy to get teachers who are willing to live at the end of the world."

Barrie sighed. "You really have thought this out."

"Yes. I'll miss you. But maybe you'll come back one day," she added. "And fight your own dragons."

Barrie shivered. "Mine are too big to fight," she said with an enigmatic smile. "But I'll root for you. What can I help you do?"

"Pack," came the immediate reply.

As fate would have it, when she contacted her old school system in Bighorn, one of the pregnant teachers had just had to go into the hospital with toxemia and they needed a replacement desperately for a fourth-grade class. It was just what Antonia wanted, and she accepted gratefully. Best of all, there had been no discussion of the reason she'd left town in the first place. Some people would remember, but she had old friends there, too, friends who wouldn't hold grudges. Powell would be there. She refused to even entertain the idea that he had any place in her reasons for wanting to go home.

She arrived in Bighorn with mixed emotions. It

made her feel wonderful to see her father's delighted expression when he was told she was coming back there to live permanently. But she felt guilty, too, because he couldn't know the real reason for her return.

"We'll have plenty of time to visit, now," she said. "Arizona was too hot to suit me, anyway," she added mischievously.

"Well, if you like snow, you've certainly come home at a good time," he replied, grinning at the five feet or so that lay in drifts in the front yard.

Antonia spent the weekend unpacking and then went along to work the following Monday. She liked the principal, a young woman with very innovative ideas about education. She remembered two of her fellow teachers, who had been classmates of hers in high school, and neither of them seemed to have any misgivings about her return.

She liked her class, too. She spent the first day getting to know the children's names. But one of them hit her right in the heart. *Maggie Long.* It could have been a coincidence. But when she called the girl's name and a sullen face with blue eyes and short black hair looked up at her, she knew right away who it was. That was Sally's face, except for the glare. The glare was Powell all over again.

She lifted her chin and stared at the child. She passed over her and went on down the line until she reached Julie Ames. She smiled at Julie, who smiled back sweetly. She remembered Danny Ames from

school, too, and his redheaded daughter was just like
him. She'd have known Danny's little girl anywhere.

She pulled out her predecessor's lesson plan and
looked over it before she took the spelling book and
began making assignments.

"One other thing I'd like you to do for Friday is
write a one-page essay about yourselves," she added
with a smile. "So that I can learn something about
you, since I've come in the middle of the year instead
of the first."

Julie raised her hand. "Miss Hayes, Mrs. Donalds
always assigned one of us to be class monitor when
she was out of the room. Whoever she picked got to
do it for a week, and then someone else did. Are you
going to do that, too?"

"I think that's a good idea, Julie. You can be our
monitor for this week," she added pleasantly.

"Thanks, Miss Hayes!" Julie said enthusiastically.

Behind her, Maggie Long glared even more. The
child acted as if she hated Antonia, and for a minute,
Antonia wondered if she knew about the past. But,
then, how could she? She was being fanciful.

She dismissed the class at quitting time. It had been
nice to have her mind occupied, not to have to think
about herself. But with the end of the day came the
terror again. And she still hadn't talked to Dr. Harris.

She made an appointment to see him when she got
home, smiling at her father as she told him glibly that
it was only because she needed some vitamins.

Dr. Harris, however, was worried when she told him Dr. Claridge's diagnosis.

"You shouldn't wait," he said flatly. "It's always best to catch these things early. Come here, Antonia."

He examined her neck with skilled hands, his eyes on the wall behind her. "Swollen lymph nodes, all right. You've lost weight?" he asked as he took her pulse.

"Yes. I've been working rather hard," she said lamely.

"Sore throat?"

She hesitated and then nodded.

He let out a long sigh. "I'll have him fax me your medical records," he said. "There's a specialist in Sheridan who's done oncology," he added. "But you should go back to Tucson, Antonia."

"Tell me what to expect," she said instead.

He was reluctant, but when she insisted, he drew in a deep breath and told her.

She sat back in her chair, pale and restless.

"You can fight it," he persisted. "You can hold it at bay."

"For how long?"

"Some people have been in remission for twenty-five years."

She narrowed her eyes as she gazed at him. "But you don't really believe I'll have twenty-five years."

His jaw firmed. "Antonia, medical research is progressing at a good pace. There's always, always, the possibility that a cure will be discovered...."

She held up a hand. "I don't want to have to decide today," she said wearily. "I just need…a little time," she added with a pleading smile. "Just a little time."

He looked as if he were biting his tongue to keep from arguing with her. "All right. A little time," he said emphatically. "I'll look after you. Perhaps when you've considered the options, you'll go ahead with the treatment, and I'll do everything I can. But, Antonia," he added as he stood up to show her out, "there aren't too many miracles in this business where cancer is concerned. If you're going to fight, don't wait too long."

"I won't."

She shook hands and left the office. She felt more at peace with herself now than she could ever remember feeling. Somehow in the course of accepting the diagnosis, she'd accepted something much more. She was stronger now. She could face whatever she had to. She was so glad she'd come home. Fate had dealt her some severe blows, but being home helped her to withstand the worst of them. She had to believe that fate would be kinder to her now that she was home.

But if Fate had kind reasons for bringing her back to Bighorn, Maggie Long wasn't one of them. The girl was unruly, troublesome and refused to do her schoolwork at all.

By the end of the week, Antonia kept her after class and showed her the zero she'd earned for her nonattempt at the spelling test. There was another one looming, because Maggie hadn't done one word of the essay Antonia had assigned the class to write.

"If you want to repeat the fourth grade, Maggie, this is a good start," she said coolly. "If you won't do your schoolwork, you won't pass."

"Mrs. Donalds wasn't mean like you," the girl said snappily. "She never made us write stupid essays, and if there was a test, she always helped me study for it."

"I have thirty-five students in this class," Antonia heard herself saying. "Presumably you were placed in this grade because you were capable of doing the work."

"I could do it if I wanted to," Maggie said. "I just don't want to. And you can't make me, either!"

"I can fail you," came the terse, uncompromising reply. "And I will, if you keep this up. You have one last chance to escape a second zero for the essay you haven't done. You can do it over the weekend and turn it in Monday."

"My daddy's coming home today," she said haughtily. "I'm going to tell him that you're mean to me, and he'll come and cuss you out, you just wait and see!"

"What will he see, Maggie?" she asked flatly. "What does it say about you if you won't do your work?"

"I'm not lazy!"

"Then do your assignment."

"Julie didn't do all of her test, and you didn't give her a zero!"

"Julie doesn't work as fast as some of the other students. I take that into account," Antonia explained.

"You like Julie," she accused. "That's why you never act mean to her! I'll bet you wouldn't give her a zero if she didn't do her homework!"

"This has nothing to do with your ability to do your work," Antonia interrupted. "And I'm not going to argue with you. Either do your homework or don't do it. Now run along."

Maggie gave her a furious glare. She jerked up her books and stomped out of the room, turning at the door. "You wait until I tell my daddy! He'll get you fired!"

Antonia lifted an eyebrow. "It will take more than your father to do that, Maggie."

The girl jerked open the door. "I hate you! I wish you'd never come here!" she yelled.

She ran down the hallway and Antonia sat back and caught her breath. The child was a holy terror. She was a little surprised that she was so unlike her mother in that one way. Sally, for all her lying, had been sweet in the fourth grade, an amiable child, not a horror like Maggie.

Sally. The name hurt. Just the name. Antonia had come home to exorcise her ghosts and she wasn't doing a very good job of it. Maggie was making her life miserable. Perhaps Powell would interfere, at least enough to get his daughter to do her homework.

She hated that it had come to this, but she hadn't anticipated the emotions Maggie's presence in her class had unleashed. She was sorry that she couldn't like the child. She wondered if anyone did. She seemed little more than a sullen, resentful brat.

Powell probably adored the child and gave her everything she wanted. But she did ride the bus to and from school and more often than not, she showed up for class in torn jeans and stained sweatshirts. Was that deliberate, and didn't her father notice that some of her things weren't clean? Surely he had a housekeeper or someone to take care of such things.

She knew that Maggie had been staying with Julie this week, because Julie had told her so. The little redheaded Ames girl was the sweetest child Antonia had ever known, and she adored her. She really was the image of her father, who'd been in Antonia's group of friends in school here in Bighorn. She'd told Julie that, and the child had been a minor celebrity for a day. It gave her something to be proud of, that her father and her teacher had been friends.

Maggie hadn't liked that. She'd given Julie the cold shoulder yesterday and they weren't speaking today. Antonia wondered at their friendship, because Julie was outgoing and generous, compassionate and kind...all the things Maggie wasn't. Probably the child saw qualities in Julie that she didn't have and liked her for them. But what in the world did Julie see in Maggie?

Chapter Four

Powell Long came home from his cattle-buying trip worn out from the long hours on the plane and the hectic pace of visiting three ranches in three states in less than a week. He could have purchased his stud cattle after watching a video, and he sometimes did if he knew the seller, but he was looking over new territory for his stock additions, and he wanted to inspect the cattle in person before he made the acquisition. It was a good thing he had, because one of the ranches had forwarded a video that must have been of someone else's cattle. When he toured the ranch, he found the stock were underfed, and some were lacking even the basic requirements for good breeding bulls.

Still, it had been a profitable trip. He'd saved several thousand dollars on seed bulls simply by going to visit the ranchers in person. Now he was home again and he didn't want to be. His house, like his life, was full of painful memories. Here was where Sally had lived, where her daughter still lived. He couldn't look at Maggie without seeing her mother. He bought the child expensive toys, whatever her heart desired. But he couldn't give her love. He didn't think he had it in him to love the product of such a painful marriage. Sally had cost him the thing he'd loved most in all the world. She'd cost him Antonia.

Maggie was sitting alone in the living room with a book. She looked up when he entered the room with eyes that avoided his almost at once.

"Did you bring me something?" she asked dully. He always did. It was just one more way of making her feel that she was important to him, but she knew better. He didn't even know what she liked, or he wouldn't bring her silly stuffed toys and dolls. She liked to read, but he hadn't noticed. She also liked nature films and natural history. He never brought her those sort of things. He didn't even know who she was.

"I brought you a new Barbie," he said. "It's in my suitcase."

"Thanks," she said.

Never a smile. Never laughter. She was a little old woman in a child's body, and looking at her made him feel guilty.

"Where's Mrs. Bates?" he asked uncomfortably.

"In the kitchen cooking," she said.

"How's school?"

She closed the book. "We got a new teacher last week. She doesn't like me," she said. "She's mean to me."

His eyebrows lifted. "Why?"

She shrugged, her thin shoulders rising and falling restlessly. "I don't know. She likes everybody else. She glares at me all the time. She gave me a zero on my test, and she's going to give me another zero on my homework. She says I'm going to fail fourth grade."

He was shocked. Maggie had always made good grades. One thing she did seem to have was a keen intelligence, even if her perpetual frown and introverted nature made her enemies. She had no close friends, except for Julie. He'd left Maggie with Julie's family, in fact, last week. They were always willing to keep her while he was out of town.

He glowered at her. "Why are you here instead of at Julie's house?" he demanded suddenly.

"I told them you were coming home and I wanted to be here, because you always bring me something," she said.

"Oh."

She didn't add that Julie's friendship with the detestable Miss Hayes had caused friction, or that they'd had a terrible argument just this morning, precipitating Maggie's return home. Fortunately Mrs. Bates was working in the house, so that it was possible for her to be here.

"The new teacher likes Julie," she said sullenly. "But she hates me. She says I'm lazy and stupid."

"She says what?"

That was the first time her father had ever reacted in such a way, as if it really mattered to him that someone didn't like her. She looked at him fully, seeing that angry flash of his black eyes that always meant trouble for somebody. Her father intimidated her. But, then, he intimidated everyone. He didn't like most people any more than she did. He was introverted himself, and he had a bad temper and a sarcastic manner when people irritated him. Over the years Maggie had discovered that she could threaten people with her father, and it always worked.

Locally he was a legend. Most of her teachers had bent over backward to avoid confrontations with him. Maggie learned quickly that she didn't have to study very hard to make good grades. Not that she wasn't bright; she simply didn't try, because she didn't need to. She smiled. Wouldn't it be nice, she thought, if she could use him against Miss Hayes?

"She says I'm lazy and stupid," she repeated.

"What's this teacher's name?" he asked coldly.

"Miss Hayes."

He was very still. "Antonia Hayes?" he asked curtly.

"I don't know her first name. She came on account

of Mrs. Donalds quit,'' she said. ''Mrs. Donalds was my friend. I miss her.''

''When did Miss Hayes get here?'' he asked, surprised that he'd heard nothing about her returning to Bighorn. Of course, he'd been out of town for a week, too.

''I told you—last week. They said she used to live here.'' She studied his hard face. It looked dangerous. ''Did she, Daddy?''

''Yes,'' he said with icy contempt. ''Yes, she used to live here. Well, we'll see how Miss Hayes handles herself with another adult,'' he added.

He went to the telephone and picked it up and dialed the principal of the Bighorn Elementary School.

Mrs. Jameson was surprised to hear Powell Long on the other end of the phone. She'd never known him to interfere in school matters before, even when Maggie was up to her teeth in trouble with another student.

''I want to know why you permit an educator to tell a child that she's lazy and stupid,'' he demanded.

There was a long pause. ''I beg your pardon?'' the principal asked, shocked.

''Maggie said that Miss Hayes told her she was lazy and stupid,'' he said shortly. ''I want that teacher talked to, and talked to hard. I don't want to have to come up there myself. Is that clear?''

Mrs. Jameson knew Powell Long. She was intimidated enough to agree that she'd speak to Antonia on Monday.

And she did. Reluctantly.

* * *

"I had a call from Maggie Long's father Friday afternoon after you left," Mrs. Jameson told Antonia, who was sitting rigidly in front of her in her office. "I don't believe for a minute that you'd deliberately make insulting remarks to that child. Heaven knows, every teacher in this school except Mrs. Donalds has had trouble with her, although Mr. Long has never interfered. It's puzzling that he would intervene, and that Maggie would say such things about you."

"I haven't called her stupid," Antonia said evenly. "I have told her that if she refuses to do her homework and write down the answers on tests, she will be given a failing grade. I've never made a policy of giving undeserved marks, or playing favorites."

"I'm sure you haven't," Mrs. Jameson replied. "Your record in Tucson is spotless. I even spoke to your principal there, who was devastated to have lost you. He speaks very highly of your intelligence and your competence."

"I'm glad. But I don't know what to do about Maggie," she continued. "She doesn't like me. I'm sorry about that, but I don't know what I can do to change her attitude. If she could only be helpful like her friend Julie," she added. "Julie is a first-rate little student."

"Everyone loves Julie," the principal agreed. She folded her hands on her desk. "I have to ask you this, Antonia. Is it possible that unconsciously you might be taking out old hurts on Maggie? I know that you were engaged to her father once.... It's a small town," she added apologetically when Antonia stiffened, "and one does hear gossip. I also know that Maggie's mother broke you up and spread some pretty terrible lies about you in the community."

"There are people who still don't think they were lies," Antonia replied tersely. "My mother eventually died because of the pressure and censure the community put on her because of them."

"I'm sorry. I didn't know that."

"She had a bad heart. I left town, to keep the talk to a minimum, but she never got over it." Her head lifted, and she forced a weak smile. "I was innocent of everything I had been accused of, but I paid the price anyway."

Mrs. Jameson looked torn. "I shouldn't have brought it up."

"Yes, you should," Antonia replied. "You had the right to know if I was deliberately persecuting a student. I despised Sally for what she did to me, and I have no more love for Maggie's father than for his late wife. But I hope I'm not such a bad person that I'd try to make a child suffer for something she didn't do."

"Nor do I believe you would, consciously," Mrs. Jameson replied. "It's a touchy situation, though. Mr. Long has enormous influence in the community. He's quite wealthy and his temper is legendary in these parts. He has no compunction about making scenes in public, and he threatened to come up here himself if this situation isn't resolved." She laughed a little unsteadily. "Miss Hayes, I'm forty-five years old. I've worked hard all my life to achieve my present status. It would be very difficult for me to find another job if I lost this one, and I have an invalid husband to support and a son in college. I plead with you not to put my job in jeopardy."

"I never would do that," Antonia promised. "I'd quit before I'd see an innocent person hurt by my actions. But Mr. Long is very wrong about the way his daughter is being treated. In fact, she's causing the problems. She refuses to do her work and she knows that I can't force her to."

"She certainly does. She'll go to her father, and he'll light fires under members of the school board. I believe at least one of them owes him money, in fact, and the other three are afraid of him." She cleared her throat. "I'll tell you flat that I'm afraid of him, myself."

"No freedom of speech in these parts, I gather?"

"If your freedom impinges on his prejudices, no, there isn't," Mrs. Jameson agreed. "He's something of a tyrant in his way. We certainly can't fault him for being concerned about his child, though."

"No," Antonia agreed. She sighed. Her own circumstances were tenuous, to say the least. She had her own problems and fear gnawed at her all the time. She wasn't afraid of Powell Long, though. She was more afraid of what lay ahead for her.

"You will try...about Maggie?" Mrs. Jameson added.

Antonia smiled. "Certainly I will. But may I come to you if the problem doesn't resolve itself and ask for help?"

"If there's any to give, you may." She grimaced. "I have my own doubts about Maggie's cooperation. And we both have a lot to lose if her father isn't happy."

"Do you want me to pass her anyway?" Antonia asked. "To give her grades she hasn't earned, because her father might be upset if she fails?"

Mrs. Jameson flushed. "I can't tell you to do that, Miss Hayes. We're supposed to educate children, not pass them through favoritism."

"I know that," Antonia said.

"But you wondered if I did," came the dry reply. "Yes, I do. But I'm job scared. When you're my age, Miss Hayes," she added gently, "I can guarantee that you will be, too."

Antonia's eyes were steady and sad. She knew that she might never have the problem; she might not live long enough to have it. She thanked Mrs. Jameson and went back to her classroom, morose and dejected.

Maggie watched her as she sat down at her desk and instructed the class to proceed with their English lesson. She didn't look very happy. Her father must have shaken them up, Maggie thought victoriously. Well, she wasn't going to do that homework or do those tests. And when she failed, her father would come storming up here, because he never doubted his little girl's word. He'd have Miss Hayes on the run in no time. Then maybe Mrs. Donalds would have her baby and come back, and everything would be all right again. She glared at Julie, who just ignored her. She was sick of Julie, kissing up to Miss Hayes. Julie was a real sap. Maggie wasn't sure who she disliked more—Julie or Miss Hayes.

There was one nice touch, and that was that Miss Hayes coolly told her that she had until Friday to turn in her essay and the other homework that Antonia had assigned the class.

The next four days went by, and Antonia asked for homework papers to be turned in that she'd assigned at the beginning of the week. Maggie didn't turn hers in.

"You'll get a zero if you don't have all of it by this afternoon, including the essay you owe me," Antonia told her, dreading the confrontation she knew was coming, despite all her hopes. She'd done her best to treat Maggie just like the other students, but the girl challenged her at every turn.

"No, I won't," Maggie said with a surly smile. "If you give me a zero, I'll tell my daddy, and he'll come up here."

Antonia studied the sullen little face. "And you think that frightens me?"

"Everybody's scared of my dad," she returned proudly.

"Well, I'm not," Antonia said coldly. "Your father can come up here if he likes and I'll tell him the same thing I've told you. If you don't do the work, you don't pass. And there's nothing he can do about it."

"Oh, really?"

Antonia nodded. "Oh, really. And if you don't turn in your homework by the time the final bell sounds, you'll find out."

"So will you," Maggie replied.

Antonia refused to argue with the child. But when the end of class came and Maggie didn't turn the homework in, she put a zero neatly next to the child's name.

"Take this paper home, please," she told the child, handing her a note with her grade on it.

Maggie took it. She smiled. And she didn't say a word as she went out the door. Miss Hayes didn't know that her daddy was picking her up today. But she was about to find out.

Antonia had chores to finish before she could go home. She didn't doubt that Powell would be along. But she wasn't going to back down. She had nothing to lose now. Even her job wasn't that important if it meant being blackmailed by a nine-year-old.

Sure enough, it was only minutes since class was dismissed and she was clearing her desk when she heard footsteps coming down the hall. Only a handful of teachers would still be in the building, but those particular steps were heavy and forceful, and she knew who they belonged to.

She turned as the door opened and a familiar tall figure came into the room with eyes as dark as death.

He didn't remove his hat, or exchange greetings. In his expensive suit and boots and Stetson, he looked very prosperous. But her eyes were seeing a younger man, a ragged and lonely young man who never fit in anywhere, who dreamed of not being poor. Sometimes she remembered that young man and loved him with a passion that even in dreams was overpowering.

"I've been expecting you," she said, putting the past away in the back drawers of her mind. "She did get a zero, and she deserved it. I gave her all week to produce her homework, and she didn't."

"Oh, hell, you don't have to pretend noble motives. I know why you're picking on the kid. Well, lay off Maggie," he said shortly. "You're here to teach, not to take out old grudges on my daughter."

She was sitting at her desk. She folded her hands together on its worn surface and simply stared at him, unblinking. "Your daughter is going to fail this grade," she said composedly. "She won't participate in class discussions, she won't do any homework, and she refuses to even attempt answers on pop tests. I'm frankly amazed that she's managed to get this far in school at all." She smiled coldly. "I understand from the principal, who is also intimidated by you, that you have the influence to get anyone fired who doesn't pass her.''

His face went rigid. ''I don't need to use any influence! She's a smart child.''

She opened her desk drawer, took out Maggie's last test paper and slid it across the desk to him. ''Really?'' she asked.

He moved into the classroom, to the desk. His lean, dark hand shot down to retrieve the paper. He looked at it with narrow, deep-set eyes, black eyes that were suddenly piercing on Antonia's face.

''She didn't write anything on this,'' he said.

She nodded, taking it back. ''She sat with her arms folded, giving me a haughty smile the whole time, and she didn't move a muscle for the full thirty minutes.''

''She hasn't acted that way before.''

''I wouldn't know. I'm new here.''

He stared at her angrily. ''And you don't like her.''

She searched his cold eyes. ''You really think I came all the way back to Wyoming to take out old resentments on Sally's daughter?'' she asked, and hated the guilt she felt when she asked the question. She knew she wasn't being fair to Maggie, but the very sight of the child was like torture.

''Sally's and mine,'' he reminded her, as if he knew how it hurt her to remember.

She felt sick to her stomach. ''Excuse me. Sally's and yours,'' she replied obligingly.

He nodded slowly. ''Yes, that's what really bothers

you, isn't it?'' he said, almost to himself. ''It's because she looks just like Sally.''

''She's her image,'' she agreed flatly.

''And you still hate her, after all this time.''

Her hands clenched together. She didn't drop her
gaze. ''We were talking about your daughter.''

''Maggie.''

''Yes.''

''You can't even bring yourself to say her name,
can you?'' He perched himself on the edge of her
desk. ''I thought teachers were supposed to be impartial, to teach regardless of personal feelings toward
their students.''

''We are.''

''You aren't doing it,'' he continued. He smiled,
but it wasn't the sort of smile that comforted. ''Let
me tell you something, Antonia. You eame home. But
this is *my* town. I own half of it, and I know everybody on the school board. If you want to stay here,
and teach here, you'd better be damn sure that you
maintain an impartial attitude toward all the students.''

''Especially toward your daughter?'' she asked.

He nodded. ''I see you understand.''

''I won't treat her unfairly, but I won't play favorites, either,'' she said icily. ''She's going to receive
no grades that she doesn't earn in my classroom. If
you want to get me fired, go ahead.''

''Oh, hell, I don't want your job,'' he said abruptly.
''It doesn't matter to me if you stay here with your

father. I don't even care why you suddenly came back. But I won't have my daughter persecuted for something that she didn't do! She has nothing to do with the past.''

"Nothing?" Her eyes glittered up into his. "Sally was pregnant with that child when you married her, and she was born seven months later," she said huskily, and the pain was a living, breathing thing. Even the threat of leukemia wasn't that bad. "You were sleeping with Sally while you were swearing eternal devotion to me!"

Antonia didn't have to be a math major to arrive at the difference. He'd married Sally less than a month after he broke up with Antonia, and Maggie was born seven months later. Which meant that Sally was pregnant when they married.

He took a slow, steady breath, but his eyes, his face, were terrible to see. He stared down at her as if he'd like to throw something.

Antonia averted her gaze to the desk, where her hands were so tightly clasped now that the knuckles were white. She relaxed them, so that he wouldn't notice how tense she was.

"I shouldn't have said that," she said after a minute. "I had no right. Your marriage was your own business, and so is your daughter. I won't be unkind to her. But I will expect her to do the same work I assign to the other students, and if she doesn't, she'll be graded accordingly."

He stood up and shoved his hands into his pockets.

The eyes that met hers were unreadable. "Maggie's paid a higher price than you know already," he said enigmatically. "I won't let you hurt her."

"I'm not in the habit of taking out my personal feelings on children, whatever you think of me."

"You're twenty-seven now," he said, surprising her. "Yet you're still unmarried. You have no children of your own."

She smiled evenly. "Yes. I had a lucky escape."

"And no inclination to find someone else? Make a life for yourself?"

"I have a life," she said, and the fear came up into her mouth as she realized that she might not have it for much longer.

"Do you?" he asked. "Your father will die one day. Then you'll be alone."

Her eyes, full of fear, fell to the desk again. "I've been alone for a long time," she said quietly. "It's something...one learns to live with."

He didn't speak. After a minute, she heard his voice, as if from a distance. "Why did you come back?"

"For my father."

"He's getting better day by day. He didn't need you."

She looked up, searching his face, seeing the young man she'd loved in his dark eyes, his sensuous mouth. "Maybe I needed someone," she said. She winced and dropped her eyes.

He laughed. It had an odd sound. "Just don't turn

your attention toward me, Antonia. You may need someone. I don't. Least of all you.''

Before she could say a word, he'd gone out the door, as quietly as he'd come in.

Maggie was waiting at the door when he walked in. He'd taken her home before he had his talk with Antonia.

"Did you see her? Did you tell her off?'' she asked excitedly. "I knew you'd show her who's boss!''

His eyes narrowed. She hadn't shown that much enthusiasm for anything in years. "What about that homework?''

She shrugged. "It was stupid stuff. She wanted us to write an essay about ourselves and do math problems and make up sentences to go with spelling words.''

He scowled. "You mean, you didn't do it—any of it?''

"You told her I didn't have to, didn't you?'' she countered.

He tossed his hat onto the side table in the hall and his eyes flashed at her. "Did you do any of the homework?''

"Well…no,'' she muttered. "It was stupid, I told you.''

"Damn it! You lied!''

She backed up. She didn't like the way he was looking at her. He frightened her when he looked that way. He made her feel guilty. She didn't lie as a rule, but this was different. Miss Hayes was hurting her, so didn't she have the right to hurt back?

"You'll do that homework, do you hear me?" he demanded. "And the next time you have a test, you won't sit through it with your arms folded. Is that clear?"

She compressed her lips. "Yes, Daddy."

"My God." He bit off the words, staring at her furiously. "You're just like your mother, aren't you? Well, this is going to stop right now. No more lies— ever!"

"But, Daddy, I don't lie…!"

He didn't listen. He just turned and walked away. Maggie stared after him with tears burning her eyes, her small fists clenched at her sides. *Just like her mother.* That's what Mrs. Bates said when she misbehaved. She knew that her father hadn't cared about her mother. Her mother had cried because of it, when she drank so much. She'd said that she told a lie and Powell had hated her for it. Did this mean that he hated Maggie, too?

She followed him out into the hall. "Daddy!" she cried.

"What?"

He turned, glaring at her.

"She doesn't like me!"

"Have you tried cooperating with her?" he replied coldly.

She shrugged, averting her eyes so that he wouldn't see the tears and the pain in them. She was used to hiding her hurts in this cold house. She went up the staircase to her room without saying anything else.

He watched her walk away with a sense of hopelessness. His daughter had used him to get back at her teacher, and he'd let her. He'd gone flaming over to the school and made all sorts of accusations and charges, and Antonia had been the innocent party. His daughter had used him to get back at her teacher, and he'd let her. He was furious at having been so gullible. It was because he didn't really know the child, he imagined. He spent as little time with her as possible, because she was a walking, talking reminder of his failed marriage.

Next time, he promised himself, he'd get his facts straight before he started attacking teachers. But he wasn't sorry about what he'd said to Antonia. Let her stew on those charges. Maybe it would intimidate her enough that she wouldn't deliberately hurt Maggie. He knew how she felt about Sally, he couldn't help but know. Her resentments were painfully visible in her thin face.

He wondered why she'd come back to haunt him. He'd almost pushed her to the back of his mind over the years. Almost. He'd gone to see her father finally to get news of her, because the loneliness he felt was eating into him like acid. He'd wondered, for one insane moment if there was any chance that they might recapture the magic they'd had together when she was eighteen.

But she'd quickly disabused him of any such fancies. Her attitude was cold and hard and uncaring. She seemed to have frozen over in the years she'd been away.

How could he blame her? All of Antonia's misfortunes could be laid at his door, because he was distrustful of people, because he'd jumped to conclusions, because he hadn't believed in Antonia's basic innocence and decency. One impulsive decision had cost him everything he held dear. He wondered sometimes how he could have been so stupid.

Like today when he'd let Maggie stampede him into attacking Antonia for something she hadn't done. It was just like old times. Sally's daughter was already a master manipulator, at age nine. And it seemed that he was just as impulsive and dim as he'd ever been. He hadn't really changed at all. He was just richer.

Meanwhile, there was Antonia's reappearance and her disturbing thinness and paleness. She looked unwell. He wondered absently if she'd had some bout with disease. Perhaps that was why she'd come home, and not because of her father at all. But, wouldn't a warm climate be the prescription for most illnesses that caused problems? Surely no doctor sent her into northern Wyoming in winter.

He had no answers for those questions, and it would do him well to stop asking them, he thought irritably. It was getting him nowhere. The past was dead. He had to let it go, before it destroyed his life all over again.

Chapter Five

Antonia didn't move for a long time after Powell left the classroom. She stared blindly at her clasped hands. Of course she knew that he didn't want her. Had she been unconsciously hoping for something different? And even if she had, she realized, there was no future at all in that sort of thinking.

She got up, cleared her desk, picked up her things and went home. She didn't have time to sit and groan, even silently. She had to use her time wisely. She had a decision to make.

While she cooked supper for her father and herself, she thought about everything she'd wanted to do that she'd never made time for. She hadn't traveled, which had been a very early dream. She hadn't been involved in church or community, she hadn't planned past the next day except to make up lesson plans for her classes. She'd more or less drifted along, assuming that she had forever. And now the line was drawn and she was close to walking across it.

Her deepest regret was losing Powell. Looking back, she wondered what might have happened if she'd challenged Sally, if she'd dared Powell to prove that she'd been two-timing him with her mother's old suitor. She'd only been eighteen, very much in love and trusting and full of dreams. It would have served her better to have been suspicious and hard-hearted, at least where Sally was concerned. She'd never believed that her best friend would stab her in the back. How silly of her not to realize that strongest friends make the best enemies; they always know where the weaknesses are hidden.

Antonia's weakness had been her own certainty that Powell loved her as much as she loved him, that nothing could separate them. She hadn't counted on Sally's ability as an actress.

Powell had never said that he loved Antonia. How strange, she thought, that she hadn't realized that until they'd gone their separate ways. Powell had been ardent, hungry for her, but never out of control. No wonder, she thought bitterly, since he'd obviously been sleeping with Sally the whole time. Why should he have been wild for any women when he was having one on the side?

He'd asked Antonia to marry him. Her parents had

been respected in the community, something his own parents hadn't been. He'd enjoyed being connected to Antonia's parents and enjoying the overflow of their acceptance by local people in the church and community. He'd spent as much time with them as he had with Antonia. And when he talked about building up his little cattle ranch that he'd inherited from his father, it had been her own father who'd advised him and opened doors for him so that he could get loans, financing. On the strength of his father's weakness for gambling, nobody would have loaned Powell the price of a theater ticket. But Antonia's father was a different proposition; he was an honest man with no visible vices.

Antonia had harbored no suspicions that an ambitious man might take advantage of an untried girl in his quest for wealth. Now, from her vantage point of many years, she could look back and see the calculation that had led to Powell's proposal of marriage. He hadn't wanted Antonia with any deathless passion. He'd wanted her father's influence. With it, he'd built a pitiful little fifty-acre ranch into a multimillion dollar enterprise of purebred cattle and land. Perhaps breaking the engagement was all part of his master plan, too. Once he'd had what he wanted from the engagement, he could marry the woman he really loved—*Sally.*

It wouldn't have surprised Antonia to discover that Sally had worked hand in glove with Powell to help him achieve his goals. The only odd thing was that he hadn't been happy with Sally, from all accounts, or she with him.

She wondered why she hadn't considered that angle all those years ago. Probably the heartbreak of her circumstances had blinded her to any deeper motives. Now it seemed futile and unreal. Powell was ancient history. She had to let go of the past. Somehow, she had to forgive and forget. It would be a pity to carry the hatred and resentment to her grave.

Grave. She stared into the pan that contained the stir-fry she was making for supper. She'd never thought about where she wanted to rest for eternity. She had insurance, still in effect, although it wasn't much. And she'd always thought that she'd rest beside her mother in the small Methodist church cemetery. Now she had to get those details finalized, just in case the treatment wasn't successful—if she decided to have it—and without her father knowing. He wasn't going to be told until the last possible minute.

She finished preparing supper and called her father to the table, careful to talk about mundane things and pretend to be happy at being home again.

But he wasn't fooled. His keen eyes probed her face. "Something's upset you. What is it?"

She grimaced. "Maggie Long," she said, sidestepping the real issue.

"I see. Just like her father when he was a kid, I hear," he added. "Little hellion, isn't she?"

"Only to me," Antonia mused. "She liked Mrs. Donalds."

"No wonder," he replied, finishing his coffee. "Mrs. Donalds was one of Sally's younger cousins. So Maggie was related to her. She petted the kid, gave her special favors, did everything but give her answers to tests. She was teacher's pet. First time any teacher treated her that way, so I guess it went to her head."

"How do you know?"

"It's a small town, girl," he reminded her with a chuckle. "I know everything." He stared at her levelly. "Even that Powell came to see you at school this afternoon. Gave you hell about the kid, didn't he?"

She shifted in her chair. "I won't give her special favors," she muttered. "I don't care if he does get me fired."

"He'll have a hard time doing that," her father said easily. "I have friends on the school board, too."

"Perhaps they could switch the girl to another class," she wondered aloud.

"It would cause gossip," Ben Hayes said. "There's been enough of that already. You just stick to your guns and don't give in. She'll come around eventually."

"I wouldn't bet on it," she said heavily. She ran a hand over her blond hair. "I'm tired," she added with a wan smile. "Do you mind if I go to bed early?"

"Of course not." He looked worried. "I thought

you went to see the doctor. Didn't he give you something to perk you up?"

"He said I need vitamins," she lied glibly. "I bought some, but they haven't had time to take effect. I need to eat more, too, he said."

He was still scowling. "Well, if you don't start getting better soon, you'd better go back and let him do some tests. It isn't natural for a woman your age to be so tired all the time."

Her heart skipped. Of course it wasn't, but she didn't want him to suspect that she was so ill.

"I'll do that," she assured him. She got up and collected the plates. "I'll just do these few dishes and then I'll leave you to your television."

"Oh, I hate that stuff," he said. "I'd much rather read in the evenings. I only keep the thing on for the noise."

She laughed. "I do the same thing in Tucson," she confessed. "It's company, anyway."

"Yes, but I'd much rather have you here," he confessed. "I'm glad you came home, Antonia. It's not so lonely now."

She had a twinge of conscience at the pleasure he betrayed. He'd lost her mother and now he was going to lose her. How would he cope, with no relatives left in the world? Her mother had been an only child, and her father's one sister had died of cancer years ago. Antonia bit her lip. He was in danger of losing his only child, and she was too cowardly to tell him.

He patted her on the shoulder. "Don't you do too

much in here. Get an early night. Leave those if you want, and I'll wash them later.''

''I don't mind,'' she protested, grinning. ''I'll see you in the morning, then.''

''Don't wake me up when you leave,'' he called over his shoulder. ''I'm sleeping late.''

''Lucky devil,'' she called back.

He only laughed, leaving her to the dishes.

She finished them and went to bed. But she didn't sleep. She lay awake, seeing Maggie Long's surly expression and hating eyes, and Powell's unwelcoming scrutiny. They'd both love to see her back in Arizona, and it looked as if they were going to do their combined best to make her life hell if she stayed here. She'd be walking on eggshells for the rest of the school year with Maggie, and if she failed the child for not doing her homework, Powell would be standing in her classroom every day to complain.

She rolled over with a sigh. Things had been so uncomplicated when she was eighteen, she thought wistfully. She'd been in love and looking forward to marriage and children. Her eyes closed on a wave of pain. Maggie would have been her child, her daughter. She'd have had blond hair and gray eyes, perhaps, like Antonia. And if she'd been Antonia's child, she'd have been loved and wanted and cared for. She wouldn't have a surly expression and eyes that hated.

Powell had said something about Maggie...what was it? That Maggie had paid a higher price than any of them. What had he meant? Surely he cared for the child. He certainly fought hard enough when he felt she was attacked.

Well, it wasn't her problem, she decided finally. And she wasn't going to let it turn into her problem. She still hadn't decided what to do about her other problem.

Julie was the brightest spot in Antonia's days. The little girl was always cheerful, helpful, doing whatever she could to smooth Antonia's path and make it easy for her to teach the class. She remembered where Mrs. Donalds had kept things, she knew what material had been covered and she was always eager to do anything she was asked.

Maggie on the other hand was resentful and ice-cold. She did nothing voluntarily. She was still refusing to turn in her homework. Talking to her did no good. She just glared back.

"I'll give you one more chance to make up this work," Antonia told her at the end of her second week teaching the class. "If you don't turn it in Monday, you'll get another zero."

Maggie smiled haughtily. "And my daddy will cuss you out again. I'll tell him you slapped me, too."

Antonia's gray eyes glittered at the child. "You would, wouldn't you?" she asked coldly. "I don't doubt that you can lie, Maggie. Well, go ahead. See how much damage you can do."

Maggie's reaction was unexpected. Tears filled her blue eyes and she shivered.

She whirled and ran out of the classroom, leaving Antonia deflated and feeling badly for the child. She clenched her hands on the desk to keep them from shaking. How could she have been so hateful and cold.

She cleaned up the classroom, waiting for Powell to storm in and give her hell. But he didn't show up. She went home and spent a nerve-rackingly quiet weekend with her father, waiting for an explosion that didn't come.

The biggest surprise arrived Monday morning, when Maggie shoved a crumpled, stained piece of paper on the desk and walked back to her seat without looking at Antonia. It was messy, but it was the missing homework. Not only that, it was done correctly.

Antonia didn't say a word. It was a small victory, of sorts. She wouldn't admit to herself that she was pleased. But the paper got an *A*.

Julie began to sit with her at recess, and shared cupcakes and other tidbits that her mother had sent to school with her.

"Mom says you're doing a really nice job on me, Miss Hayes," Julie said. "Dad remembers you from school, did you know? He said you were a sweet girl, and that you were shy. Were you, really?"

Antonia laughed. "I'm afraid so. I remember your father, too. He was the class clown."

"Dad? Really?"

''Really. Don't tell him I told you, though, okay?'' she teased, smiling at the child.

From a short distance away, Maggie glared toward them. She was, as usual, alone. She didn't get along with the other children. The girls hated her, and the boys made fun of her skinny legs that were always bruised and cut from her tomboyish antics at the ranch. There was one special boy, Jake Weldon. Maggie pretended not to notice him. He was one of the boys who made fun of her, and it hurt really bad. She was alone most of the time these days, because Julie spent her time with the teacher instead of Maggie.

Miss Hayes liked Julie. Everyone knew it, too. Julie had been Maggie's best friend, but now she seemed to be Miss Hayes's. Maggie hated both of them. She hadn't told her father what Miss Hayes had said about her homework. She wanted her teacher to know that she wasn't bad like her mother. She knew what her mother had done, because she'd heard them talking about it once. She remembered her mother crying and accusing him of not loving her, and him saying that she'd ruined his life, she and her premature baby. There had been something else, something about him being drunk and out of his mind or Maggie wouldn't have been born at all.

It hadn't made sense then. But when she was older, she'd heard him say the same thing to the housekeeper, that Maggie had been born prematurely.

After that, she'd stopped listening. That was when she knew her father didn't love her. That was when she'd stopped trying to make him notice her by being good.

Her daddy knew Miss Hayes. She heard him tell the housekeeper that Antonia had come to Bighorn to make his life miserable and that he didn't want her here. If she'd been able to talk to Miss Hayes, she'd have told her that her father hated both of them, and that it made them sort of related.

She wondered if her dad hadn't wanted to marry her mother, and why he had. Maybe it had something to do with why her daddy hated her. People had said that Sally didn't love her little child, that Maggie was just the rope she'd used to tie up Powell Long with. Maybe they were right, because her mother never spent any time doing things with her. She never liked Maggie, either.

She slid down against the tree into the dirt, getting her jeans filthy. Mrs. Bates, the housekeeper, would rage and fuss about that, and she didn't care. Mrs. Bates had thrown away most of her clothes, complaining that they were too dirty to come clean. She hadn't told her dad. When she ran out of clothes, maybe somebody would notice.

She wished Mrs. Bates liked her. Julie did, when she wasn't fawning over teachers to make them give her special privileges. She liked Julie, she did, but Julie was a kiss-up. Sometimes she wondered why she let Julie be her friend at all. She didn't need any friends. She could make it all by herself. She'd show them all that she was somebody special. She'd make them love her one day. She sighed and closed her eyes. Oh, if only she knew Julie's secret; if only she knew how to make people like her.

"There's Maggie," Julie commented, grimacing as she glanced toward her friend. "Nobody likes her except me," she confided to Miss Hayes. "She beats up the boys and she can bat and catch better than any of them, so they don't like her. And the girls think she's too rough to play with. I sort of feel sorry for her. She says her daddy doesn't like her. He's always going away somewhere. She stays with us when he's gone, only she doesn't want to this week because—" She stopped, as if she was afraid she'd already said too much.

"Because?" Antonia prompted curiously.

"Oh, nothing," Julie said. She couldn't tell Miss Hayes that she'd fought with Maggie over their new teacher. "Anyway, Maggie mostly stays with us if her dad's away longer than overnight."

Involuntarily, Antonia glanced toward the child and found her watching them with those cold, sullen eyes. The memories came flooding back—Sally jealous of Antonia's pretty face, jealous of Antonia's grades, jealous of Antonia having any other girlfriends, jealous...of her with Powell.

She shivered faintly and looked away from the child. God forgive her, it was just too much. She wondered if she could possibly get Maggie transferred to another class. If she couldn't then there was no other option. The only teaching job available was the one she had. She couldn't wait for another opening. Her eyes closed. She was running out of time. Why, she asked herself, why was she wasting it like this? She'd told herself she was coming home to cope with her memories, but they were too much for her. She couldn't fight the past. She couldn't even manage to get through the present. She had to consider how she would face the future.

"Miss Hayes?"

Her eyes opened. Julie was looking worried. "Are you all right?" the little girl asked, concerned.

"I'm tired, that's all," Antonia said, smiling. "We'd better go in now."

She called the class and led them back into the building.

Maggie was worse than ever for the rest of the day. She talked back, refused to do a chore assigned to her, ignored Antonia when she was called on in class. And at the end of the day, she waited until everyone else left and came back into the room, to stand glaring at Antonia from the doorway.

"My dad says he wishes you'd go away and never come back," she said loudly. "He says you make his life miserable, and that he can't stand the sight of you! He says you make him sick!"

Antonia's face flushed and she looked stunned.

Maggie turned and ran out the door. Her father had said something like that, to himself, and it made her feel much better that she'd told Miss Hayes about it.

That had made her look sick, all right! And it wasn't a lie. Well, not a real lie. It was just something to make her feel as bad as Maggie had felt when Miss Hayes looked at her on the playground and shuddered. She knew the teacher didn't like her. She didn't care. She didn't like Miss Hayes, either.

Maggie was smug the next day. She didn't have any more parting shots for Antonia, and she did her work in class. But she refused to do her homework, again, and dared Antonia to give her a zero. She even dared her to send a note home to her father.

Antonia wanted to call her bluff, but she was feeling sicker by the day and it was increasingly hard for her to get up in the mornings and go to work at all. The illness was progressing much more quickly than she'd foreseen. And Maggie was making her life hell.

For the rest of the week, Antonia thought about the possibility of getting Maggie moved out of her class. Surely she could approach the principal in confidence.

And that was what she did, after school.

Mrs. Jameson smiled ruefully when Antonia sat down beside her desk and hesitated.

"You're here about Maggie Long again," she said at once.

Antonia's eyes widened. "Why...yes."

"I was expecting you," the older woman said with resignation. "Mrs. Donalds got along quite well with her, but she's the only teacher in the past few years who hasn't had trouble with Maggie. She's a rebel, you see. Her father travels a good deal. Maggie is left with Julie's family.'' She grimaced. ''We heard that he was thinking of marrying again, but once that rumor started, Maggie ran away from home. She, uh, isn't keen on the widow Holton.''

Antonia was wondering if anyone was keen about the widow Holton, from what she'd already heard from Barrie. It was a surprise to hear that Powell had considered marrying the woman—if it was true and not just gossip.

The principal sighed, her attention returning to the task at hand. ''You want Maggie moved, I suppose. I wish I could oblige you, but we only have one fourth-grade class, because this is such a small school, and you're teaching it.'' She lifted her hands helplessly. ''There it is. I'm really sorry. Perhaps if you spoke with her father?''

''I already have,'' Antonia replied calmly.

''And he said...?''

''That if I pushed him, he'd do his best to have me removed from my position here,'' she said bluntly.

The older woman pursed her lips. ''Well, as we've already discussed, he wouldn't have to work that hard to do it. It's a rather ticklish situation. I'm sorry I can't be more optimistic.''

Antonia leaned back in her seat with a long sigh. ''I shouldn't have come back to Bighorn,'' she said, almost to herself. ''I don't know why I did.''

''Perhaps you were looking for something.''

''Something that no longer exists,'' Antonia replied

absently. "A lost part of my life that I won't find here."

"You are going to stay, aren't you?" Mrs. Jameson asked. "After this school term, I mean. Your students say wonderful things about you. Especially Julie Ames," she added with a grin.

"I went to school with her father," Antonia confessed. "To this school, as a matter of fact. She's just like her dad."

"I've met him, and she is a lot like him. What a pity all our students can't be as energetic and enthusiastic as our Julie."

"Yes, indeed."

"Well, I'll give you all the moral support I can," Mrs. Jameson continued. "We do have a very good school counselor. We've sent Maggie to her several times, but she won't say a word. We've had the counselor talk to Mr. Long, but he won't say a word, either. It's a difficult situation."

"Perhaps it will work itself out," Antonia replied.

"Do think about staying on," the older woman said seriously.

Antonia couldn't promise that. She forced a smile. "I'll certainly think about it," she agreed.

But once out of the principal's office, she was more depressed than ever. Maggie hated her, and obviously would not cooperate. It was only a matter of time before she had to give Maggie a failing grade for her noneffort, and Powell would either come back for some more heated words or get her fired. She didn't know if she could bear another verbal tug-of-war with him, especially after the last one. And as for getting fired, she wondered if that really mattered anymore. At the rate her health was failing, it wasn't going to matter for much longer, anyway.

She wandered back to her schoolroom and found Powell sitting on the edge of her desk, looking prosperous in a dark gray suit and a red tie, with a gray Stetson and hand-tooled leather boots that complemented his suit. He was wearing the same signet ring on his little finger that he'd worn when they were engaged, a script letter *L*. The ring was very simple, 10K gold and not very expensive. His mother had given it to him when he graduated from high school, and Antonia knew how hard the woman had had to work to pay for it. The Rolex watch on his left wrist was something he'd earned for himself. The Longs had never had enough money at any time in their lives to pay for a watch like that. She wondered if Powell ever thought back to those hard days of his youth.

He heard her step and turned his head to watch her enter the classroom. In her tailored beige dress, with her blond hair in a bun, she looked thinner than ever and very dignified.

"How you've changed," he remarked involuntarily.

"I was thinking the same thing about you," she said wearily. She sat down behind the desk, because just the walk to the office had made her tired. She looked up at him with the fatigue in her face. "I really need to go home. I know why you're here. She can't be moved to another class, because there isn't one. The only alternative is for me to leave...."

"That isn't why I came," he said, surprised.

"No?"

He picked up a paper clip from the desk and looked at it intently. "I thought you might have something to eat with me," he said. "We could talk about Maggie."

She was nauseated and trying not to let it overwhelm her. She barely heard him. "What?"

"I said, let's get together tonight," he repeated, frowning. "You look green. Put your head down."

She turned sideways and lowered her head to the hands resting on her knees, sucking in air. She felt nauseous more and more these days, and faint. She didn't know how much longer she was going to be mobile. The thought frightened her. She would have to make arrangements to get on with the therapy, while there was still time. It was one thing to say that dying didn't matter, but it was quite another when the prospect of it was staring her in the face.

"You're damn thin." He bit off the words. "Have you seen a doctor?"

"If one more person asks me that...!" She erupted. She took another breath and lifted her head, fighting the dizziness as she pushed back a wisp of hair from her eyes. "Yes, I've seen a doctor. I'm just run-down. It's been a hard year."

"Yes, I know," he said absently, watching her.

She met his concerned eyes. If she'd been less feeble, she might have wondered at the expression in them. As it was, she was too tired to care.

"Maggie's been giving everyone fits," he said unexpectedly. "I know you're having trouble with her. I thought if we put our heads together, we might come up with some answers."

"I thought my opinion didn't matter," she replied dully.

He averted his gaze. "I've had a lot on my mind," he said noncommittally. "Of course your opinion matters. We need to talk."

She wanted to ask what good he thought it would do to talk, when he'd told his daughter that he was sick of Miss Hayes and wanted her out of town because she was making his life miserable. She wasn't going to mention that. It would be like tattling. But it hurt more than anything else had in recent days.

"Well?" he persisted impatiently.

"Very well. What time shall I meet you, and where?"

The question seemed to surprise him. "I'll pick you up at your home, of course," he said. "About six."

She really should refuse. She looked into his dark eyes and knew that she couldn't. One last date, she was thinking sadly. She could have one last date with him before the ordeal began....

She managed a smile. "All right."

He watched her sort out the papers on her desk and put them away methodically. His eyes were on her hands, on the unusual thinness of them. She looked unwell. Her mother's death surely had affected her, but this seemed much more than worry. She was all but skeletal.

"I'll see you at six," she said when she'd put up the classroom and walked out into the hall with him.

He looked down at her, noting her frailty, her slenderness. He still towered over her, as he had years before. She was twenty-seven, but his eyes saw a vivacious, loving girl of eighteen. What had happened to change her whole personality so drastically? She was an old soul in a young body. Had he caused all that?

She glanced up at him curiously. "Was there something else?"

He shrugged. "Maggie showed me an *A* on her homework paper."

"I didn't give her the grade," she replied. "She earned it. It was good work."

He stuck his hands into his pockets. "She has a bright mind, when she wants to use it." His eyes narrowed. "I said some harsh things the last time I was here. Now's as good a time as any to apologize. I was out of line." He couldn't go further and admit that Maggie had lied to him. He was still raw, as Antonia surely was, about Sally's lies. It was too much to admit that his daughter was a liar as well.

"Most parents who care about their children would have challenged a zero," she said noncommittally.

"I haven't been much of a parent," he said abruptly. "I'll see you at six."

She watched him with sad eyes as he walked away, the sight of his long back reminding her poignantly of the day he'd ended their engagement.

He paused at the door, sensing her eyes, and he turned unexpectedly to stare at her. It was so quick that she didn't have time to disguise her grief. He actually winced, because he knew that she'd looked like that nine years ago. He hadn't looked back, so he hadn't known.

She drew in a steadying breath and composed her features. She didn't say anything. There was nothing to say that he hadn't already read in her face.

He started to speak, but apparently he couldn't find the words, either.

"At six," she repeated.

He nodded, and this time he went through the doorway.

Chapter Six

Antonia went through every dress she had in her closet before she settled on a nice but simple black crepe dress with short sleeves and a modest neckline. It reached just below her knees and although it had once fit her very nicely, it now hung on her. She had nothing that looked the right size. But it was cold and she could wear a coat over it, the one good leather one she'd bought last season on sale. It would cover the dress and perhaps when she was seated, it wouldn't look so big on her. She paired the dress with a thin black leather belt, gold stud earrings and a small gold cross that her mother had given her when she graduated from high school. She wore no other jewelry, except for the serviceable watch on her wrist. She saw the engagement ring that Powell had bought for her, a very modest little diamond in a thin gold setting. She'd sent it back to him, but he'd refused to accept it from her father. It had found its way back to her, and she kept it here in her jewelry box, the only keepsake she had except for the small cross she always wore.

She picked the ring up and looked at it with sad gray eyes. How different her life, and Powell's, might have been if he hadn't jumped to conclusions and she hadn't run away.

She put the ring back into the box, into the past, where it belonged, and closed it up. This would be the last time she'd go out with Powell. He only wanted to talk about Maggie. If he was serious about the widow Holton, of whom she'd heard so much, then this would certainly not be an occasion he'd want to repeat. And even if he asked, Antonia knew that she would have to refuse a second evening out with him. Her heart was still all too vulnerable. But for tonight, she took special care with her makeup and left her blond hair long around her shoulders. Even thin, she looked good. She hoped Powell would think so.

She sat in the living room with her curious but silent father, waiting for the clock to chime six. He had ten minutes left to make it on time. Powell had been very punctual in the old days. She wondered if he still was.

"Nervous?" her father asked gently.

She smiled and nodded. "I don't know why he wanted to take me out to talk about Maggie. We could have talked here, or at school."

He smoothed a hand over his boot, crossed over his other leg. "Maybe he's trying to make things up with you."

"I doubt that," she replied. "I hear he's been spending time with the widow Holton...."

"So has Dawson. But love isn't the reason. They both want her south pasture. It borders on both of theirs."

"Oh. Everybody says she's very pretty."

"So she is. But Dawson won't have anything to do with women in a romantic way, and Powell is playing her along."

"I heard that he was talking marriage."

"Did you?" He frowned. "Well...that's surprising."

"Mrs. Jameson said his daughter ran away when she thought he was going to marry Mrs. Holton."

Her father shook his head. "I'm not surprised. That child doesn't get along with anyone. She'll end up in jail one day if he doesn't keep a better eye on her."

She traced a pattern in the black crepe purse that matched her dress. "I haven't been quite fair to her," she confessed. "She's so much like Sally." She grimaced. "She must miss her."

"I doubt it. Her mother left her with any available baby-sitter and stayed on the road until the drinking started taking its toll on her. She never was much of a driver. That's probably why she went into the river."

Into the river. Antonia remembered hearing about the accident on the news. Powell had been rich enough that Sally's tragic death made headlines. She'd felt sorry for him, but she hadn't gone to the funeral. There was no point. She and Sally had been enemies for so long. For so long.

The sound of a car in the driveway interrupted her musings. She got up and reached the door just as Powell knocked.

She felt embarrassed when she saw how he was dressed. He was wearing jeans and a flannel shirt with a heavy denim jacket and old boots. If she was surprised, so was he. She looked very elegant in that black dress and the dark leather coat she wore with it.

His face drew in sharply at the sight of her, because even in her depleted condition, she took his breath away.

"I'm running late." She improvised to explain the way she was dressed. "I've just now come back from town," she lied, redfaced. "I'll hurry and change and be ready in a jiffy. Dad can talk to you while I get ready. I'm sorry…!"

She dashed back into the bedroom and closed the door. She could have died of shame. So much for her dreams of the sort of date they'd once shared. He was dressed for a cup of coffee and a sandwich at a fast-food joint, and here she was rigged out for a restaurant. She should have asked him where they were going in the first place, and not tried to second-guess him!

She quickly changed into jeans and a sweatshirt and put her hair up in its usual bun. At least the jeans fit her better than the dress, she thought dryly.

Powell stared after her and grimaced. "I had an emergency on the ranch with a calving heifer," he murmured. "I didn't realize she'd be dressed up, so I didn't think about changing...."

"Don't make it worse," her father said curtly. "Spare her pride and go along with what she said."

He sighed heavily. "I never do the right thing, say the right thing." His dark eyes were narrow and sad. "She's the one who was hurt the most, and I just keep right on adding to the pain."

Ben Hayes was surprised at the remark, but he had no love for Powell Long. He couldn't forget the torment the man had caused his daughter, nor what Antonia had said about Powell using his influence to open financial doors for him. All Powell's pretended concern for his health hadn't changed what he thought of the man. And tonight his contempt knew no bounds. He hated seeing Antonia embarrassed like that.

"Don't keep her out long," Ben said coldly. "She isn't well."

Powell's eyes cut around to meet the older man's. "What's wrong with her?" he asked.

"Her mother's barely been dead a year," he reminded him. "Antonia misses her a lot."

"She's lost weight, hasn't she?" he asked Ben.

Ben shifted in the chair. "She'll pick back up, now that she's home." He glared at Powell. "Don't hurt her again, boy," he said evenly. "If you want to talk to her about your daughter, fine. But don't expect anything. She's still raw about the past, and I don't blame her. You were wrong and you wouldn't listen. But she's the one who had to leave town."

Powell's jaw went taut. He stared at the older man with eyes that glittered, and he didn't reply.

It was a tense silence that Antonia walked back into. Her father looked angry, and Powell looked... odd.

"I'm ready," she said, sliding into her leather coat.

Powell nodded. "We'll go to Ted's Truck Stop. It's open all night and he serves good coffee, if that suits you."

She read an insult into the remark, and flushed. "I told you I was dressed up because I'd just come back from town," she began. "Ted's suits me fine."

He was stunned by the way she emphasized that, until he realized what he'd said. He turned on his heel and opened the front door for her. "Let's go," he said.

She told her father goodbye and went through the door. Powell closed it behind them, shutting them in the cold, snowy night. A metallic gold Mercedes-Benz was sitting in the driveway, not the four-wheel-drive vehicle he usually drove. Although it had chains to get through snow and ice, it was a luxury car and a far cry from the battered old pickup truck Powell had driven when they'd been engaged.

Flakes of snow fell heavily on the windshield as he drove the mile down the highway to Ted's, which was a bar and grill, just outside the Bighorn city limits. Ted sold beer and wine and good food, but Antonia had never been inside the place before. It wasn't considered a socially respectable place, and she wondered if Powell had a reason for taking her there. Perhaps he was trying to emphasize the fact that this wasn't a routine date. It was to be a business discussion, but he didn't want to take her anyplace where they might be recognized. So if that was the case, maybe he really was serious about the widow Holton after all. It made her sad, even though she knew she had no future with him, or with anyone.

"You're quiet," he remarked as he pulled up in the almost deserted parking lot. It was early for Ted's sort of trade, although a couple of tractor trailers were sitting apart in the lot.

"I suppose so," she replied.

He felt the unease about her, the muted sadness. He felt guilty about bringing her here. She'd dressed up for him, and he'd slapped her down unintentionally. He hadn't even considered that she might think of this as a date. She was as sensitive now as she had been at eighteen.

He went around the car to open her door, but she was already out of it and standing in the snow when he got there. She joined him at the fender and walked toward the bar. Her sneakers were getting wet and the snow was deep enough that it leaked in past her socks, but it didn't matter. She was so miserable already that cold feet just seemed to go with her general mood.

Powell noticed, though, and his lips compressed. It was already a bust of an evening, and it was his own damn fault.

They sat down in a booth and the waitress, a big brunette named Darla, smiled and handed them a menu.

"Just coffee for me," Antonia said with a quiet smile.

Powell's eyes flashed. "I brought you here for a meal," he reminded her firmly.

She evaded his angry eyes. "I'll have a bowl of chili, then. And coffee."

He ordered steak and salad and coffee and handed the menu back to the waitress. He couldn't remember a time when he'd felt as helpless, or as ashamed.

"You need more than that," he said softly.

The tone of his voice brought back too many memories. They'd gone out to eat very rarely in the old days, in his old Ford pickup truck with the torn seat and broken dash. A hamburger had been a treat, but it was being together that had made their dates perfect. They'd wolf down their food and then drive out to the pasture near Powell's house. He'd shut off the engine and turn to her, and she'd go into his arms like a homing pigeon.

She could still taste those hot, deep, passionate kisses they'd shared so hungrily. It was amazing that he'd had the restraint to keep their dates innocent. She'd rushed headlong into desire with no self-preservation at all, wanting him so much that nothing else had mattered. But he'd put on the brakes, every time. That hadn't bothered her at the time. She'd thought it meant that he respected her enough to wait for the wedding ceremony. But after he'd called off the wedding and married Sally, and Maggie was born seven months later, his restraint had made a terrible sort of sense. He hadn't really wanted Antonia. He'd wanted her father's influence. She'd been too much in love to realize it.

"I said, you need to eat more than that," he repeated.

She looked up into his dark eyes with the memories slicing through her. She swallowed. "I haven't felt too good today," she said evasively. "I'm not really hungry."

He saw the shadows under her eyes and knew that lack of sleep had certainly added to her depleted health.

"I wanted to talk to you about Maggie," he said

suddenly, because it bothered him to be with Antonia and remember their old relationship. "I know she's given you problems. I hope we can work out something."

"There's nothing to work out," Antonia said. "She's done her homework. I think she'll adjust to me eventually."

"She had a lot to say about you last night," he continued, as if she hadn't spoken. "She said that you threatened to hit her."

She looked him right in the eye. "Did she?"

He waited, but she didn't offer any defense. "And she said that you told her that you hated her and that you didn't want her in your class, because she reminded you too much of her mother."

Her eyes didn't fall. It wasn't the truth, but there was enough truth in it to twist. Maggie certainly was perceptive, she thought ruefully. And Powell sat there with his convictions so plain on his lean face that he might as well have shouted them.

She knew then why he'd invited her here, to this bar. He was showing her that he thought too little of her to take her to a decent place. He was putting her down in a cold, subtle way, while he raked her over the coals of his anger for upsetting his little girl.

She managed a smile. "Does the city cab run out this far?" she asked in a tone that was tight enough to sound choked. "Then I won't even have to ask you to take me home." She started to get up, but he rose, too, and blocked her way out of the booth.

"Here it is." The waitress interrupted them, bringing steaming black coffee in two mugs. "Sorry I took so long. Is anything wrong?" she added when Powell didn't move.

"No," he said after a minute, his eyes daring Antonia to move as he sat back down. "Nothing at all. But we'll just have the coffee, if it isn't too late to change the order."

"It's all right, I'll take care of it," the waitress said quickly. She'd seen the glint of tears in Antonia's eyes, and she recognized a kindling argument when she saw one starting. She put down the cream pitcher and wrote out the check. If she was any judge of angry women, there would barely be time for them to drink their one cup each before the explosion.

She thanked them, put down the check and got out of the line of fire.

"Don't cry," Powell said through his teeth as he stared at Antonia's white face. "Don't!"

She took a steadying breath and put both hands around the coffee cup. She stared at it instead of him, but her hands trembled.

He closed his eyes, fighting memories and prejudices and gossip and pain. He'd forgotten nothing. *Forgiven nothing.* Seeing her alone like this brought it all back.

She was fighting memories of her own. She lifted the coffee to her lips and burned them trying to drink it.

"Go ahead," he invited coldly. "Tell me she's lying."

"I wouldn't tell you the time of day," she said in a voice like warmed-over death. "I never learn. You said we'd discuss the problem, but this isn't a discussion, it's an inquisition. I'll tell you flat out—I've already asked Mrs. Jameson to move Maggie out of my class. She can't do that, and the only option I have left is to quit my job and go back to Arizona."

He stared at her without speaking. He hadn't expected that.

She met his startled eyes. "Do you think she's a little angel?" she asked. "She's rebellious, haughty, and she lies better than her mother ever did."

"Damn you!"

The whip of his voice made her sick inside. She reached for her purse and this time she got up. She pushed past him, and ran out into the snow with tears streaming down her face. She'd walk back to town, she would…!

Her foot slipped on a patch of ice, and she went down hard. She felt the snow on her hot face and lifted it, to the cooling moisture of fresh snowflakes, just as a pair of steely hands jerked her back to her feet and propelled her toward the car.

She didn't react as he unlocked the door and put her inside. She didn't look at him or say a word, even when he fastened her shoulder harness and sat glaring at her before he finally started the car and headed it back toward town.

When they arrived at her father's house, she reached for the catch that would unfasten the harness, but his hand was there, waiting.

"Why can't you admit the truth?" he demanded. "Why do you keep lying about your relationship with George Rutherford? He bought your wedding dress, he paid your college tuition. The whole damn town knew you were sleeping with him, but you've convinced everyone from your father to George's own son that it was perfectly innocent! Well, you never convinced me and you never will!"

"I know that," she said without looking at him. "Let me go, Powell."

His hand only tightened. "You slept with him!" he accused through his teeth. "I would have died for you…!"

"You were sleeping with my best friend!" she accused hotly. "You got her pregnant while you were engaged to me! Do you think I give a damn about your opinion or your feelings? You weren't jealous of George! You never even loved me! You got engaged to me so that my father's influence could get you a loan that you needed to save your family ranch!"

The accusation startled him so much that he didn't have the presence of mind to retaliate. He stared at her in the dim light from the front porch as if she'd gone mad.

"Sally's people didn't have that kind of clout," she continued, tears of anger and pain running down her cheeks like tiny silver rivers. "But mine did. You used me! The only decent thing you did was to keep from seducing me totally, but then, you didn't need to go that far, because you were already sleeping with Sally!"

He couldn't believe what he was hearing. It was the first time in his life that he'd been at a loss for words, but he was literally speechless.

"And *you* can accuse *me* of lying?" she demanded in a choked tone. "Sally lied. But you wanted to believe her because it got you out of our engagement the day before the wedding. And you *still* believe her, because you can't admit that I was only a means to an end for your ambition. It isn't a broken heart you're nursing, it's broken pride because you couldn't get anywhere without a woman's family name to get you a loan!"

He took a short breath. "I got that loan on my own collateral," he said angrily.

"You got it on *my* father's name," she countered. "Mr. Sims, the bank president, said so. He even laughed about it, about how you were already making use of your future father-in-law to help you mend your family fortunes!"

He hadn't known that. He'd put the land up for security and he'd always assumed that it had been enough. He should have realized that his father's reputation as a gambler would have made him a dangerous risk as a borrower.

"Antonia," he began hesitantly, reaching out a hand.

She slapped it away immediately. "Don't you touch me," she said hotly. "I've had the Longs to hell and back! You can take this for gospel—if your daughter doesn't study, she won't pass. And if that costs me my job, I don't care!"

She jerked open the door and got out, only to find Powell there waiting for her, dark-eyed and glowering.

"I'm not going to let you take out any sort of vengeance on Maggie," he said shortly. "And if you don't stop giving her hell because of grudges against her mother, you'll be out of a job, I promise you."

"Do your worst," she invited with soft venom, her gray eyes flashing at him. "You can't hurt me more than you already have. Very soon now, I'll be beyond the reach of any vengeance you like to pursue!"

"Think so?" With a lightning quick movement, he jerked her against his lean, hard body and bent to her mouth.

The kiss was painful, and not just physically. He kissed her without tenderness, with nothing more than a need to punish. His tongue insinuated itself past her lips in a cold, calculating parody of sex, while his hands twisted her body against his lean hips.

She stiffened, trying to fight, but she was too weak to force him to let go. She opened her eyes and looked at him, stared at him, until he thought she'd had enough. Just at the last, he relented. His mouth became soft and slow and sensuous, teasing, testing. His hands slid up to her waist and he nibbled at her lower lip with something like tenderness. But she refused him even the semblance of response. She stood like a statue in his grasp, her eyes open, wet with tears, her mouth rigid.

When his eyes opened again, he looked oddly guilty. Her mouth was swollen and her face was very pale.

He winced. "I shouldn't have done that," he said curtly.

She laughed coldly. "No, it wasn't necessary," she agreed. "I'd already gotten the message. You held me in such contempt that you didn't even change out of your working clothes. You took me to a bar...." She pulled away from him, a little shakily. "You couldn't have made your opinion of me any plainer."

He pushed his hat back on his head. "I didn't mean it to turn out like this," he said angrily.

"Didn't you?" She stared up at him with eyes that hated him and loved him, with eyes that would soon lose the ability to see him at all. She took a breath and it ended on a sob.

"Oh, God, don't," he groaned. He pulled her into his arms, but this time without passion, without anger. He held her against his heart with hands that protected, cherished, and she felt his lips in her hair, at her temple. "I'm sorry. I'm sorry, Annie." He bit off the words.

It was the first time he'd used the nickname he'd called her when she was eighteen. The sound of his deep voice calmed her. She let him hold her. It would be the last time. She closed her eyes and it was as if it was yesterday—*she was a girl in love, and he was the beginning of her world.*

"It was...so long ago," she whispered brokenly.

"A lifetime," he replied in a hushed tone. His arms cradled her and she felt his cheek move tenderly against her blond hair. "Why didn't I wait?" he whispered almost to himself, and his eyes closed. "Another day, just one more day..."

"We can't have the past back," she said. His arms were warm against the cold, and strong, comforting. She savored the glory of them around her for one last time. No matter how he felt about her, she would have this memory to take down into the dark with her.

She fought tears. Once, he would have done anything for her. Or she'd thought that he would. It was cruel to think that he had only used her as a means to an end.

"You're skin and bones," he said after a minute.

"I've had a hard year."

He nuzzled his cheek against her temple. "They've all been hard years, one way or another." He sighed heavily. "I'm sorry about tonight. God, I'm sorry!"

"It doesn't matter. Maybe we needed to clear the air."

"I'm not sure we cleared anything." He drew back and looked down at her sad face. He touched her swollen mouth tenderly, and he looked repentant. "In the old days, I never hurt you deliberately," he said quietly. "I've changed, haven't I, Annie?"

"We've both changed. We've grown older."

"But not wiser, in my case. I'm still leading with my chin." He pushed a few wisps of blond hair away from her mouth. "Why did you come home? Was it because of me?"

She couldn't tell him that. "My father hasn't been well," she said, evading a direct answer. "He needs me. I never realized how much until Christmas."

"I see."

She looked up into his black eyes with grief already building in her face.

"What's wrong?" he asked gently. "Can't you tell me?"

She forced a smile. "I'm tired. That's all, I'm just tired." She reached up and smoothed her hand slowly over his lean cheek. "I have to go inside." On an impulse, she stood on tiptoe. "Powell...would you kiss me, just once...the way you used to?" she asked huskily, her gray eyes pleading with him.

It was an odd request, but the stormy evening had robbed him of the ability to reason properly. He didn't answer. He bent, nuzzling her face, searching for her lips, and he kissed her as he had on their very first date, so long ago. His mouth was warm and searching and cautious, as if he didn't want to frighten her. She reached up to him and held him close. For a few precious seconds, there was no dreaded future, no painful past. She melted into the length of him, moaning softly when she felt the immediate response of his body to hers. He half lifted her against him, and his mouth became demanding, insistent, intimate. She gave what he asked, holding him close. For this moment, he belonged to her and she loved him so...!

An eternity later, she drew gently away without looking at him, pulling her arms from around his neck. The scent of his cologne was in her nostrils, the taste of him was in her mouth. She hoped that she could remember this moment, at the end.

She managed a smile as she stood on shaky legs. "Thanks," she said huskily. She stared up at him as if she wanted to memorize his face. In fact, she did.

He scowled. "I took you out because I wanted to talk to you," he said heavily.

"We talked," she replied, moving back. "Even if nothing got settled. There are too many scars, Powell. We can't go back. But I won't hurt Maggie, even if it means leaving the job, okay?"

"You don't have to go that far," he snapped.

She just smiled. "It will come to that," she replied. "She's got the upper hand, you see, and she knows it. It doesn't matter," she added absently as she stared at him. "In the long run, it doesn't matter at all. Maybe it's even for the best.'' She took a long, slow breath, drinking in the sight of him. ''Goodbye, Powell. I'm glad you've been so successful. You've got everything you ever wanted. Be happy.''

She turned and went into the house. She hadn't thanked him for the coffee. But, then, he probably didn't expect it. She was glad that her father was watching a television program intently, because when she called good-night, he didn't ask how it had gone. It saved her the pain of telling him. It spared her his pity when he saw the tears she couldn't stem.

Powell's step was slow and leaden as he went into his house. He was drained of emotion, tired and disheartened. Always he'd hoped that one day he and Antonia would find their way back together again, but he couldn't seem to get past the bitterness, and she'd closed doors tonight. She'd kissed him as if she were saying goodbye. Probably she had been. She didn't like Maggie, and that wouldn't change. Maggie didn't like her, either. Sally was gone, but she'd left a barrier between them in the person of one small belligerent girl. He couldn't get to Antonia because Maggie stood in the way. It was a sad thought, when he'd realized tonight how much Antonia still meant to him.

Surprisingly he found his daughter sitting on the bottom step of the staircase in her school clothes, waiting for him when he walked into his house.

"What are you doing up? Where's Mrs. Bates?" he asked.

She shrugged. "She had to go home. She said I'd be okay since you weren't supposed to be gone long." She studied his face with narrowed, resentful eyes. "Did you tell Miss Hayes that she'd better be nice to me from now on?"

He frowned. "How did you know I took Miss Hayes out?"

"Mrs. Bates said you did." She glared harder. "She said Miss Hayes was sweet, but she's not. She's mean to me. I told her that you hated her. I told her that you wanted her to go away and never come back. You did say that, Daddy, you know you did."

He felt frozen inside. No wonder Antonia had been so hostile, so suspicious! "When did you tell Miss Hayes that?" he demanded.

"Last week." Her lower lip protruded. "I want her to go away, too. I hate her!"

"Why?" he asked.

"She's so stupid," she muttered, "she goes all gooey when Julie brings her flowers and plays up to her. She doesn't even know that Julie's just doing it so she can be teacher's pet. Julie doesn't even come over to play with me anymore, she's too busy drawing pictures for Miss Hayes!"

The resentment in his daughter's face was a revelation. He remembered Sally being that way about Antonia. When they'd first been married, she'd been scathing about Antonia going to college and getting a job as a teacher. Sally hadn't wanted to go away to school. She'd wanted to marry Powell. She'd said that Antonia had laughed about his calling off the wedding and saying that she'd marry George who was richer anyway...lies, all lies!

"I want you to do your homework from now on," Powell told the child. "And stop behaving badly in class."

"I do not behave badly! And I did my homework! I did!"

He wiped a hand over his brow. Maggie was a disagreeable child. He bought her things, but he couldn't bear to spend any time around her. She always made him feel guilty.

"Did she tell you I wasn't behaving?" she demanded.

"Oh, what does it matter what she said?" He glared at her angrily, watching the way she backed up when he looked at her. "You'll toe the line or else."

He stormed off, thoroughly disgusted. He didn't think how the impulsive outburst might hurt a sensitive child who carefully hid her sensitivity from the cold adults around her. All her belligerence was nothing more than a mask she wore to keep people from seeing how much they could hurt her. But now, the mask was down. She stared up after her father with blue eyes brimming with tears, her small fists clenched at her sides.

"Daddy," she whispered to herself, "why don't you love me? Why can't you love me? I'm not bad. I'm not bad, Daddy!"

But he didn't hear her. And when she went to bed, her head was full of wicked Miss Hayes and ways to make her sorry for the way her daddy had just treated her.

Chapter Seven

The class had a test the following Monday. Maggie didn't answer a single question on it. As usual, she sat with her arms folded and smiled haughtily at Antonia. When Antonia stopped beside her desk and asked if she wasn't going to try to answer any of the questions, things came to a head.

"I don't have to," she told Antonia. "You can't make me, either."

Antonia promptly took Maggie to the principal's office and decided to let Powell carry through with his threat to get her fired. It no longer mattered very much. She was tired of the memories and the future, and she was no closer to an answer about her own dilemma. Part of her wanted to take the chance that drastic therapy might save her. Another part was scared to death of it.

"I'm sorry," she said when Mrs. Jameson came out into the waiting room, "but Maggie refuses to do the test I'm giving the class. I thought perhaps if you explained the seriousness of the situation to her..."

This was Maggie's best chance, and she took it at once. "She hates me!" Maggie cried piteously, pointing at Antonia. "She said I was just like my mommy and that she hated me!" She actually sobbed. Real tears welled in her blue eyes.

Antonia's face went red. "I said no such thing, and you know it!" she said huskily.

"Yes, you did," Maggie lied. "Mrs. Jameson, she said that she was going to fail me and there was nothing I could do about it. She hates me 'cause my daddy married my mommy instead of her!"

Antonia leaned against the door facing for support, staring at the child with eyes that were full of disbelief. The attack was so unexpected that she had no defense for it. Had Powell been merciless enough to tell the child that? Had he been that angry?

"Antonia, surely this isn't true," Mrs. Jameson began hesitantly.

"No, it's not true," Antonia said in a stilted tone. "I don't know who's been saying such things to her, but it wasn't me."

"My daddy told me," Maggie lied. Actually she'd overheard Mrs. Bates telling that to one of her friends last night on the telephone. It had given Maggie a trump card that she was playing for all she was worth.

Antonia felt the blow all the way to her heart. She'd known that Powell was angry, but she hadn't realized that he was heartless enough to tell Maggie such a painful truth, knowing that she'd use it as a weapon against her despised teacher. And it was a devastating remark to make in the school office. One of the mothers was in there to pick up a sick child, and the two secretaries were watching with wide, eager eyes. What Maggie had just said would be all over town by nightfall. Another scandal. Another humiliation.

"She's awful to me," Maggie continued, letting tears fall from her eyes. It wasn't hard to cry; all she had to do was think about how her father hated her. Choking, she pointed at Antonia. "She says she can be as mean to me as she wants to, because nobody will believe me when I tell on her! I'm scared of her! You won't let her hit me, will you, Mrs. Jameson?" she added, going close to the older woman to look up at her helplessly. "She said she was going to hit me!" she wailed.

Mrs. Jameson had been wavering. But Maggie's eyes were overflowing with tears and she wasn't a hard enough woman to ignore them. She opened her office door. "Go inside and sit down, please, dear," she said. "Don't cry, now, it will be all right. No one will hurt you."

The little girl sniffed back more tears and wiped her eyes on the back of her hand. "Yes, ma'am," she said, keeping her eyes down so that Antonia wouldn't see the triumph in them. *Now you'll have to go away,* she thought gleefully, *and Mrs. Donalds will come back.*

She closed the door behind her. Antonia just stared at Mrs. Jameson.

"Antonia, she's never been that upset," Mrs. Jameson said reluctantly. "I've never seen her cry. I think she's really afraid of you."

Hearing the indecision in the other woman's voice, Antonia knew what she was thinking. She'd heard all the old gossip, and she didn't know Antonia well. She was afraid of Powell's influence. And Maggie had cried. It didn't take a mind reader to figure the outcome. Antonia knew she was beaten. It was as if fate had taken a hand here, forcing her to go back to Arizona. Perhaps it was for the best, anyway. She couldn't have told her father the truth. It would have been too cruel, and very soon now her health was going to break. She couldn't be a burden on the man she loved most.

She met the older woman's eyes tiredly. "It's just as well," she said gently. "I wouldn't have been able to work much longer, anyway."

"I don't understand," Mrs. Jameson said, frowning.

She only smiled. She would understand one day. "I'll save you the trouble of firing me. I quit. I hope you'll release me without proper notice, and I'll forfeit my pay in lieu of it," she said. "Maybe she was

right," she said, nodding toward the office. "Maybe
I could have been kinder to her. I'll clear out my desk
and leave at once, if you can have someone take over
my class."

She turned and walked out of the office, leaving a
sad principal staring after her.

When Maggie came back to the classroom, after a
long talk with Mrs. Jameson and then lunch, Miss
Hayes was no longer there. Julie was crying quietly
while the assistant principal put the homework assignment on the board.

Julie glared at Maggie for the rest of the day, and
she even refused to speak to her until they left the
building to catch the bus home.

"Miss Hayes left," Julie accused. "It was because
of you, wasn't it? I heard Mr. Tarleton say they fired
her!"

Maggie's face flushed. "Well, of course you liked
her, teacher's pet! But she was mean to me!" Maggie
snapped. "I hated her. I'm glad she's gone!"

"She was so kind," Julie sobbed. "You lied!"

Maggie went even redder. "She deserved it! She
would have failed me!"

"She should have!" Julie said angrily. "You lazy,
hateful girl!"

"Well, I don't like you, either," Maggie yelled at
her. "You're a kiss-up, that's all you are! Mrs. Donalds doesn't like you, she likes me, and she's coming
back!"

"She's having a baby, and she isn't coming back!" Julie raged at her.

"Why did Miss Hayes have to leave?" one of the boys muttered as he and his two friends joined them at the bus queue.

"Because Maggie told lies about her and she got fired!" Julie said.

"Miss Hayes got fired? You little brat!" the boy, Jake, said to Maggie, and pushed her roughly when the bus started loading. "She was the best teacher we ever had!"

"She wasn't, either!" Maggie said defensively. She hadn't realized that people were going to know that she got Miss Hayes fired, or that the teacher had been so well liked by her class.

"You got her fired because she didn't like you," Jake persisted, holding up the line. "Well, they ought to fire the whole school, then, because nobody likes you! You're ugly and stupid and you look like a boy!"

Maggie didn't say a word. She ignored him and the others and got on the bus, but she sat alone. Nobody spoke to her. Everybody glared and whispered. She huddled in her seat, trying not to look at Jake. She was crazy about him, and he hated her, too. It was a good thing that nobody knew how she felt.

At least, Miss Hayes was gone, she thought victoriously. That was one good thing that had come out of the horrible day.

* * *

Antonia had to tell her father that she'd lost her job and she was leaving town again. It was the hardest thing she'd ever had to do.

"That brat!" he raged. He went to the telephone. "Well, she's not getting away with those lies. I'll call Powell and we'll make her tell the truth!"

Antonia put her hand over his on the receiver and held it in place. She coaxed him back into his easy chair and she sat on the very edge of the sofa with her hands clenched together.

"Powell believes her," she said firmly. "He has no reason not to. Apparently she doesn't tell lies as a rule. He won't believe you any more than he believed me. He'll side with Maggie and nothing will change. Nothing at all."

"Oh, that child," Ben Hayes said through his teeth.

She smoothed down her skirt. "I disliked her and it showed. That wasn't her fault. Anyway, Dad, it doesn't matter. I'll still come back and visit and you can come and see me. It won't be so bad. Really."

"I'd only just got you home again," he said heavily.

"And maybe I'll come back one day," she replied, smiling. She'd spared him the truth, at least. She hugged him. "I'll leave in the morning. It's best if I don't drag it out."

"What will they do about a teacher?" he demanded.

"They'll hire the next person on their list," she said simply. "It isn't as if I'm not expendable."

"You are to me."

She kissed him. "And you are to me. Now, I'd better go pack."

She phoned Barrie that night and was invited to share her apartment for the time being. She didn't tell Barrie what was wrong. That could wait.

She said goodbye to her father, climbed into her car and drove off toward Arizona. He'd wanted her to take the bus, but she wanted to be alone. She had plenty of thinking to do. She had to cope with her fears. It was time for that hard decision that she might already have put off for too long.

Back in Arizona, Barrie fed her cake and coffee and then waited patiently for the reason behind her best friend's return.

When Antonia told her about Powell's daughter's lies, she was livid.

Barrie bit her lower lip, a nervous habit that sometimes left them raw. "I could shake them both," she said curtly. "You're so thin, Annie, so worn. Maybe it's for the best that you came back here. You look worse than ever."

"I'll perk up now that I'm back. I need to see about my job, if they've got something open."

"Your replacement, Miss Garland, was offered a job in industry at three times the pay and she left without notice," Barrie told her. "I expect they'd love you to replace her. There aren't many people who'll work as hard as we do for the pay.''

That made Antonia smile. ''Absolutely. That's a bit of luck at last! I'll phone first thing tomorrow.''

''It's good to have you back,'' Barrie said. ''I've really missed you.''

''I've missed you, too. Have you heard from Dawson…Barrie!''

Barrie had bitten right through her lip.

Antonia handed her a tissue. ''You have to stop doing that,'' she said, glad to be talking about something less somber than her sudden departure from Bighorn.

''I do try, you know.'' She dabbed at the spot of blood and then stared miserably at her friend. ''Dawson came to see me. We had an argument.''

''About what?''

Barrie clammed up.

''All right, I won't pry. You don't mind if I stay here? Really?''

''Idiot,'' Barrie muttered, hugging her. ''You're family. You belong here.''

Antonia fought tears. ''You're family, too.''

She patted the other woman's back. ''I know. Now let's eat something before we start wailing, and I'll tell you about the expansion plans they've just announced for the math department. I may be offered the head teaching position in the department!''

''I'm so happy for you!''

''So am I. Oh, I'm so lucky!'' Her enthusiasm was

catching. Antonia closed her eyes and leaned silently on Barrie's strength. She had to keep going, she told herself. There must be a reason why she was here, now, instead of happily teaching for what was left of her life in Bighorn. There had to be some purpose to the chain of events that had brought her back to Arizona. The thought of the treatments still frightened her, but not as much as they had only three weeks before. She would go back and see the doctor, and discuss those options.

Maggie was spending the weekend without any company. Julie wouldn't speak to her, and she had no other friends. Mrs. Bates, having heard all about why Miss Hayes had to leave, was avoiding the child as well. She'd moved into the house just to take care of Maggie, because she refused to stay with Julie. But it was a very tense arrangement, and Mrs. Bates muttered while she kept house.

Powell had gone to a business meeting in Denver on Thursday. He'd been out of town when the trouble started. He arrived back without knowing about Antonia's sudden departure. He'd thought about nothing except his disastrous date with Antonia and the things she'd said to him. He'd finally admitted to himself that she really was innocent of any affair with George Rutherford. Her accusations that he'd only used her for financial gain had clinched it.

Of course that wasn't true; he'd never thought of doing such a thing. But if she believed it, it would explain why she hadn't tried to defend herself. She'd never thought he cared one way or the other about her. Presumably she thought he'd been in love with Sally all along, and the fact that Maggie had been premature had helped convince her that he was sleeping with Sally during their engagement. It wasn't true. In fact, he'd only ever slept with Sally once, the night after Antonia left town. He'd been heartbroken, betrayed, and so drunk he hardly knew what he was doing.

When he woke the next morning beside Sally, the horror of what he'd done had killed something inside him. He'd known that there was no going back. He'd seduced Sally, and he'd had to marry her, to prevent another scandal. He'd been trapped, especially when she missed her regular period only two weeks later and turned to him to protect her from scandal. Ironically, he had.

Antonia didn't know that. She didn't know he'd loved her, because he'd never told her so. He hadn't been able to bring himself to say the words. Only when it was too late did he realize what he'd lost. The years between had been empty and cold and he'd grown hard. Sally, knowing he didn't love her at all, knowing he hated her for breaking up his engagement to Antonia, had paid the price, along with her daughter.

Sally had turned to alcohol to numb her pain, and once she'd started, she'd become an alcoholic. Powell had sent her to one doctor after another, to treatment centers. But nothing had worked. His total rejection had devastated her, and even after she'd died he hadn't been able to mourn her.

Neither had Maggie. The child had no love for either of her parents, and she was as cold a human being as Powell had ever known. Sometimes he wondered if she was his child, because there seemed to be nothing of him in her. Sally had hinted once that Powell hadn't been her first lover. She'd even hinted that Powell wasn't Maggie's father. He'd wondered ever since, and it had colored his relationship with the gloomy child who lived in his house.

He tossed his suitcase onto the floor in the hall and looked around. The house was empty, or seemed to be. He looked up the staircase and Maggie was sitting there, by herself, in torn jeans and a stained sweatshirt. As usual, she was glowering.

"Where's Mrs. Bates?" he asked.

She shrugged. "She went to the store."

"Don't you have anything to do?"

She lowered her eyes to her legs. "No."

"Well, go watch television or something," he said irritably when she didn't look up. A thought struck him. "You didn't get in trouble at school again, did you?" he asked.

Her shoulder moved again. "Yes."

He moved to the bottom step and stared at her. "Well?"

She shifted restlessly. "Miss Hayes got fired."

He didn't feel his heart beating. His eyes didn't

move, didn't blink. "Why did she get fired?" he asked in a soft, dangerous tone.

Maggie's lower lip trembled. She clenched her hands around her thin knees. "Because I lied," she said under her breath. "I wanted her...to go away, because she didn't like me. I lied. And they fired her. Everybody hates me now. Julie especially." She swallowed. "I don't care!" She looked up at him belligerently. "I don't care! She didn't like me!"

"Well, whose fault is that?" he asked harshly.

She hid the pain, as she always did. Her stubborn little chin came up. "I want to go live somewhere else," she said with a pathetic kind of pride.

He fought down guilt. "Where would you go?" he asked, thinking of Antonia. "Sally's parents live in California and they're too old to take care of you, and there isn't anybody else."

She averted her wounded eyes. He sounded as if he wanted her to leave, too. She was sick all over.

"You'll go to school with me in the morning, and you'll tell the principal the truth, do you understand?" he asked flatly. "And then you'll apologize to Miss Hayes."

She clenched her teeth. "She's not here," she said.

"What?"

"She left. She went to Arizona." She winced at the look in his dark eyes.

He took an unsteady breath. The expression in his eyes was like a whiplash to Maggie.

"You don't like her," she accused in a broken

voice. "You said so! You said you wished she'd go away!"

"You had no right to cost her that job," he said coldly. "Not liking people doesn't give you the right to hurt them!"

"Mrs. Bates said I was bad like my mama," she blurted out. "She said I was a liar like my mama." Tears filled her eyes. "And she said you hate me like you hated my mama."

He didn't speak. He didn't know what to say, how to deal with this child, his daughter. He hesitated, and in that split second, she got up and ran up the stairs with a heart that broke in two, right inside her. Mrs. Bates was right. Everybody hated her! She ran into her room and closed the door and locked it.

"I'm bad," she whispered to herself, choking on the words. "I'm bad! That's why everybody hates me so."

It had to be true. Her mother had gotten drunk and told her how much she hated her for trapping her in a loveless marriage, for not looking like her father, for being a burden. Her father didn't know that. She couldn't talk to him, she couldn't tell him things. He didn't want to spend any time with her. She was unlovable and unwanted. And she had no place at all to go. Even if she ran away, everybody knew her and they'd just bring her back. Only it would make things worse, because her dad would be even madder at her if she did something like that.

She sat down on the carpeted floor and looked

around at the pretty, expensive things that lined the spacious room. All those pretty things, and not one of them was purchased with love, was given with love. They were substitutes for affectionate hugs and kisses, for trips to amusement parks and zoos and carnivals. They were guilt offerings from a parent who didn't love her or want her. She stared at them with anguish in her eyes, and wondered why she'd ever been born.

Powell got into his car and drove over to Antonia's father's house. He didn't expect to be let in, but Ben opened the door wide.

"I won't come in," Powell said curtly. "Maggie told me what she did. She and I will go to Mrs. Jameson in the morning and she'll tell the truth and apologize. I'm sure they'll offer Antonia her job back."

"She won't come," Ben replied in a lackluster tone. "She said it was just as well that things worked out that way, because she didn't want to live here."

Powell took off his hat and smoothed back his black hair. "I can only say I'm sorry," he said. "I don't know why Maggie dislikes her so much."

"Yes, you do," Ben said unexpectedly. "And you know why she dislikes Maggie, too."

His chest rose and fell in a soundless breath. "Maybe I do. I've made a hell of a lot of mistakes. She said I wouldn't believe the truth because I couldn't admit that." His shoulders shifted. "I suppose she was right. I knew it wasn't true about her and George. But admitting it meant admitting that I had ruined not only her life, but mine and Sally's as well. My pride wouldn't let me do that.''

"We pay a high price for some mistakes," Ben said. "Antonia's still paying. After all these years, she's never looked at another man."

His heart jumped. He searched Ben's eyes. "Is it too late?"

Ben knew what the other man was asking. "I don't know," he said honestly.

"Something's worrying her," Powell said. "Something more than Maggie, or the past. She looks ill."

"I made her go see Dr. Harris. She said he prescribed vitamins."

Powell stared at him. He recognized the suspicion in the other man's eyes, because he'd felt it himself. "You don't buy that, Ben. Neither do I." He took a long breath. "Look, why don't you call Dr. Harris and ask him what's going on?"

"It's Sunday."

"If you don't, I will," the younger man said.

Ben hesitated only for a minute. "Maybe you're right. Come in."

He phoned Dr. Harris. After a few polite words, he asked him point-blank about Antonia.

"That's confidential, Ben," the doctor said gently. "You know that."

"Well, she's gone back to Arizona," Ben said

hotly. "And she looks bad. She said you told her all she needed was vitamins. I want the truth."

There was a hesitation. "She asked me not to tell anyone. Not even you."

Ben glanced at Powell. "I'm her father."

There was a longer hesitation. "She's under the care of a doctor in Tucson," Dr. Harris said after a minute. "Dr. Harry Claridge. I'll give you his number."

"Ted, tell me," Ben pleaded.

There was a heavy sigh. "Ben, she's taking too long to make up her mind about having treatment. If she doesn't hurry, it...may be too late."

Ben sat down heavily on the sofa, his face pale and drawn. "She needs treatment...for what?" he asked, while Powell stood very still, listening, waiting.

"God, I hate having to tell you this!" the doctor said heavily. "I'm violating every oath I ever took, but it's in her best interest...."

"She's dragging her feet over treatment for what?" Ben burst out, glancing at Powell, whose face was rigid with fear.

"For cancer, Ben. The blood work indicates leukemia. I'm sorry. You'd better speak with Dr. Claridge. And see if you can talk some sense into her. She could stay in remission for years, Ben, years, if she gets treatment in time! They're constantly coming up with new medicines, they're finding cures for different sorts of cancer every day! You can't let her give up now!"

Ben felt tears stinging his eyes. "Yes. Of course. Give me...that number, will you, Ted?"

The phone number of the doctor in Arizona was passed along.

"I won't forget you for this. Thank you," Ben said, and hung up.

Powell was staring at him with dawning horror. "She refused treatment. For what?"

"Leukemia," Ben said heavily. "She didn't come home to be with me. She came home to die." He looked up into Powell's white, drawn face, furiously angry. "And now she's gone, alone, to face that terror by herself!"

Chapter Eight

Powell didn't say a word. He just stared at Ben while all the hurtful things he'd said to Antonia came rushing back to haunt him. He remembered how brutally he'd kissed her, the insulting things he'd said. And then, to make it worse, he remembered the way she'd kissed him, just at the last, the way she'd looked up at him, as if she were memorizing his face.

"She was saying goodbye," he said, almost choking on the words.

"What?"

Powell drew in a short breath. There was no time for grief now. He couldn't think of himself. He had to think of Antonia, of what he could do for her. Number one on the list was to get her to accept help.

"I'm going to Arizona." He put his hat back on and turned.

"You hold on there a minute," Ben said harshly. "She's my daughter…!"

"And she doesn't want you to know what's wrong with her," Powell retorted, glaring over his shoulder at the man. "I'll be damned if I'm going to stand around and let her do nothing! She can go to the Mayo Clinic. I'll take care of the financial arrangements. But I'm not going to let her die without a fight!"

Ben felt a glimmer of hope even as he struggled with his own needs, torn between agreeing that it was better not to let her know that he was aware of her condition and wanting to rush to her to offer comfort. He knew that Powell would do his best to make her get treatment; probably he could do more with her than Ben could. But Powell had hurt her so badly in the past.…

Powell saw the hesitation and relented. He could only imagine how Ben felt about his only child. He wasn't close enough to his own daughter to know how he might react to similar news. It was a sobering, depressing thought. "I'll take care of her. I'll phone you the minute I can tell you something," he told Ben quietly. "If she thinks you know, it will tear her up. Obviously she kept it quiet to protect you."

Ben grimaced. "I figured that out for myself. But I hate secrets."

"So do I. But keep this one for her. Give her peace of mind. She won't care if I know," he said with a bitter laugh. "She thinks I hate her."

Ben was realizing that whatever Powell felt, it wasn't hate. He nodded, a curt jerk of his head. "I'll stay here, then. But the minute you know something…!"

"I'll be in touch."

Powell drove home with his heart in his throat. Antonia wouldn't have told anyone. She'd have died from her stubborn refusal to go ahead and have treatment, alone, thinking herself unwanted.

He went upstairs and packed a suitcase with memories haunting him. He'd have given anything to be able to take back his harsh accusations.

He was vaguely aware of eyes on his back. He turned. Maggie was standing there, glowering again.

"What do you want?" he asked coldly.

She averted her eyes. "You going away again?"

"Yes. To Arizona."

"Oh. Why are you going there?" she asked belligerently.

He straightened and looked at the child, unblinking. "To see Antonia. To apologize on your behalf for costing her her job. She came back here because she's sick," he added curtly. "She wanted to be with her father." He averted his eyes. The shock was wearing off. He felt real fear. He couldn't imagine a world without Antonia.

Maggie was an intelligent child. She knew from the way her father was reacting that Miss Hayes meant something to him. Her eyes flickered. "Will she die?" she asked.

He took a breath before he answered. "I don't know."

She folded her thin arms over her chest. She felt worse than ever. Miss Hayes was dying and she had to leave town because of Maggie. She lowered her eyes to the floor. "I didn't know she was sick. I'm sorry I lied."

"You should be. Furthermore, you're going to go with me to see Mrs. Jameson when I get back, and tell her the truth."

"Yes, sir," she said in a subdued tone.

He finished packing and shouldered into his coat.

Her wounded blue eyes searched over the tall man who didn't like her. She'd hoped all her young life that he'd come home just once laughing, happy to see her, that he'd catch her up in his arms and swing her around and tell her he loved her. That had never happened. Julie had that sort of father. Maggie's dad didn't want her.

"You going to bring Miss Hayes back?" she asked.

"Yes," he said flatly. "And if you don't like it, that's too bad."

She didn't answer him. He seemed to dislike her all over again now, because she'd lied. She turned and went back into her room, closing the door quietly. Miss Hayes would hate her. She'd come back, but she wouldn't forget what Maggie had done. There'd be one more person to make her life miserable, to make her feel unloved and unwanted. She sat down on her bed, too sad even to cry. Her life had never seemed so hopeless before. She wondered suddenly if this was how Miss Hayes felt, knowing she was going to die and then losing the only job she could get in town, so she had to go live in a place where she didn't have any family.

"I'm really sorry, Miss Hayes," Maggie said under her breath. The tears started and she couldn't stop them. But there was no one to comfort her in the big, elegant empty house where she lived.

Powell found Mrs. Bates and told her that he was going to Arizona, but not why. He left at once, without seeing Maggie again. He was afraid that he wouldn't be able to hide his disappointment at what she'd done to Antonia.

He made it to Tucson by late afternoon and checked into a hotel downtown. He found Antonia's number in the telephone directory and called it, but the number had been disconnected. Of course, surely she'd had to give up her apartment when she went back to Bighorn. Where could she be?

He thought about it for a minute, and knew. She'd be staying with Dawson Rutherford's stepsister. He looked up Barrie Bell in the directory. There was only one B. Bell listed. He called that number. It was Sunday evening, so he expected the women to be home.

Antonia answered the phone, her voice sounding very tired and listless.

Powell hesitated. Now that he had her on the phone, he didn't know what to say. And while he hesitated, she assumed it was a crank call and hung up on him. He put the receiver down. Perhaps talking to her over the phone was a bad idea, anyway. He noted the address of the apartment, and decided that he'd just go over there in the morning. The element of surprise couldn't be discounted. It would give him an edge, and he badly needed one. He got himself a small bottle of whiskey from the refrigerator in the room and poured it into a glass with some water. He didn't drink as a rule, but he needed this. It had occurred to him that he could lose Antonia now to something other than his own pride. He was afraid, for the first time in his life.

He figured that Antonia wouldn't be going immediately back to work, and he was right. When he rang the doorbell at midmorning the next day after a sleepless night, she came to answer it, Barrie having long since gone to work.

When she saw Powell standing there, her shock gave him the opportunity to ease her back into the apartment and close the door behind him.

"What are you doing here?" she demanded, recovering.

He looked at her, really seeing her, with eyes dark

with pain and worry. She was wearing a sweatshirt
and jeans and socks, and she looked pitifully thin
and drawn. He hated the pain he and Maggie had
caused her.

"I talked to Dr. Harris," he said shortly, bypass-
ing her father so that she wouldn't suspect that Ben
knew about her condition.

She went even paler. *He knew everything.* She
could see it in his face. "He had no right…!"

"You have no right," he snapped back, "to sit
down and die!"

She took a sharp breath. "I can do what I like
with my life!" she replied.

"No."

"Go away!"

"I won't do that, either. You're going to the doctor. And you'll start whatever damn treatment he
tells you to get," he said shortly. "I'm through asking. I'm telling!"

"You aren't telling me anything! You have no
control over me!"

"I have the right of a fellow human being to stop
someone from committing suicide," he said quietly,
searching her eyes. "I'm going to take care of you.
I'll start today. Get dressed. We're going to see Dr.
Claridge. I made an appointment for you before I
came here."

Her mind was spinning. The shock was too sudden, too extreme. She simply stared at him.

His hands went to her shoulders and he searched

her eyes slowly. "I'm going to take Maggie to see Mrs. Jameson. I know what happened. You'll get your job back. You can come home."

She pulled away from him. "I don't have a home anymore," she said, averting her face. "I can't go back. My father would find out that I have leukemia. I can't do that to him. Losing mother almost killed him, and his sister died of cancer. It was terrible, and it took a long time for her to die." She shuddered, remembering. "I can't put him through any more. I must have been crazy to try to go back there in the first place. I don't want him to know."

He couldn't tell her that her father already knew. He shoved his hands into his pockets and stared at her straight back.

"You need to be with people who care about you," he said.

"I am. Barrie is like family."

He didn't know what else to say, how to approach her. He jingled the loose change in his pocket while he tried to find ways to convince her.

She noticed his indecision and turned back to him. "If you'd made this decision, if it was your life, you wouldn't thank anyone for interfering."

"I'd fight," he said, angry with her for giving up. "And you know it."

"Of course you would," she said heavily. "You have things to fight for—your daughter, your wealth, your businesses."

He frowned.

She saw the look and laughed bitterly. "Don't you understand? I've run out of things to fight for," she told him. "I have nothing! Nothing! My father loves me, but he's all I have. I get up in the morning, I go to work, I try to educate children who'd rather play than do homework. I come home and eat supper and read a book and go to bed. That's my life. Except for Barrie, I don't have a friend in the world." She sounded as weary as she felt. She sat down on the edge of an easy chair with her face propped in her hands. It was almost a relief that someone knew, that she could finally admit how she felt. Powell wouldn't mind talking about her condition because it didn't matter to him. "I'm tired, Powell. It's gaining on me. I've been so sick lately that I'm barely able to get around at all. I don't care anymore. The treatment scares me more than the thought of dying does. Besides, there's nothing left that I care enough about to want to live. I just want it to be over."

The terror was working its way into his heart as he stared at her. He'd never heard anyone sound so defeated. With that attitude, all the treatment in the world wouldn't do any good. She'd given up.

He stood there, staring down at her bent head, breathing erratically while he searched for something to say that would inspire her, that would give her the will to fight. What could he do?

"Isn't there anything you want, Antonia?" he asked slowly. "Isn't there something that would give you a reason to hold on?"

She shook her head. "I'm grateful to you for coming all this way. But you could have saved yourself the trip. My mind is made up. Leave me alone, Powell."

"Leave you alone…!" He choked on the words. He wanted to rage. He wanted to throw things. She sounded so calm, so unmoved. And he was churning inside with the force of his emotions. "What else have I done for nine long, empty damn years?" he demanded.

She leaned forward, letting her long, loose blond hair drape over her face. "Don't lose your temper. I can't fight anymore. I'm too tired."

She looked it. His eyes lingered on her stooped posture. She looked beaten. It was so out of character for her that it devastated him.

He knelt in front of her, taking her by the wrists and pulling her toward him so that she had to look up.

His black eyes bit into her gray ones from point-blank range. "I've known people who had leukemia. With treatment, you could keep going for years. They could find a cure in the meantime. It's crazy to just let go, not to even take the chance of being able to live!"

She searched his black eyes quietly, with an ache deep inside her that had seemed to have been there forever. Daringly, her hand tugged free of his grasp and found his face. Such a beloved face, she thought brokenly. So dear to her. She traced over the thick

hair that lay unruly against his broad forehead, down
to the thick black eyebrows, down his nose to the
crook where it had been broken, over one high
cheekbone and down the indented space to his jutting chin. Beloved. She felt the muscles clench and
saw the faint glitter in his eyes.

He was barely breathing now, watching her watch
him. He caught her hand roughly and held it against
his cheek. What he saw in her unguarded face tormented him.

"You still love me," he accused gruffly. "Do you
think I don't know?"

She started to deny it, but there was really no reason to. Not anymore. She smiled sadly. "Oh, yes,"
she said miserably. Her fingers touched his chiseled,
thin mouth and felt it move warmly beneath them as
he reacted with faint surprise to her easy admission.
"I love you. I never stopped. I never could have."
She drew her fingers away. "But everything ends,
Powell. Even life."

He caught her hand, pulling it back to his face.
"This doesn't have to," he said quietly. "I can get
a license today. We can be married in three days."

She had to fight the temptation to say yes. Her
eyes fell to his collar, where a pulse hammered relentlessly. "Thank you," she said with genuine feeling. "That means more to me than you can know,
under the circumstances. But I won't marry you. I
have nothing to give you."

"You have the rest of your life," he said shortly. "However long that is!"

"No." Her voice was weaker. She was fighting tears. She turned her head away and tried to get up, but he held her there.

"You can live with me. I'll take care of you," he said heavily. "Whatever you need, you'll get. The best doctors, the best treatment."

"Money still can't buy life," she told him. "Cancer is...pretty final."

"Stop saying that!" He gripped her arms, hard. "Stop being a defeatist! You can beat anything if you're willing to try!"

"Oh, that sounds familiar," she said, her eyes misting over with memory. "Remember when you were first starting to build your pedigree herd up? And they told you you'd never manage it with one young bull and five heifers. Remember what you said? You said that anything was possible." Her eyes grew warm. "I believed you'd do it. I never doubted it for a minute. You were so proud, Powell, even when you had nothing, and you fought on when so many others would have dropped by the wayside. It was one of the things I admired most about you."

He winced. His face clenched; his *heart* clenched. He felt as if he was being torn apart. He let her go and got to his feet, moving away with his hands tight in his pockets.

"I gave up on you, though, didn't I?" he asked

with his back to her. "A little gossip, a few lies and I destroyed your life."

She studied her thin hands. It was good that they were finally discussing this, that he'd finally admitted that he knew the truth. Perhaps it would make it easier for him, and for her, to let go of the past.

"Sally loved you," she said, making excuses for her friend for the first time. "Perhaps love makes people act out of character."

His fists clenched in his pockets. "I hated her, God forgive me," he said huskily. "I hated her every day we were together, even more when she announced that she was pregnant with Maggie." He sighed wearily. "God, Annie, I resent my own child because I'm not even sure she's mine. I'll never be sure. Even if she is, every time I look at her, I remember what her mother did."

"You did very well without me," she said without malice. "You built up the ranch and made a fortune doing it. You have respect and influence...."

"And all it cost me was you." His head bowed. He laughed dully. "What a price to pay."

"Maggie is a bright child," she said uncertainly. "She can't be so bad. Julie likes her."

"Not recently. Everybody's mad at her for making you leave," he said surprisingly. "Julie won't speak to her."

"That's a shame," she said. "She's a child who needs love, so much." Antonia had been thinking of what had happened the past few weeks, and Maggie's role in it.

He turned, scowling. "What do you mean?"

She smiled. The reasons for Maggie's bad behavior were beginning to be so clear. "Can't you see it in her? She's so alone, Powell, just like you used to be. She doesn't mix with the other children. She's always apart, separate. She's belligerent because she's lonely."

His face hardened. "I'm a busy man..."

"Blame me. Blame Sally. But don't blame Maggie for the past," she pleaded. "If nothing else comes out of this, there should be something for Maggie."

"Oh, God, St. Antonia speaks!" he said sarcastically, because her defense of his daughter made him ashamed of his lack of feeling for the child. "She got you fired, and you think she deserves kindness?"

"She does," she replied simply. "I could have been kinder to her. She reminded me of Sally, too. I was holding grudges of my own. I wasn't deliberately unkind, but I made no overtures toward her at all. A child like Julie is easy to love, because she gives love so generously. A child like Maggie is secretive and distrustful. She can't give love because she doesn't know how. She has to learn."

He thought about that for a minute. "All right. If she needs it, you come home with me and teach me how to give it."

She searched over his rigid expression with eyes that held equal parts of love and grief. "I'm already going downhill," she said slowly. "I can't do that to her, or to you and my father." Her eyes skimmed over his broad shoulders lovingly. "I'll stay with Barrie until I become a liability, then I'll go into a hospice…Powell!"

He had her up in his arms, clear off the floor, his hot face buried in her throat. He didn't speak, but his arms had a fine tremor and his breathing was ragged. He held her so close that she felt vaguely bruised, and he paced the floor with her while he tried to cope with the most incredible emotional pain he'd ever felt.

"I won't let you die," he said roughly. "Do you hear me? I won't!"

She slid her arms around his neck and let him hold her. He did care, in his own way, and she was sorry for him. She'd had weeks to come to grips with her condition, but he'd only had a day or so. Denial was a very real part of it, as Dr. Claridge had already told her.

"It's because of the night you took me to the bar, isn't it?" she asked quietly. "There's no need to feel guilty about what you said. I know it hasn't been an easy nine years for you, either. I don't hold any more grudges. I don't have time for them now. I've put things into perspective in the past few weeks. Hatred, guilt, anger, revenge…they all become so insignificant when you realize your time is limited."

His arms contracted. He stopped pacing and stood holding her, cold with fear.

"If you take the treatments, you have a chance," he repeated.

"Yes. I can live, from day to day, with the fear of it coming back. I can have radiation sickness, my hair will fall out, the very quality of my life will be impaired. What there is left of it, that is."

He drew in a sharp breath, rocking her against him. His eyes, if she could have seen them, were wide and bleak in a face gone rigid with grief.

"I'll be there. I'll help you through it! Life is too precious to throw away." His mouth searched against her throat hungrily. "Marry me, Annie. If it's only for a few weeks, we'll make enough memories to carry us both into eternity!"

His voice was husky as he spoke. It was the most beautiful thing he'd ever said to her. She clung, giving way to tears at last.

"Yes?" he whispered.

She didn't speak. It was too much of a temptation to resist. She didn't have the willpower to say no, despite her suspicion of his motives.

"I want you," he said harshly. "I want you more than I've ever wanted anything in my life, sick or well. Say yes," he repeated insistently. "Say yes!"

If it was only physical, if he didn't love her, was she doing the right thing to agree? She didn't know. But it was more than she could do to walk away from him a second time. Her arms tightened around his neck. "If you're sure...if you're really sure."

"I'm sure, all right." His cheek slid against hers. He searched her wet eyes. His mouth closed them and then slid down to cover her soft, trembling, tear-wet mouth. He kissed her tenderly, slowly, feeling her immediate response.

The kisses quickly became passionate, intense, and he drew back, because this was a time for tenderness, not desire. "If you'll have the treatments," he said carefully, "if it's even remotely possible afterward, I'll give you a child."

As bribery went, it was a master stroke. She looked as if she thought he was going insane. Her pale eyes searched his dark ones warily.

"Don't you want a child, Antonia?" he asked curtly. "You used to. It was all you talked about while we were engaged. Surely you didn't give up those dreams."

She felt the heat rush into her cheeks. It was an intimate thing to be talking about. Her eyes escaped his, darting down to the white of his shirt.

"Don't," she said weakly.

"We'll be married," he said firmly. "It will all be legal and aboveboard."

She sighed miserably. "Your daughter won't like having me in the house, for however long I have."

"My daughter had better like it. Having you around her may be the best thing that ever happened to her. But you keep harping on my daughter—I told you before, I don't even think Maggie's mine!''

Her eyes came up sharply.

''Oh, you think you're the only one who paid the price, is that it?'' he asked bluntly. ''I was married to an alcoholic, who hated me because I couldn't bear to touch her. She told me that Maggie wasn't mine, that she'd been with other men.''

She tried to pull away, but he wouldn't let her. He put her back on her feet, but he held her there in front of him. His eyes were relentless, like his hold on her. ''I told you that I believed Sally about George, but I didn't. After that one, she told so many lies...so many...!'' He let go of her abruptly and turned his back, ramming his hands into the pockets of his slacks as he went to look out the window that overlooked the city of Tucson with ''A'' Mountain in the distance. ''I've lived in hell. Until she died, and afterward. You said you couldn't bear Maggie in your class because of the memories, and I accused you of cruelty. But it's that way with me, too.''

The child's behavior made a terrible kind of sense. Her mother hadn't wanted her, and neither did her father. She was unloved, unwanted. No wonder she was a behavioral problem.

''She looks like Sally,'' she said.

''Oh, yes. Indeed she does. But she doesn't look like me, does she?''

She couldn't argue that point, as much as she might have liked to reassure him.

She joined him at the window. Her eyes searched his. The pain and the anguish of his life were carved into his lean face, in deep lines and an absence of happiness. He looked older than he was.

"What stupid mistakes we make, Antonia, when we're young. I didn't believe you, and that hurt you so much that you ran away. Then I spent years pretending that it wasn't a lie, because I couldn't bear to see the waste and know that I caused it. It's hard to admit guilt, fault. I fought it tooth and nail. But in the end, there was no one else to blame."

She lowered her eyes to his chest. "We were both much younger."

"I never used you to get loans on your father's name," he said bluntly. "That was the farthest thing from my mind."

She didn't answer him.

He moved closer, so that as she stared at the floor, his legs filled her line of vision. They were long legs, muscular and powerful from hours working in the saddle.

He took her cold hands in his. "I was a loner and a misfit. I grew up in poverty, with a father who'd gamble the food out of a baby's mouth and a mother who was too afraid of him to leave. It was a rough childhood. The only thing I ever wanted was to get out of the cycle of poverty, to never have to go hungry again. I wanted to make people notice me."

"You did," she said. "You have everything you ever wanted—money and power and prestige."

"There was one other thing I wanted," he said, correcting her. "I wanted you."

She couldn't meet his eyes. "That didn't last."

"Yes, it did. I still want you more than any woman I've ever known."

"In bed," she scoffed.

"Don't knock it," he replied. "Surely by now you've learned how passion can take you over."

She looked up. Her eyes were guileless, curious, totally innocent.

He caught his breath. "No?"

She lowered her gaze again. "I stopped taking risks after you. Nobody got close enough to hurt me again. In any way."

He caught her small hand in his and rubbed his thumb slowly over its delicate back. He watched the veins in it, traced their blue paths to her fingers. "I can't say the same," he replied quietly. "It would have been more than I could bear to go without a woman for years."

"I suppose it's different for men."

"For some of us," he agreed. He clasped her fingers tight. "They were all you," he added on a cold laugh. "Every one was you. They numbed the pain for a few minutes, and then it came back full force and brought guilt with it."

She reached out hesitantly and touched his dark hair. It was cool under her fingers, clean and smelling of some masculine shampoo.

"Hold me," he said quietly, sliding his arms around her waist. "I'm as frightened as you are."

The words startled her. By the time she reacted to them, he had her close, and his face was buried in her throat.

Her hands hovered above his head and then finally gave in and slid into his hair, holding his cheek against hers.

"I can't let you die, Antonia," he said in a rough whisper.

Her fingers smoothed over his hair protectively. "The treatments are scary," she confessed.

He lifted his head and searched her eyes. "If I went with you, would it be so bad?" he asked softly. "Because I will."

She was weakening. "No. It wouldn't be...so bad, then."

He smiled gently. "Leukemia isn't necessarily fatal," he continued. "Remission can last for years." He traced her mouth. "Years and years."

Tears leaked out of her eyes and down into the corners of her mouth.

"You'll get better," he said, his voice a little rough with the control he was exercising. "And we'll have a baby together."

Her lips compressed. "If I have to have radiation, I don't think I can ever have children."

He hadn't wanted to think about that. He took her hand and brought it hungrily to his mouth. "We'll talk to the doctor. We'll find out for certain."

It was like being caught in a dream. She stopped thinking and worrying altogether. Her eyes searched his and she smiled for the first time.

"All right?" he prompted.

She nodded. "All right."

Dr. Claridge was less than optimistic about pregnancy, and he said so. "You can't carry a child while you're undergoing the treatment," he explained patiently, and watched their faces fall. He hated telling them that.

"And afterward?" she asked, clinging to Powell's strong hand.

"I can't make any promises." He looked at her file, frowning. "You have a rare blood type, which makes it even more dangerous...."

"Rare blood type?" she echoed. "I thought Type O positive was garden variety."

He stared at her. "Yours is not O positive—it's much more rare."

"It is not!" she argued, surprised. "Dr. Claridge, I certainly do know my own blood type. I had an accident when I was in my teens and they had to give me blood. You remember," she told Powell. "I wrecked my bike and cut a gash in my thigh on some tin beside the house."

"I remember," he said.

She looked back at Dr. Claridge. "You can check with Dr. Harris. He'll tell you I'm Type O."

He was frowning as he read the test results again.

"But, this is your file," he said to himself. "This is the report that came back from the lab. The names match." He buzzed his nurse and had her come in and verify the file.

"Have we ever done a complete blood profile on Antonia in the past?" he asked. "There's no record of one here."

"No, we haven't," the nurse agreed.

"Well, do one now. Something is wrong here."

"Yes, sir."

The nurse went out and came back a minute later with the equipment to draw blood. She drew two vials.

"Get a rush on that. Get a local lab to do it. I want to know something by morning," he told her.

"Yes, sir."

The doctor turned back to Antonia. "Don't get your hopes up too high," he said. "It might be a misprint on the blood type and everything else could still be correct. But we'll double-check it. Meanwhile," he added, "I think it would be wise to wait until tomorrow to make any more decisions. You can call me about ten. I should know something then."

"I'll do that. Thank you."

"Remember. Don't expect too much."

She smiled. "I won't."

"But, just on the off chance, has anyone you've been in contact with had infectious mononucleosis lately?"

She blinked. "Why, yes. One of my female students had it a few weeks ago,'' she said. ''I remember that her mother was very concerned because the girl had played spin the bottle at a party. Ten years old, can you imagine…?'' She laughed nervously.

He went very still. ''Did you come into contact with any of her saliva?''

She chuckled weakly. ''I don't go around kissing my girls.''

''Antonia!''

''We shared a soda,'' she recalled.

He began to smile. ''Well, well. Of course, there's still the possibility that we're no better off, but mono and leukemia are very similar in the way they show up in blood work. A lab technician could have mixed them up.''

''It might have been a mistake?'' she asked hopefully.

''Maybe. But only maybe. We can't discount the other symptoms you've had.''

''A maybe is pretty good,'' she said. ''What are the symptoms of mononucleosis?''

''Same as leukemia,'' he confirmed. ''Weakness, sore throat, fatigue, fever…'' He glanced at Powell and cleared his throat. ''And highly contagious.''

Powell smiled crookedly. ''I wouldn't care.''

The doctor chuckled. ''I know how you feel. Well, go home, Antonia. We'll know something in the morning. The labs are careful, but mistakes can happen.''

"If only this is one," she said huskily. "Oh, if only!"

When they were outside, Powell held her hand tight in his, and paused to bend and kiss her very gently on her mouth.

"I can't think of anything I'd rather have than mononucleosis," he remarked.

She smiled tearfully. "Neither can I!"

"You're sure about that blood type."

"Positive."

"Well, we'll cross our fingers and pray. Right now, let's get some lunch. Then we might go for a drive."

"Okay."

He took her back to his hotel for lunch and then they drove out of town, through the Saguaro National Monument and looked at the giant cacti. The air was cold, but the sun was out and Antonia felt a little more hopeful than she had before.

They didn't talk. Powell simply held her hand tight in his and the radio played country and western music.

Barrie was home when they drove up to her apartment building. She was surprised to see Powell, but the expression on his face and on Antonia's made her smile.

"Good news, I hope?" she asked.

"I hope so," Antonia said.

Barrie frowned, and then Antonia realized that she didn't know what was going on.

"We're getting married," Powell said, covering for her.

"We are?" Antonia asked, shocked.

"You said yes, remember? What else did you think I meant when I started talking about children?" he asked haughtily. "I won't live in sin with you."

"I didn't ask you to!"

"Good. Because I won't. I'm not that kind of man," he added, and he smiled at her with a new and exciting tenderness.

Antonia caught her breath at the warmth in the look he gave her, tingling from head to toe with new hope. *Please God,* she thought, *let this be a new beginning.*

Barrie was smiling from ear to ear. "Do I say congratulations?"

"Does she?" Powell asked Antonia.

Antonia hesitated. She knew that Powell only wanted her; maybe he felt sorry for her, too. He hadn't really had time to get used to the possibility that she might die. His motives disturbed her. But she'd never stopped loving him. Would it be so bad to marry him? He might learn to love her, if there was enough time.

"I'll tell you tomorrow," she promised.

He searched her eyes quietly. "It will be all right," he promised. "I know it."

She didn't. She was afraid to hope. But she didn't argue.

"There's a nice film on television tonight, if you're staying," Barrie told Powell. "I thought I'd make popcorn."

"That's up to Antonia," he said.

Antonia smiled at him. "I'd like you to stay."

He took off his hat. "I like butter on my popcorn," he said with a grin.

Chapter Nine

It was the longest night of Antonia's life. Powell went to his hotel at midnight, and she went to bed, still without having told Barrie what she had to face in the morning.

After Barrie went to work, Antonia got dressed. When Powell came for her at nine, she was more than ready to sit in the doctor's waiting room. She wasn't about to trust the telephone about anything that important. And apparently, neither was he.

They drove around until ten, when they went to Dr. Harris's office for their appointment. They sat in his waiting room and waited patiently through an emergency until he invited Antonia into his office, with Powell right behind her.

They didn't need to ask what he'd found. He was grinning from ear to ear.

"You're garden variety Type O," he told her without preamble, smiling even wider at her delight as she hugged an equally jubilant Powell. "Furthermore, I called the lab that did the blood work before, and they'd just fired a technician who kept mixing up test results. Yours was one he did. The other assistants turned him in, apparently. They're very professional. They don't tolerate sloppy work."

"Oh, thank God!" Antonia burst out.

"I'm very sorry for the ordeal you've had because of this," he added.

"I hid my head in the sand," she said. "If I'd come right in for treatment, and you'd done more blood work, you'd have discovered it sooner."

"Well, there is some bad news," he added with a rueful smile. "You really do have mononucleosis."

Dr. Claridge explained the course of the disease, and then warned them again about how contagious mono was.

"I've seen this run through an entire school in the cafeteria in the old days," he recalled. "And sometimes people spend weeks in bed with it. But I don't believe that'll be necessary in your case. I don't think you will lose a lot of work time."

"She won't have to worry about that," Powell said. "She's marrying me. She won't have to work. And I don't think she'll mind a few days in bed, getting rid of the infection."

She looked up at his suddenly grim face and realized that he was going through with the marriage regardless of her new diagnosis. It didn't make sense for a minute, and then it made terrible sense. He'd given his word. He wouldn't go back on it, no matter what. His pride and honor were as much a part of his makeup as his stubbornness.

"We'll talk about that later," she said evasively. "Dr. Claridge, I can't thank you enough."

"I'm just happy to be able to give a cheerful prognosis on your condition now," he said with genuine feeling. "These things happen, but they can have tragic consequences. There was such a lab work mix-up in a big eastern city many years ago...it caused a man to take his own life out of fear. Generally I encourage people to have a second blood test to make sure. Which I would have certainly done in your case, had you come back to see me sooner," he added deliberately.

She flushed. "Yes. Well, I'll try to show a little more fortitude in the future. I was scared to death and I panicked."

"That's a very human reaction," Dr. Claridge assured her. "Take care. If you have any further problems, let me know."

"We'll be going back to Bighorn," Powell said. "But Dr. Harris will be in touch if he needs to."

"Good man, Harris," Dr. Claridge said. "He was very concerned about you when he contacted me. He'll be happy with the new diagnosis."

"I'm sure he will. I'll phone him the minute I get home and tell him," Antonia added.

They left the doctor's office and Antonia paused on the sidewalk to look around her with new eyes. "I thought I'd lost everything," she said aloud, staring with unabashed delight at trees and people and the distant mountains. "I'd given up. And now, it's all new, it's all beautiful."

He caught her hand in his and held it tight. "I wish I'd known sooner," he said.

She smiled faintly. "It was my problem, not yours."

He didn't answer that. He could tell from her attitude that she was going to try to back out of their wedding. Well, he thought, she was going to find that it was more difficult than she imagined. He had her. He wasn't letting go now.

"If you're hungry, we can have something to eat. Late breakfast or early lunch, whichever you like. But first, we'll get these filled," he added, putting the prescriptions into his pocket.

They filled the prescriptions and then went straight to Powell's hotel, and up in the elevator to his luxurious suite overlooking the Sonoran Desert.

"We can eat up here, and we can talk in private," he said, "without prying eyes. But first, I want to phone your father."

"My father? Why?"

He picked up the telephone, got an outside line and dialed. "Because he knew," he said.

"How?"

He glanced at her. "I made him phone Dr. Harris. We both felt that something was wrong. He wanted to rush down here, but I didn't want you to know... Hello, Ben? There was a mix-up at the lab. She has mononucleosis, not cancer, and she'll be back on her feet in no time." He smiled at the excitement on the other end of the line. "He wants to talk to you," he said, holding out the receiver.

"Hi, Dad," Antonia said softly, glaring at Powell. "I didn't know you knew."

"Powell wouldn't rest until he had the truth. It is the truth, this time?" Ben asked sharply. "It really was a mistake?"

"It really was, thank God," she said with genuine relief. "I was scared to death."

"You weren't the only one. This is wonderful news, girl. Really wonderful news! When are you coming back? Powell tell you Maggie was going to tell the truth? You can get your old job back."

She glanced at Powell warily. He was listening, watching, intently. "Nothing's definite yet. I'll phone you in a day or two and let you know what I decide to do. Okay?"

"Okay. Thank God you're all right," he said heavily. "It's been a hell of a couple of days, Antonia."

"For me, too. I'll talk to you soon. Love you, Dad.''

"Love you."

She hung up, turning to glare at Powell. "You had to interfere!"

"Yes, I did," he agreed. "I agree with your father—I don't like secrets, either."

He took off his hat, holding her gaze the whole time. He looked incredibly grim. He slipped off his jacket and his tie, and loosened the top buttons of his shirt, exposing a dark, muscular chest thick with black hair.

The sight of him like that brought back long-buried needs and hungers.

"What are you doing?" she asked when his belt followed the rest and he'd dropped into a chair to shed his boots.

"Undressing," he said. He got back up again and moved toward her.

She started to sidestep, but she was seconds too late. He picked her up and carried her into the bedroom. He threw her onto the bed, following her down with a minimum of exertion.

With his arms on either side of her supporting his weight, she was trapped.

"Powell…"

His black eyes were faintly apologetic. "I'm sorry," he murmured as his mouth eased down against hers.

In the old days, their lovemaking had been passionate, but he'd always been the one to draw back. His reserve was what had convinced her later that he hadn't loved her.

Now, there was no reserve at all, and he was kissing her in a way he never had. His lips didn't cherish, they aroused, and aroused violently. He made her tremble with longings she'd never felt, even with him. His hands were as reckless as his mouth, touching, invading, probing, against her naked skin while the only sounds in the room were his quick, sharp breaths and the thunder of his heart beating against her bare breasts.

She didn't even realize he'd half undressed her. She was too involved in the pleasure he was giving her to care about anything except that she wanted him to have access to her soft, warm skin. She needed the feel of his mouth on her, ached for it, hurt to have it. She arched up against him, moaning when the pleasure became more than she could bear.

Vaguely she was aware that a lot of skin was touching other skin. She felt the warm strength of his body against hers and there didn't seem to be any fabric separating them anymore. The hair on his long legs brushed her bare ones as he separated them and moved so that he was lying completely against her in an intimacy they'd never shared.

She panicked then, freezing when she felt his aroused body in intimate contact with her own.

His mouth softened on hers, gentled, so tender that

she couldn't resist him. His hands smoothed up and down her body, and he smiled against her lips.

"Easy," he whispered, lifting his head so that he could see her wet, dazed eyes. His hips moved and she stiffened. "Does that hurt?" he asked softly.

She bit her lower lip. Her hands clenched against his hard arms. "It...yes."

"You're embarrassed. Shocked, too." He brushed his lips against hers as he moved again, tenderly, but even so, the pain was there again and she flinched. His eyes searched hers and the look on his face became strained, passionate, almost grim. "I guess it has to hurt this time," he said unsteadily, "but it won't for long."

She swallowed. "It's...wrong."

He shook his head. "We're going to be married. This is my insurance."

"In...surance?" She gasped, because he was filling her...

"Yes." He moved again, and this time she gasped because it was so sweet, and her hips lifted to prolong it. "I'm giving you a baby, Antonia," he breathed reverently, and even as the words entered her ear, his mouth crushed down over hers and his body moved urgently, and the whole world dissolved in a sweet, hot fire that lifted her like a bird in his arms and slung her headlong up into the sky...

He didn't *look* guilty. That was her first thought when his face came into vivid focus above her. He was smiling, and the expression in his black eyes made her want to hit him. She flushed to the very roots of her hair, as much from the intimacy of their position as from her memories of the past few hectic, unbelievably passionate minutes.

"That settles all the arguments you might have against marriage, I trust?" he asked outrageously. He drew a strand of damp blond hair over her nose playfully. "If we'd done this nine years ago, nothing could have come between us. It was sweeter than I dreamed it would be, and believe me, I dreamed a lot in nine years."

She sighed heavily, searching his black eyes. They were warm and soft now and she waited for the shame and guilt to come, but it didn't. It was very natural to lie naked in his arms and let him look at her and draw his fingers against her in lazy, intimate caresses.

"No arguments at all?" he asked at her lips, and kissed her gently. "You look worried."

"I am," she said honestly. Her wide eyes met his. "I'm midway between periods."

He smiled slowly. "The best time," he mused.

"But a baby so soon…!"

His fingers covered her lips and stopped the words. "So late," he replied. "You're already twenty-seven."

"I know, but there's Maggie," she said miserably. "She doesn't like me. She won't want me there at all…and a baby, Powell! It will be so hard on her."

"We'll cross bridges when we come to them," he

said. His eyes slid down her body and back up and desire kindled in their black depths again. His face began to tauten, his caresses became arousing. When she shivered and a soft moan passed between her parted lips, he bent to kiss them with renewed hunger.

"Can you take me again?" he whispered provocatively. "Will it hurt?"

She slid closer to him, feeling the instant response of his body, feeling him shiver as she positioned her body to accept his. She looked into his eyes and caught her breath when he moved down.

He stilled, watching her, his heartbeat shaking them both. He lifted and pushed, watched. Her eyes dilated and he eased down again, harder this time, into complete possession.

She gasped. But her hands were pulling at him, not pushing. He smiled slowly and bent to cover her mouth with his. There had never been a time in his life when he felt more masculine than now, with her soft cries in his ear and her body begging for his. He closed his eyes and gave in to the glory of loving her.

Eventually they had lunch and went to Barrie's apartment when she was due home. One look at them told the story, and she hugged Antonia warmly.

"Congratulations. I told you it would work out one day."

"It worked out, all right," Antonia said, and then

told her friend the real reason why she'd come back to Arizona.

Barrie had to sit down. Her green eyes were wide, her face drawn as she realized the agony her friend had suffered.

"Why didn't you tell me?" she burst out.

"For the same reason she didn't tell me," Powell murmured dryly, holding Antonia's hand tight in his. "She didn't want to worry anyone."

"You idiot!" Barrie muttered. "I'd have made you go back to the doctor."

"That's why I didn't tell you," Antonia said. "I would have told you eventually, though."

"Thanks a lot!"

"You'd have done exactly the same thing, maybe worse," Antonia said, unperturbed, as she grinned at Barrie. "You have to come to the wedding."

"When is it?"

"Ten in the morning, day after tomorrow, at the county courthouse here," Powell said with a chuckle. "I have the license, Dr. Claridge did the blood work this morning and we're going back to Bighorn wearing our rings."

"I have a spare room," Barrie offered.

Powell shook his head. "Thanks, but she's mine now," he said possessively, searching Antonia's face with quick, hungry eyes. "I'm not letting her out of my sight."

"I can understand that," Barrie agreed. "Well, do you have plans for the evening, or do you want to take in a movie with me? That new period piece is on at the shopping center.''

"That might be fun," Antonia said, looking up at Powell.

"I like costume dramas," he seconded. "Suits me."

Besides, he told Antonia later, when they were briefly alone, she wasn't going to be in any shape for what he really wanted for another day or so. That being the case, a movie was as good as anything to pass the time. As long as they were together, he added quietly. If she felt like it. He worried about not keeping her still. She ignored that. She could rest when they got back to Bighorn, she informed him.

Antonia clung to his hand during the movie, and that night, she slept in his arms. It was as if the past nine years had never happened. He still hadn't said anything about love, but she knew that he wanted her. Perhaps in time, love would come. Her real concern was how they were going to cope with Maggie's resentment, especially if their passion for each other bore fruit. It was too soon for a baby, but Powell's ardor had been too headlong to allow for precautions, and his hunger for a child with her was all too obvious. He wasn't thinking about Maggie. He was thinking about all those wasted years and how quickly he could make up for them. But Antonia worried.

The wedding service was very small and sedate and dignified. Antonia wore a cream-colored wool suit to be married in, and a hat with a small veil that covered her face until the justice of the peace pronounced them man and wife. Powell lifted the veil and looked at her face for a long moment before he bent and kissed her. It was like no kiss he'd ever given her before. She looked into his eyes and felt her legs melt under her. She'd never loved him so much.

Barrie had been one of their witnesses and a sheriff's deputy who was prevailed upon by the justice of the peace was the other. The paperwork was completed, the marriage license handed back with the date and time of the wedding on it. They were married.

The next day they were on the way to Bighorn in Powell's Mercedes-Benz. He was more tense than he'd been for three days and she knew it was probably because her body was still reeling from its introduction to intimacy. She was better, but any intimacy, even the smallest, brought discomfort. She hated that. Powell had assured her that it was perfectly natural, and that time would take care of the problem, but his hunger for her was in his eyes every time he looked at her. At this stage of their new relationship, she hated denying him what he craved. After all, it was the only thing they did have right now.

"Stop looking so morose," he taunted when they neared the Wyoming border hours later. "The world won't end because we can't enjoy each other in bed again just yet."

"I was thinking of you, not me," she said absently.

He didn't reply. His eyes were straight ahead. "I thought you enjoyed it."

She glanced at him and realized that she'd unintentionally hurt his ego. "Of course I did," she said. "But I think it must be more of a need for a man. I mean…"

"Never mind," he mused, glancing at her. "You remembered what I said, didn't you—that I can't go for a long time without a woman? I was talking about years, Antonia, not days."

"Oh."

He chuckled softly. "You little green girl. You're just as you were at eighteen."

"Not anymore."

"Well, not quite." He reached out his hand and she put hers into it, feeling its comforting strength. "We're on our way, honey," he said gently, and it was the first time that he'd used an endearment to address her. "It will be all right. Don't worry."

"What about Maggie?" she asked.

His face hardened. "Let me worry about Maggie."

Antonia didn't say anything else. But she had a bad feeling that they were going to have trouble in that quarter.

They stopped by her father's house first, for a tearful reunion. Then they dropped the bombshell.

"Married?" Ben burst out. "Without even telling me, or asking if I wanted to be there?"

"It was my idea," Powell confessed, drawing Antonia close to his side. "I didn't give her much choice."

Ben glared at him, but only for a minute. He couldn't forget that Powell had been more than willing to take on responsibility for Antonia when he thought she was dying. That took courage, and something more.

"Well, you're both old enough to know what you're doing," he said grudgingly, and he smiled at his daughter, who was looking insecure. "And if I get grandkids out of this, I'll shut up."

"You'll have grandchildren," she promised shyly. "Including a ready-made one to start with."

Powell frowned slightly. She meant Maggie.

Antonia looked up at him with a quiet smile. "Speaking of whom, we'd better go, hadn't we?"

He nodded. He shook hands with Ben. "I'll take care of her," he promised.

Ben didn't say anything for a minute. But then he smiled. "Yes. I know you will."

Powell drove them to his home, palatial and elegant, sitting on a rise overlooking the distant mountains. There were several trees around the house and long, rolling hills beyond where purebred cattle grazed. In the old days, the house had been a little shack with a leaking roof and a porch that sagged.

"What a long way you've come, Powell," she said.

He didn't look at her as he swung the car around to the side of the house and pressed the button that opened the garage.

The door went up. He drove in and closed the door behind them. Even the garage was spacious and clean.

He helped Antonia out. "I'll come back for your bags in a few minutes. You remember Ida Bates, don't you? She keeps house for me."

"Ida?" She smiled. "She was one of my mother's friends. They sang together in the choir at church."

"Ida still does."

They went in through the kitchen. Ida Bates, heavy-set and harassed, turned to stare at Antonia with a question in her eyes.

"We were married in Tucson," Powell announced. "Meet the new lady of the house."

Ida dropped the spoon in the peas she was stirring and rushed to embrace Antonia with genuine affection. "I can't tell you how happy I am for you! What a surprise!"

"It was to us, too," Antonia murmured with a shy glance at her new husband, who smiled back warmly.

Ida let her go and cast a worried look at Powell. "She's up in her room," she said slowly. "Hasn't come out all day. Won't eat a bite."

Antonia felt somehow responsible for the child's torment. Powell noticed that, and his jaw tautened. He took Antonia's hand.

"We'll go up and give her the news."

"Don't expect much," Ida muttered.

The door to Maggie's room was closed. Powell didn't even knock. He opened it and drew Antonia in with him.

Maggie was sitting on the floor looking at a book. Her hair was dirty and straggly and the clothes she was wearing looked as if they'd been slept in.

She looked at Antonia with real fear and scrambled to her feet, backing until she could hold on to the bedpost.

"What's the matter with you?" Powell demanded coldly.

"Is she…real?" she asked, wide-eyed.

"Of course I'm real," Antonia said quietly.

"Oh." Maggie relaxed her grip on the bedpost. "Are you…real sick?"

"She doesn't have what we thought," Powell said without preamble. "It was a mistake. She has something else, but she's going to be all right."

Maggie relaxed a little, but not much.

"We're married," Powell added bluntly.

Maggie didn't react at all. Her blue eyes lifted to Antonia and she didn't smile.

"Antonia is going to live with us," Powell continued. "I'll expect you to make her feel welcome here."

Maggie knew that. Antonia would certainly be welcome, as Maggie never had been. She looked at her father with an expression that made Antonia want to cry. Powell never even noticed the anguish in it.

Pick her up, she wanted to tell him. *Hold her. Tell her you still love her, that it won't make any difference that you've remarried.* But he didn't do that. He stared at the child with an austerity that made terrible

sense of what he'd said to Antonia. He didn't know
if Maggie was his, and he resented her. The child
certainly knew it. His attitude all but shouted it.

"I'll have to stay in bed for a while, Maggie,"
Antonia said. "It would be nice if you'd read to me
sometimes," she added, nodding toward the book on
the floor.

"You going to be my teacher, too?" Maggie asked.

"No," Powell said firmly, looking straight at Antonia. "She's going to have enough to do getting
well."

Antonia smiled ruefully. It looked as if she was
going to have a war on her hands if she tried to take
that teaching job back.

"But you and I are still going to see Mrs. Jameson," he told his daughter. "Don't think you're going
to slide out of that."

Maggie lifted her chin and looked at him. "I already done it."

"What?" he demanded.

"I told Mrs. Jameson," she said, glaring up at him.
"I told her I lied about Miss Hayes. I told her I was
sorry."

Powell was impressed. "You went to see her all
by yourself?" he asked.

She nodded, a curt little jerk of her head. "I'm
sorry," she said gruffly to Antonia.

"It was a brave thing to do," Antonia remarked.
"Were you scared?"

Maggie didn't answer. She just shrugged.

"Don't leave that book lying there," Powell instructed, nodding toward it on the carpet. "And take a bath and change those clothes."

"Yes, Daddy," she said dully.

Antonia watched her put the book away, and wished that she could do something, say something, interfere enough that she could wipe that look from Maggie's little face.

Powell tugged her out of the room before she could say anything else. She went, but she was determined that she was going to do something about this situation.

Antonia and Maggie had not started out on the right foot, because of what had happened in the past. But now Antonia wanted to try with this child. Now that she saw the truth in Powell's early words—that Maggie had paid a high price. That price had been love.

Maggie might not like her, but the child needed a champion in this household; and Antonia was going to be her champion.

Chapter Ten

When they were in the master bedroom where Powell slept, Antonia went close to him.

"Don't you ever hug her?" she asked softly. "Or kiss her, and tell her you're glad to see her?"

He stiffened. "Maggie isn't the sort of child who wants affection from adults."

His attitude shocked Antonia. "Powell, you don't really believe that, do you?" she asked, aghast.

The way she was looking at him made him uncomfortable. "I don't know if she's mine." He bit off the words defensively.

"Would it matter so much?" she persisted. "Powell, she's lived in your house since she was born. You've been responsible for her. You've watched her grow. Surely you feel something for her!"

He caught her by the waist and pulled her to him. "I want a child with you," he said quietly. "I promise you, it will be loved and wanted. It will never lack for affection."

She touched his lean cheek. "I know that. I'll love it, too. But Maggie needs us as well. You can't turn your back on her."

His eyebrows went up. "I've always fulfilled my responsibilities as far as Maggie is concerned. I've never wanted to see her hurt. But we've never had a good relationship. And she isn't going to accept you. She's probably already plotting ways to get rid of you."

"Maybe I know her better than you think," she replied. She smiled. "I'm going to love you until you're sick of it," she whispered, going close to him. "Love will spill out of every nook and cranny, it will fill you up. You'll love Maggie because I'll make you love her." She drew his head down and nibbled at his firm mouth until it parted, until he groaned and dragged her into his arms, to kiss her hungrily, like a man demented.

She returned his kisses until sheer exhaustion drained her of strength and she lay against his chest, holding on for support.

"You're still very weak," he remarked. He lifted her gently and carried her to the bed. "I'll have Ida bring lunch up here. Dr. Claridge said you'd need time in bed and you're going to get it now that we're home."

"Bully," she teased softly.

He chuckled, bending over her. "Only when I need to be." He kissed her softly.

Maggie, passing the door, heard him laugh, saw the happiness he was sharing with Antonia, and felt more alone than she ever had in her young life. She walked on, going down the stairs and into the kitchen.

"Mind you don't track mud in here," Ida Bates muttered. "I just mopped."

Maggie didn't speak. She walked out the door and closed it behind her.

Antonia had her lunch on a tray with Powell. It was so different now, being with him, loving him openly, watching the coldness leave him. He was like a different man.

But she worried about Maggie. That evening when Ida brought another tray, this time a single one because Powell had to go out, she asked about Maggie.

"I don't know where she is," Ida said, surprised. "She went out before lunch and never came back."

"But aren't you concerned?" Antonia asked sharply. "She's only nine!"

"Little monkey goes where she pleases, always has. She's probably out in the barn. New calf out there. She likes little things. She won't go far. She's got no place to go."

That sounded so heartless. She winced.

"You eat all that up, now. Do you good to have

some hot food inside you.'' Ida smiled and went out, leaving the door open. ''Call if you need me!''

Antonia couldn't enjoy her meal. She was worried, even if nobody else was.

She got up and searched in her suitcases for a pair of jeans, socks, sneakers and a sweatshirt. She put them on and eased down the stairs, through the living room and out the front door. The barn was to the side of the house, a good little walk down a dirt road. She didn't think about how tired she was. She was worried about Maggie. It was late afternoon, and growing dark. The child had been out all day.

The barn door was ajar. She eased inside it and looked around the spacious, shadowy confines until her eyes became accustomed to the dimness. The aisle was wide and covered in wheat straw. She walked past one stall and another until she found a calf and a small child together in the very last one.

''You didn't have anything to eat,'' she said.

Maggie was shocked. She stared up at the woman she'd caused so much trouble for and felt sick to her stomach. Nobody else cared if she starved. It was ironic that her worst enemy was concerned about her.

Her big blue eyes stared helplessly up at Antonia.

''Aren't you hungry?'' Antonia persisted.

Maggie shrugged. ''I had a candy bar,'' she said, avoiding those soft gray eyes.

Antonia came into the stall and settled down beside the calf in the soft, clean hay. She touched the calf's soft nose and smiled. "Their noses are so soft, aren't they?" she asked. "When I was a little girl, I used to wish I had a pet, but my mother was allergic to fur, so we couldn't have a dog or cat."

Maggie fidgeted. "We don't have dogs and cats. Mrs. Bates says animals are dirty."

"Not if they're groomed."

Maggie shrugged again.

Antonia smoothed the calf's forehead. "Do you like cattle?"

Maggie watched her warily. Then she nodded. "I know all about Herefords and black Angus. That's what my daddy raises. I know about birth weights and weight gain ratios and stuff."

Antonia's eyebrows arched. "Really? Does he know?"

Maggie's eyes fell. "It wouldn't matter. He hates me on account of I'm like my mother."

Antonia was surprised that the child was that perceptive. "But your mother did have wonderful qualities," Antonia said. "When we were in school, she was my best friend."

Maggie stared at her. "She married my daddy instead of you."

Antonia's hand stilled on the calf. "Yes. She told a lie, Maggie," she explained. "Because she loved your daddy very much."

"She didn't like me," Maggie said dully. "She used to hit me when he wasn't home and say it was my fault that she was unhappy."

"Maggie, it wasn't your fault," Antonia said firmly.

Maggie's blue eyes met hers. "Nobody wants me here," she said stiffly. "Now that you're here, Daddy will make me go away!"

"Over my dead body," Antonia said shortly.

The child sat there like a little statue, as if she didn't believe what she'd heard. "You don't like me."

"You're Powell's little girl," she replied. "I love him very much. How could I possibly hate someone who's part of him?"

For the first time, the fear in the child's eyes was visible. "You don't want to make me go away?"

"Certainly not," Antonia said.

She nibbled on her lower lip. "They don't want me here," she muttered, nodding her head curtly toward the house. "Daddy goes off and leaves me all the time, and she," she added in a wounded tone, "hates having to stay with me. It was better when I could stay with Julie, but she hates me, too, on account of I got you fired."

Antonia's heart went out to the child. She wondered if in all her life any adult had taken the time to sit down and really talk to her. Perhaps Mrs. Donalds had, and that was why Maggie missed her so much.

"You're very young to try to understand this," she told Maggie slowly. "But inadvertently it was because I lost my job that I went back to the doctor and discovered that I didn't have cancer. Your dad made me go to the doctor,'' she added with a reflective smile. ''He came after me when I left. If he hadn't, I don't know what might have happened to me. Things seem fated sometimes, to me,'' she added thoughtfully. ''You know, as if they're meant to happen. We blame people for playing their part in the scheme of things, and we shouldn't. Life is a test, Maggie. We have obstacles to overcome, to make us stronger.'' She hesitated. ''Is any of this making sense to you?''

''You mean God tests us,'' the child said softly.

Antonia smiled. ''Yes. Does your dad take you to church?''

She shrugged and looked away. ''He doesn't take me anywhere.''

And it hurt, Antonia thought, because she was beginning to understand just how much this child was enduring. ''I like going to church,'' she said. ''My grandparents helped build the Methodist Church where I went when I was little. Would you...'' She hesitated, not wanting to lose ground by rushing the child.

Maggie turned her head and looked at her. ''Would I...?'' she prompted softly.

''Would you like to go to church with me sometimes?''

The change the question made in that sullen face was remarkable. It softened, brightened, with interest. ''Just you and me?'' she asked.

"At first. Your dad might come with us, eventually."

She hesitated, toying with a piece of wheat straw. "You aren't mad at me anymore?" she asked.

Antonia shook her head.

"He won't mind?"

She smiled. "No."

"Well…" She shifted and then she frowned, glancing up at the woman with sad eyes. "Well, I would like to," she said. "But I can't."

"Can't? Why not?"

Maggie's shoulders hunched forward. "I don't got a dress."

Tears stung Antonia's gray eyes. Hadn't Powell noticed? Hadn't anybody noticed?

"Oh, my dear," she said huskily, grimacing.

The note in her voice got the child's attention. She saw the glitter of tears in the woman's eyes and felt terrible.

"Antonia!"

The deep voice echoed through the barn. Powell saw them together and strode forward.

"What the hell are you doing out of bed?" he demanded, lifting her to her feet with firm hands. He saw the tears and his face hardened as he turned to the child on her knees by the calf. "She's crying. What did you say to her?" he demanded.

"Powell, no!" She put her hand across his lips. "No! She didn't make me cry!"

"You're defending her!"

"Maggie," Antonia said gently, "you tell your dad what you just told me. Don't be afraid," she added firmly. "Tell him."

Maggie gave him a belligerent glare. "I don't got a dress," she said accusingly.

"Don't *have* a dress," Antonia corrected her belatedly.

"I don't have a dress," Maggie said obligingly.

"So?" he asked.

"I want to take her to church with me. She doesn't have anything to wear," Antonia told him.

He looked down at his daughter with dawning realization. "You haven't got a dress?"

"No, I don't!" Maggie returned.

He let out a heavy breath. "My God."

"Tomorrow after school you and I are going shopping," Antonia told the child.

"You and me?" Maggie asked.

"Yes."

Powell stared from one of them to the other with open curiosity. Maggie got to her feet and brushed herself off. She looked up at Antonia warily. "I read this fairy tale about a woman who married a man with two little kids and she took them off and lost them in the forest."

Antonia chuckled. "I couldn't lose you, Maggie," she told the child. "Julie told me that you could track like a hunter."

"She did?"

"Who taught you how to track?" Powell demanded.

Maggie glared at him. "Nobody. I read it in a Boy Scout manual. Jake loaned me his."

"Why didn't you ask your dad to buy you one of your own?" she asked the child.

Maggie glared at him again. "He wouldn't," she said. "He brings me dolls."

Antonia's eyebrows lifted. She looked at Powell curiously. "Dolls?"

"She's a girl, isn't she?" he demanded belligerently.

"I hate dolls," Maggie muttered. "I like books."

"Yes, I noticed," Antonia said.

Powell felt like an idiot. "You never said," he muttered at his daughter.

She moved a little closer to Antonia. "You never asked," she replied. She brushed at the filthy sweatshirt where wheat straw was sticking to it.

"You look like a rag doll," Powell said. "You need a bath and a change of clothes."

"I don't got no more clothes," she said miserably. "Mrs. Bates said she wouldn't wash them because I got them too dirty to get clean."

"*What?*"

"She threw away my last pair of blue jeans," Maggie continued, "and this is the only sweatshirt I got left."

"Oh, Maggie," Antonia said heavily. "Maggie,

why didn't you tell her you didn't have any other clothes?''

''Because she won't listen,'' the child said. ''Nobody listens!'' She looked at her father with his own scowl. ''When I grow up, I'm going to leave home and never come back! And when I have little kids, I'm going to love them!''

Powell was at a complete loss for words. He couldn't even manage to speak.

''Go and have a bath,'' Antonia told the child gently. ''Have you a gown and robe?''

''I got pajamas. I hid them or she'd have throwed them away, too,'' she added mutinously.

''Then put them on. I'll bring up your supper.''

Powell started to speak, but she put her hand over his mouth again.

''Go ahead, Maggie,'' she urged the child.

Maggie nodded and with another majestic glare at her father, she stalked off down the aisle.

''Oh, she's yours, all right,'' Antonia mused when she'd gone out of the barn and they were alone. ''Same scowl, same impatient attitude, same temper, same glare…''

He felt uncomfortable. ''I didn't know she didn't have any damned clothes,'' he said.

''Now you do. I'm going to take her shopping to buy new ones.''

''You aren't in any shape to go shopping or to carry trays of food,'' he muttered. ''I'll do it.''

"You'll take her shopping?" she asked with mischief twinkling in her gray eyes.

"I can take a kid to a dress shop," he said belligerently.

"I'm sure you can," she agreed. "It's just the shock of having you volunteer to do it, that's all."

"I'm not volunteering," he said. "I'm protecting you."

She brightened. "Was that why? You sweet man, you."

She reached up and kissed him softly, lingeringly, on his hard mouth. He only resisted for a split second. Then he lifted her clear of the ground, and kissed her with muted hunger, careful not to make any more demands on her than she was ready for. He turned and carried her down the aisle, smiling at her warmly between kisses.

Mrs. Bates was standing in the middle of the floor looking perplexed when they walked in, although she smiled at the sight of the boss with his wife in his arms.

"Carrying her over the threshold?" she teased Powell.

"Sparing her tired legs," he corrected. "Did Maggie go through here?"

"Indeed she did," Mrs. Bates said with a rueful smile. "I'm a wicked witch because I threw away the only clothes she had and now she has to go shopping for more."

"That's about the size of it," he agreed, smiling at Antonia.

"I didn't know," Mrs. Bates said.

"Neither did I," replied Powell.

They both looked at Antonia.

"I'm a schoolteacher," she reminded them. "I'm used to children."

"I guess I don't know anything," Powell said with a heavy sigh.

"You'll learn."

"How about taking a tray up to Maggie?" Powell asked Mrs. Bates.

"It's the least I can do," the older woman said sheepishly. "I'll never live that down. But you can't imagine the shape those jeans were in. And the sweatshirts!"

"I'm taking her shopping tomorrow after school," Powell said. "We'll get some new stuff for her to wear out."

Mrs. Bates was fascinated. In all the years she'd worked here, Powell Long hadn't taken his daughter anywhere if she wasn't in trouble.

"I know," he said, reading the look accurately. "But there has to be a first step."

Mrs. Bates nodded. "I guess so. For both of us."

Antonia just smiled. Progress at last!

Powell felt out of place in the children's boutique. The saleslady was very helpful, but Maggie didn't know what to get and neither did he.

They looked at each other helplessly.

"Well, what do you want to buy?" he demanded.

She glared at him. "I don't know!"

"If I could suggest some things." The saleslady intervened diplomatically.

Powell left her to it. He couldn't imagine that clothes were going to do much for his sullen child, but Antonia had insisted that it would make a difference if he went with her. So far, he didn't see any difference.

But when the child went into the dressing room with the saleslady and reappeared five minutes later, he stared at her as if he didn't recognize her.

She was wearing a ruffled pink dress with lace at the throat, a short-skirted little thing with white leggings and patent leather shoes. Her hair was neatly brushed and a frilly ribbon sat at a jaunty angle in it beside her ear.

"Maggie?" he asked, just to be sure.

The look on her dad's face was like a miracle. He seemed surprised by the way she looked. In fact, he smiled. She smiled back. And the change the expression made in her little face was staggering.

For the first time, he saw himself in the child. The eyes were the wrong color, but they were the same shape as his own. Her nose was going to be straight like his—well, like his used to be before he got it broken in a fight. Her mouth was thin and wide like his, her cheekbones high.

Sally had lied about this, too, about Maggie not being his. He'd never been so certain of anything.

He lifted an ironic eyebrow. "Well, well, from ugly duckling to swan," he mused. "You look pretty."

Maggie's heart swelled. Her blue eyes sparkled. Her lips drew up and all at once she laughed, a gurgle of sound that hit Powell right in the heart. He had never heard her laugh. The impact of it went right through him and he seemed to see down the years with eyes full of sorrow and regret. This child had never had a chance at happiness. He'd subconsciously blamed her for Sally's betrayal, for the loss of Antonia. He'd never been a proper father to her in all her life. He wondered if it was going to be too late to start now.

The laughter had changed Maggie's whole appearance. He laughed at the difference.

"Hell," he said under his breath. "How about something blue, to match her eyes?" he asked the saleslady. "And some colorful jeans, not those old dark blue things she's been wearing."

"Yes, sir," the saleslady said enthusiastically.

Maggie pirouetted in front of the full-length mirror, surprised to see that she didn't look the way she usually did. The dress made her almost pretty. She wondered if Jake would ever get to see her in it, and her eyes brightened even more. Now that Antonia was back, maybe everyone would stop hating her.

But Antonia was sick, and she wouldn't be teaching. And that was still Maggie's fault.

"What's the matter?" Powell asked gently. He went down on one knee in front of the child, frowning. "What's wrong?"

Maggie was surprised that he was concerned, that he'd even noticed her sudden sadness. He didn't, usually.

She lifted her eyes to his. "Miss Hayes won't be teaching. It's still my fault."

"Antonia." He corrected her. "She isn't Miss Hayes anymore."

A thought occurred to her. "Is she…my mom, now?"

"Your stepmother," he said tersely.

She moved closer. Hesitantly she reached out and put her hand on his shoulder. It barely touched and then rested, like a butterfly looking for a place to light. "Now that she's back, you don't…hate me anymore, do you?" she asked softly.

His face contorted. With a rough sound, deep in his throat, he swept her close and held her, standing with her in his arms. He hugged her and rocked her, and she clung to him with a sound like a muffled sob.

"Please don't…hate me…anymore!" She wept. "I love you, Daddy!"

"Oh, dear God," Powell whispered huskily, his eyes closed as he weighed his sins. His arms contracted. "I don't hate you," he said curtly. "God knows, I never hated you, Maggie!"

She laid her head on his shoulder and closed her own eyes, savoring the newness of a father's arms, a father's comfort. This was something she'd never known. It was so nice, being hugged. She smiled through her tears.

"Say," he said after a minute, "this is nice."

She gurgled.

He put her down and looked into her uplifted face. Tears were streaming down it, but she was smiling.

He dug in his pocket and cursed under his breath. "Hell. I never carry handkerchiefs," he said apologetically.

She wiped her eyes on the back of her hands. "Me, neither," she said.

The saleslady came back with an armload of dresses. "I found a blue suit," she said gaily, "and another skirt and top in blue."

"They're very pretty!" Maggie said enthusiastically.

"Indeed they are. Why don't you try them on?" he said invitingly.

"Okay!"

She danced off with the saleslady and he watched, astonished. That was his child. He had a very pretty daughter, and she loved him in spite of all the mistakes he'd made. He smiled reflectively. Well, well, and they said miracles didn't happen. He felt in the middle of one right now. And somehow, it all went back to Antonia, a cycle that had begun and ended with her in his life. He smiled as he thought about the process that had brought them, finally, together and made such a vital change in the way things had been. He glanced at himself in the mirror and wondered where the bitter, hard man he'd been only weeks before, had gone.

Chapter Eleven

Maggie ran into Antonia's bedroom ahead of her father, wearing the blue dress and leggings and new shoes.

She came to a sudden stop at the side of the bed and seemed to become suddenly shy as she looked at the pink-clad woman in the bed. Antonia's blond hair was around her shoulders and she was wearing a pink lacy gown with an equally lacy bed jacket. She looked fragile, but she also looked welcoming, because she smiled.

"Oh, how nice," Antonia said at once, wondering at the change in the child. "How very nice! You look like a different girl, Maggie!"

Maggie felt breathless. "Daddy got me five new

outfits and jeans and shirts and sweatshirts and shoes," she sputtered. "And he hugged me!"

Antonia's face lit up. "He did?"

Maggie smiled shyly. "Yeah, he did!" She laughed. "I think he likes me!"

"I think he does, too," Antonia said in a loud whisper.

Maggie had something in her hand. She hesitated, glancing warily at Antonia. "Me and Daddy got you something," she said shyly.

"You did?" she asked, too surprised to correct the child's grammar.

Maggie moved forward and put it into Antonia's hands. "It plays a song."

It was a small box. Antonia unwrapped it and opened it. Inside was a music box, a fragile, porcelain-topped miniature brass piano that, when wound and opened, played "Clair de Lune."

"Oh," she exclaimed. "I've never had anything so lovely!"

Maggie smiled crookedly.

"Did your dad pick it out?" she asked, entranced by the music.

Maggie's face fell.

Antonia saw the expression and could have hit herself for what she'd asked. "You picked it out, didn't you?" she asked immediately, and watched the child's face brighten again. She would have to be careful not to do any more damage to that fragile self-esteem. "What wonderful taste you have, Maggie. Thank you!"

Maggie smiled. "You're welcome."

Powell came in the door, grinning when he saw Antonia with the music box. "Like it?" he asked.

"I love it," she replied. "I'll treasure it, always," she added with a warm glance at Maggie.

Maggie actually blushed.

"You'd better put your clothes away," Powell said.

Maggie winced at the authority in his tone, but when she looked up at him, he wasn't angry or impatient. He was smiling.

Her eyes widened. She smiled back. "Okay, Dad!"

She glanced again at Antonia and darted out the door.

"I hear we're handing out hugs today," Antonia murmured dryly.

He chuckled. "Yes, we are. I could get to like that."

"She could, too."

"How about you?" he asked with a speculative glance.

She held out her arms. "Why don't you come down here and find out?"

He laughed softly as he tossed his hat into the chair and eased down on the bed beside her, his arms on either side of her to balance him. She reached up to draw him down, smiling under the warm, slow crush of his mouth.

He kissed her hungrily, but with a tenderness she remembered from their early days together. She loved the warmth of his kisses, the feel of his body against her. She writhed under his weight suggestively and felt him tense.

"No," he whispered, easing to one side.

She sighed wistfully. "Heartless man."

"It's for your own good," he said, teasing her lips with his forefinger. "I want you to get well."

"I'm trying."

He smiled and bent to nuzzle her nose against his. "Maggie looks pretty in blue," he murmured.

"Yes, she does." She searched his black eyes. "You noticed, didn't you?"

"Noticed what?"

"How much she favors you. I saw it when she smiled. She has the same wrinkles in her face that you have in yours when you smile. Of course, she has your nasty temper, too."

"Curses with the blessings." He chuckled. His eyes searched hers and he drew in a heavy breath. "I never dreamed when I went off to Arizona to find you that it would end up like this."

"Is that a complaint?"

"What do you think?" he murmured and kissed her again.

He carried her down to the table, and for the first time, he and Antonia and Maggie had a meal together.

Maggie was nervous, fidgeting with the utensils because she didn't know which one to use.

"There's plenty of time to learn that," Powell said when he saw her unease. "You aren't under the microscope, you know. I thought it might be nice to have a meal together for a change."

Maggie looked from one adult to the other. "You aren't going to send me away, are you?" she asked her father.

"Idiot," he muttered, glaring at her.

She glared right back. "Well, you didn't like me," she reminded him.

"I didn't know you," he replied. "I still don't. That's my fault, but it's going to change. You and I need to spend more time together. So suppose instead of riding the bus, I take you to and from school all the time?"

She was elated and then disappointed. Jake rode the bus. If she didn't, she wouldn't get to see him.

Powell didn't know about Jake. He scowled even more at her hesitation.

"I'd like to," Maggie said. She blushed. "But…"

Antonia remembered what Julie had told her. "Is there someone who rides the bus that you don't want to miss seeing?" she asked gently, and the blush went nuclear.

Powell pursed his lips. "So that's it," he said, and chuckled. "Do I know this lucky young man who's caught my daughter's eye?"

"Oh, Daddy!" Maggie groaned.

"Never mind. You can go on riding the bus," he said, with a wicked glance at Antonia. "But you might like to come out with me some Saturdays when I'm checking up on my cattle operation."

"I'd like to do that," Maggie said. "I want to know about your weight gain ratios and heritability factors."

Powell's fork fell from his fingers and made a clanging noise against his plate. To hear those terms coming from a nine-year-old floored him.

Maggie saw that, and grinned. "I like to read about cattle, too. He's got these herd books," she explained to Antonia, "and they have all the statistics on proper genetic breeding. Do you breed genetically, Daddy?"

"Good God," he said on a heavy breath. "She's a cattleman."

"Yes, she is," Antonia agreed. "Surprise, surprise. Speaking of genetics, I wonder who she inherited that from?"

He looked sheepish, but he grinned from ear to ear. "Yes, I do breed genetically," he told his daughter. "If you're that interested, I'll take you around the operation and show you the traits I'm breeding for."

"Like easy calving and low birth weight?" Maggie asked.

Powell let out another breath, staring at his daughter with pure admiration. "And here I was worried that I wouldn't have anyone to leave the ranch to."

Antonia burst out laughing. "It looks as if you're

going to leave it in the right hands," she agreed, glancing warmly at Maggie.

Maggie blushed and beamed, all at once. She was still in shell shock from the sudden change of her life. She owed that to Antonia. It was like coming out of the darkness into the sunshine.

Antonia felt the same when she looked at her ready-made family.

"That reminds me," she said. "Your granddad would like to take you with him on an antique-buying binge next weekend. He's going to drive over to an auction in Sheridan."

"But I don't got a granddad," Maggie said, perplexed.

"Don't *have*," Antonia corrected her. She smiled. "And yes, you do have one. My father."

"A real granddaddy of my own?" Maggie asked, putting down her fork. "Does he know me?"

"You went to see him with your dad. Don't you remember?"

"He lived in a big white house. Oh, yes." Her face brightened, and then it fell. "I was scared and I didn't speak to him. He won't like me."

"He likes you very much," Antonia said. "And he'll enjoy teaching you about antiques, if you'd like to learn. It's his hobby."

"That would be fun!"

"I can see that you're going to be much in demand from now on, Maggie," Antonia said, smiling. "Will you mind?"

Maggie shook her head. She smiled a little unsteadily. "Oh, no, I won't mind at all!"

Antonia was half asleep when Powell slid into bed beside her with a long sigh and stretched.

"She beat me," he said.

Antonia rolled over, pillowing her head on his bare, hair-roughened chest. "At what?" she murmured drowsily.

"Checkers. I still don't see how she set me up." He yawned. "God, I'm sleepy!"

"So am I." She curved closer. "Good night."

"Good night."

She smiled as she slipped back into oblivion, thinking as she did how lucky they were to have each other. Powell had changed so much. He might not love her as she loved him, but he seemed very content. And Maggie was friendly enough. It would take time, but she felt very much at home here already. Things looked bright.

The next morning, she was afraid she'd spoken too soon. Maggie went off to school, and Powell went to a cattle sale, leaving Antonia at home by herself on what was Mrs. Bates's day off. The persistent ringing of the doorbell got her out of bed, and she went downstairs in a long white robe, still half asleep, to answer it.

The woman standing on the other side of the door came as a total shock.

If Antonia was taken aback, so was the gorgeous
redhead gaping at her with dark green eyes.

"Who are you?" she demanded haughtily.

Antonia looked her over. Elegant gray suit, pink
camisole a little too low-cut, short skirt and long legs.
Nice legs. Nice figure. But a little ripe, she thought
wickedly. The woman was at least five years older
than she was; perhaps more.

"I'm Mrs. Powell Long," Antonia replied with
equal hauteur. "What can I do for you?"

The woman just stared at her. "You're joking!"

"I'm not joking." Antonia straightened. "What do
you want?"

"I came to see Powell. On a private matter," she
added with a cold smile.

"My husband and I don't have secrets," Antonia
said daringly.

"Really? Then you know that he's been at my
house every night working out the details of a merger,
don't you?"

Antonia didn't know how to answer that. Powell
had been working late each night, but she'd never
thought it was anything other than business. Now, she
didn't know. She was insecure, despite Powell's hunger for her. Desire wasn't love, and this woman was
more beautiful than any that Antonia had ever seen.

"Powell won't be home until late," Antonia said
evasively.

"Well, in that case, I won't wait," the redhead
murmured.

"Can I take a message?"

"Yes. Tell him Leslie Holton called to see him," she replied. "I'll, uh, be in touch, if he asks. And I'm sure he will." Her cold eyes traveled down Antonia's thin body and back up again with faint contempt. "There's really no understanding the male mind, is there?" she mused aloud and with a nod, turned and walked back to her lafe-model Cadillac.

Antonia watched her get in it and drive away. The woman even drove with an attitude, haughty and efficient. She wished and wished that the car would run over four big nails and have all four tires go flat at once. But to her disappointment, the car glided out of sight without a single wobble.

So that was the widow Holton, who was trying to get her claws into Dawson Rutherford and Powell. Had she succeeded with Powell? She seemed very confident. And she was certainly lovely. Obviously he hadn't been serious about marrying the widow, but had there been something between them?

Antonia found herself feeling uncertain and insecure. She didn't have the beauty or sophistication to compete with a woman like that. Powell did want her, certainly, but that woman would know all the tricks of seduction. What if she and Powell had been lovers? What if they still were? Antonia hadn't been up to bouts of lovemaking, since that one long night she'd spent with Powell. Was abstinence making him desperate? He'd teased her about not being able to go without a woman for long periods of time, and he'd

said years, not weeks. But was he telling the truth or
just sparing Antonia's feelings? She had to find out.

Late that afternoon, another complication presented
itself. Julie Ames came home with Maggie and pro-
ceeded to make herself useful, tidying up Antonia's
bedroom and fluffing up her pillows. She'd come in
with a bouquet of flowers, too, and she'd rushed up
to hug Antonia at once, all loving concern and friend-
liness.

Maggie reacted to this as she always had, by withdrawing, and Antonia wanted so badly to tell her that
Julie didn't mean to hurt her.

"I'll go get a vase," Maggie said miserably, turning.

"I'll bet Julie wouldn't mind doing that," Antonia
said, surprising both girls. "Would you?" she asked
Julie. "You could ask Mrs. Bates to find you one and
put water in it."

"I'd be happy to, Mrs. Long!" Julie said enthusiastically, and rushed out to do as she was asked.

Antonia smiled at Maggie, who was still staring at
her in a puzzled way.

"Whose idea was it to pick the flowers?" she
asked knowingly.

Maggie flushed. "Well, it was mine, sort of."

"Yes, I thought so. And Julie got the credit, and it
hurt."

Maggie was surprised. "Yes," she admitted absently.

"I'm not as dim as you think I am," she told Maggie. "Just try to remember one thing, will you? *You're* my daughter. You belong here."

Maggie's heart leaped. She smiled hesitantly.

"Or I'm your stepmother, if you'd rather..."

She moved closer to the bed. "I'd rather call you Mom," she said slowly. "If...you don't mind."

Antonia smiled gently. "No, Maggie. I don't mind. I'd be very, very flattered."

Maggie sighed. "My mother didn't want me," she said in a world-weary way. "I thought it was my fault, that there was something wrong with me."

"There's nothing wrong with you, darling," Antonia said gently. "You're fine just the way you are."

Maggie fought back tears. "Thanks."

"Something's still wrong, isn't it?" she asked softly. "Can you tell me?"

Maggie looked at her feet. "Julie hugged you."

"I like being hugged."

She looked up. "You do?"

She smiled, nodding.

Maggie hesitated, but Antonia opened her arms, and the child went into them like a homing pigeon. It was incredible, this warm feeling she got from being close to people. First her own dad had hugged her, and now Antonia had. She couldn't remember a time when anyone had wanted to hug her.

She smiled against Antonia's warm shoulder and sighed.

Antonia's arms contracted. "I do like being hugged."

Maggie chortled. "So do I."

Antonia let her go with a smile. "Well, we'll both have to put in some practice, and your dad will, too. You're very pretty when you smile," she observed.

"Here's the vase!" Julie said, smiling as she came in with it. She glanced at Maggie, who was beaming. "Gosh, you look different lately."

"I got new clothes," Maggie said pointedly.

"No. You smile a lot." Julie chuckled. "Jake said you looked like that actress on his favorite TV show, and he was sort of shocked. Didn't you see him staring at you in class today?"

"He never!" Maggie exclaimed, embarrassed. "Did he?" she added hopefully.

"He sure did! The other boys teased him. He didn't even get mad. He just sort of grinned."

Maggie's heart leaped. She looked at Antonia with eyes brimming with joy and discovery.

Antonia felt that same wonder. She couldn't ever regret marrying Powell, regardless of how it all ended up. She thought of the widow Holton and grew cold inside. But she didn't let the girls see it. She only smiled, listening to their friendly discussion with half an ear, while she wondered what Powell was going to say when she told him about their early-morning visitor.

He said nothing at all, as it turned out. And that made it worse. He only watched her through narrowed black eyes when she mentioned it, oh, so carelessly, as they prepared for bed that night.

"She didn't tell me what she wanted to discuss with you. She said that it was personal. I told her I'd give you the message. She did say that she'd be in touch." She peered up at him.

His hard face didn't soften. He searched her eyes, looking for signs of jealousy, but none were there. She'd given him the bare bones of Leslie's visit with no emotion at all. Surely if he meant anything to her, it would have mattered that he was carrying on private, personal discussions with another woman. And Leslie's name had been linked with his in past years. She must have known that, too.

"Was that all?" he asked.

She shrugged. "All that I remember." She smiled. "She's a knockout, isn't she?" she added generously. "Her hair is long and thick and wavy. I've never seen a human being with hair like that...it's almost alive. Does she model?"

"She was a motion picture actress until the death of her husband. She was tired of the pace so when she inherited his fortune, she gave it up."

"Isn't it boring for her here, in such a small community?"

"She spends a lot of time chasing Dawson Rutherford."

That was discouraging, for Barrie, anyway. Antonia wondered if Barrie knew about her stepbrother's contact with the woman. Then she remembered what her father had said about Dawson.

"Does he like her?" she asked curiously.

"He likes her land," he replied. "We're both trying to get her to sell a tract that separates his border from mine. Her property has a river running right through it. If he gets his hands on it, I'll have an ongoing court battle over water rights, and vice versa."

"So it really is business," she blurted out.

He cocked an eyebrow. "I didn't say that was all it was," he replied softly, mockingly. "Rutherford is a cold fish with women, and Leslie is, how can I put it, overstimulated."

Her breath caught in her throat. "How overstimulated is she?" she demanded suddenly. "And by whom?"

He pursed his lips and toyed with his sleeve. "My past is none of your concern."

She glared at him and sat upright in the bed. "Are you sleeping with her?"

His eyebrows jumped up. "What?"

"You heard me!" she snapped. "I asked if you were so determined to get that land that you'd forsake your marriage vows to accomplish it!"

"Is that what you think?" he asked, and he looked vaguely threatening.

"Why else would she come here to the house to see you?" she asked. "And at a time when she knew you were usually home and Maggie was in school?"

"You're really unsettled about this, aren't you? What did she say to you?"

"She said you'd been at her house every evening when you were supposedly working late," she muttered sharply. "And she acted as if I were the interloper, not her."

"She wanted to marry me," he remarked, digging the knife in deeper.

"Well, you married me," she said angrily. "And I'm not going to be cuckolded!"

"Antonia! What a word!"

"You know what I mean!"

"I hope I do," he said quietly, searching her furious eyes. "Why don't you explain it to me?"

"I wish I had a bottle, I'd explain it," she raged at him, "right over your hard head!"

His dark eyes widened with humor. "You're so jealous you can't see straight," he said, chuckling.

"Of that skinny redheaded cat?" she retorted.

He moved closer to the bed, still grinning. "Meow."

She glared at him, her fists clenched on the covers. "I'm twice the woman she is!"

He cocked one eyebrow. "Are you up to proving it?" he challenged softly.

Her breath came in sharp little whispers. "You go lock that door. I'll show you a few things."

He laughed with sheer delight. He locked the door and turned out the top light, turning back toward the bed.

She was standing beside it by then, and while he watched, she slid her negligee and gown down her arms to the floor.

"Well?" she asked huskily. "I may be a little thinner than I like, but I…"

He was against her before she could finish, his arms encircling her, his mouth hungry and insistent on her lips. She yielded at once, no argument, no protest.

He laid her down and quickly divested himself of everything he was wearing.

"Wait a minute," she protested weakly, "I'm supposed to be…proving something."

"Go ahead," he said invitingly as his mouth opened on her soft breast and his hands found new territory to explore.

She tried to speak, but it ended on a wild little cry. She arched up to him and her nails bit into his lean hips. By the time his mouth shifted back to hers and she felt the hungry pressure of his body over her, she couldn't even manage a sound.

Later, storm-tossed and damp all over from the exertion, she lay panting and trembling in his arms, so drained by pleasure that she couldn't even coordinate her body.

"You were too weak," he accused lazily, tracing her mouth with a lazy finger as he arched over her. "I shouldn't have done that."

"Yes, you should," she whispered huskily, drawing his mouth down over hers. "It was beautiful."

"Indeed it was." He smiled against her lips. "I

hope you were serious about wanting children. I meant to stop by the drugstore, but I forgot.''

She laughed. ''I love children, and we've only got one so far.''

He lifted his head and searched her eyes. ''You've changed her.''

''She's changed me. And you.'' Her arms tightened around his neck. ''We're a family. I've never been so happy. And from now on, it will only get better.''

He nodded. ''She's very forgiving,'' he replied. ''I've got to earn back the trust I lost along the way. I'm ashamed for what I've put her through.''

''Life is all lessons,'' she said. ''She's got you now. She'll have sisters and brothers to spoil, too.'' Her eyes warmed him. ''I love you.''

He traced the soft line of her cheek. ''I've loved you for most of my life,'' he said simply, shocking her, because he'd never said the words before. ''I couldn't manage to tell you. Funny, isn't it? I didn't realize what I had until I lost it.'' His eyes darkened. ''I wouldn't have wanted to live, if you hadn't.''

''Powell,'' she whispered brokenly.

He kissed away the tears. ''And you thought I wanted the widow Holton!''

''Well, she's skinny, but she is pretty.''

''Only on the outside. You're beautiful clean through, especially when you're being Maggie's mom.''

She smiled. ''That's because I love Maggie's dad so much,'' she whispered.

"And he loves you," he whispered back, bending. "Outrageously."

"Is that so?" she teased. "Prove it."

He groaned. "The spirit is willing, but you've worn out the flesh. Besides," he added softly, "you aren't up to long sessions just yet. I promise when you're completely well, I'll take you to the Bahamas and we'll see if we can make the world record book."

"Fair enough," she said. She held him close and closed her eyes, aglow with the glory of loving and being loved.

Chapter Twelve

The new teacher for Maggie's class found a cooperative, happy little girl as ready to help as Julie Ames was. And Maggie came home each day with a new outlook and joy in being with her parents. There were long evenings with new movies in front of the fire, and books to look at, and parties, because Antonia arranged them and invited all the kids Maggie liked—especially Jake.

Powell had done some slowing down, although he was still an arch rival of Dawson Rutherford's over that strip of land the widow Holton was dangling between them.

"She's courting him," Powell muttered one evening. "That's the joke of the century. The man's ice

clean through. He avoids women like the plague, but
she's angling for a weekend with him.''

"Yes, I know. I spoke to Barrie last week. She said
he's tried to get her to come home and chaperone
him, but they had a terrible fight over it and now
they're not speaking at all. Barrie's jealous of her, I
think.''

"Poor kid,'' he replied, drawing Antonia closer.
"There's nothing to be jealous of. Rutherford doesn't
like women.''

"He doesn't like men, either.''

He chuckled. "Me, especially. I know. What I
meant was that he's not interested in sexual esca-
pades, even with lovely widows. He just wants land
and cattle.''

"Women are much more fun,'' she teased, snug-
gling close.

"Barrie might try showing him that.''

"She'd never have the nerve.''

"Barrie? Are we talking about the same woman
who entertained three admirers at once at dinner?''

"Dawson is different,'' she replied. "He matters.''

"I begin to see the light.''

She closed her eyes with a sigh. "He's a nice
man,'' she said. "You don't like him because of his
father, but he's not as ruthless as George was.''

He stiffened. "Let's not talk about George.''

She lifted away and looked at him. "You don't still
believe…!''

"Of course not,'' he said immediately. "I meant

that the Rutherfords have been a thorn in my side for years, in a business sense. Dawson and I will never be friends.''

"Never is a long time. Barrie is my friend."

"And a good one," he agreed.

"Yes, well, I think she might end up with Dawson one day."

"They're related," he said shortly.

"They are not. His father married her mother."

"He hates her, and vice versa."

"I wonder," Antonia said quietly. "That sort of dislike is suspicious, isn't it? I mean, you avoid people you really dislike. He's always making some excuse to see Barrie and give her hell."

"She gives it right back," he reminded her.

"She has to. A man like that will run right over a woman unless she stands up to him." She curled her fingers into his. "You're like that, too," she added, searching his black eyes quietly. "A gentle woman could never cope with you."

"As Sally found out," he agreed. His fingers contracted. "There's something about our marriage that I never told you. I think it's time I did. Maggie was born two months premature. I didn't sleep with Sally until after I broke our engagement. And I was so drunk that I thought you'd come back to me," he added quietly. "You can't imagine how sick I felt when I woke up with her the next morning and realized what I'd done. And it was too late to put it right."

She didn't say anything. She swallowed down the pain. "I see."

"I was cruel, Antonia," he said heavily. "Cruel and thoughtless. But I paid for it. Sadly, Sally and Maggie paid with me, and so did you." He searched her eyes. "From now on, baby, if you tell me green is orange, I'll believe it. I wanted to tell you that from the day you came back to your father's house and I saw you there."

"You made cutting remarks instead."

He smiled ruefully. "It hurts to see what you've lost," he replied. "I loved you to the soles of your feet, and I couldn't tell you. I thought you hated me."

"Part of me did."

"And then I found out why you'd really come here to teach," he said. "I wanted to die."

She went into his arms and nuzzled closer to him. "You mustn't look back," she said. "It's over now. I'm safe, and so are you, and so is Maggie."

"My Maggie," he sighed, smiling. "She's a hell of a cattlewoman already."

"She's your daughter."

"Mmmm. Yes, she is. I'm glad I finally realized that Sally had lied about that. There are too many similarities."

"Far too many." She smiled against his chest. "It's been six weeks since that night I offered to prove I was more of a woman than the widow Holton," she reminded him.

"So it has."

She drew away a little, her eyes searching his while a secret smile touched her lips. But he wasn't waiting for surprises. His lean hand pressed softly against her flat stomach and he smiled back, all of heaven in his dark eyes.

"You know?" she whispered softly.

"I sleep with you every night," he replied. "And I make love to you most every one. I'm not numb. And," he added, "you've lost your breakfast for the past week."

"I wanted to surprise you."

"Go ahead," he suggested.

She glared at him. "I'm pregnant," she said.

He jumped up, clasped his hands over his heart and gave her such a look of wonder that she burst out laughing.

"Are you, truly?" he exclaimed. "My God!"

She was all but rolling on the floor from his ex-aggerated glee. Mrs. Bates stuck her head in the door to see what the commotion was all about.

"She's pregnant!" he told her.

"Well!" Mrs. Bates exclaimed. "Really?"

"The home test I took says I am," she replied. "I still have to go to the doctor to have it confirmed."

"Yes," Powell said. "And the results from this test won't be frightening."

She agreed wholeheartedly.

They told Maggie that afternoon. She was apprehensive when they called her into the living room. Things had been so wonderful lately. Perhaps they'd changed their minds about her, and she was going to be sent off to school…

"Antonia is pregnant," Powell said softly.

Maggie's eyes lit up. "Oh, is that it!" she said, relieved. "I thought it was going to be something awful. You mean we're going to have a real baby of our own?" She hugged Antonia warmly and snuggled close to her on the sofa. "Julie will be just green, just green with envy!" she said, laughing. "Can I hold him when he's born, and help you take care of him? I can get books about babies.…"

Antonia was laughing with pure delight. "Yes, you can help," she said. "I thought it might be too soon, that you'd be unhappy about it."

"Silly old Mom," Maggie said with a frown. "I'd love a baby brother. It's going to be a boy, isn't it?"

Powell chuckled. "I like girls, too," he said.

Maggie grinned at him. "You only like me on account of I know one end of a cow from another," she said pointedly.

"Well, you're pretty, too," he added.

She beamed. "Now, I'll have something really important to share at show and tell." She looked up. "I miss you at school. So does everybody else. Miss Tyler is nice, but you were special."

"I'll go back to teaching one day," Antonia promised. "It's like riding a bike. You never forget how."

"Shall we go over and tell your granddad?" Powell asked.

"Yes," Maggie said enthusiastically. "Right now!"

* * *

Ben was overwhelmed by the news. He sat down heavily in his easy chair and just stared at the three of them sitting smugly on his couch.

"A baby," he exclaimed. His face began to light up. "Well!"

"It's going to be a boy, Granddad," Maggie assured him. "Then you'll have somebody who'll appreciate those old electric trains you collect. I'm sorry I don't, but I like cattle."

Ben chuckled. "That's okay, imp," he told her. "Maybe some day you can help teach the baby about Queen Anne furniture."

"He likes that a lot," Maggie told the other adults. "We spend ever so much time looking at furniture."

"Well, it's fun," Ben said.

"Yes, it is," Maggie agreed, "but cattle are so much more interesting, Granddad, and it's scientific, too, isn't it, Dad?"

Powell had to agree. "She's my kid. You can tell."

"Oh, yes." Ben nodded. He smiled at the girl warmly. Since she'd come into his life, whole new worlds had opened up for him. She came over sometimes just to help him organize his books. He had plenty, and it was another love they shared. "That reminds me. Found you something at that last sale."

He got up and produced a very rare nineteenth-century breed book. He handed it to Maggie with great care. "You look after that," he told her. "It's valuable."

"Oh, Granddad!" She went into raptures of enthusiasm.

Powell whistled through his teeth. "That's expensive, Ben."

"Maggie knows that. She'll take care of it, too," he added. "Never saw anyone take the care with books that she does. Never slams them around or leaves them lying about. She puts every one right back in its place. I'd even lend her my first editions. She's a little jewel."

Maggie heard that last remark and looked up at her grandfather with an affectionate smile. "He's teaching me how to take care of books properly," she announced.

"And she's an excellent pupil." He looked at Antonia with pure love in his eyes. "I wish your mother was here," he told her. "She'd be so happy and proud."

"I know she would. But, I think she knows, Dad," Antonia said gently. And she smiled.

That night, Antonia phoned Barrie to tell her the news. Her best friend was overjoyed.

"You have to let me know when he's born, so that I can fly up and see him."

"Him?"

"Boys are nice. You should have at least one. Then you'll have a matched set. Maggie and a boy."

"Well, I'll do my best." There was a pause. "Heard from Dawson?"

There was a cold silence. "No."

"I met the widow Holton not so long ago," Antonia remarked.

Barrie cleared her throat. "Is she old?"

"About six years older than I am," Antonia said. "Slender, redheaded, green-eyed and very glamorous."

"Dawson should be ecstatic to have her visiting every weekend."

"Barrie, Dawson really could use a little support where that woman is concerned," she said slowly. "She's hard and cold and very devious, from what I hear. You never know what she might do."

"He invited her up there," Barrie muttered. "And then had the audacity to try and get me to come play chaperone, so that people wouldn't think there was anything going on between them. As if I want to watch her paw him and fawn all over him and help him pretend it's all innocent!"

"Maybe it is innocent. Dawson doesn't like women, Barrie," she added. "They say he's, well, sexually cold."

"Dawson?"

"Dawson."

Barrie hesitated. She couldn't very well say what she was thinking, or what she was remembering.

"Are you still there?" Antonia asked.

"Yes." Barrie sighed. "It's his own fault, he wants that land so badly that he'll do anything to get it."

"I don't think he'd go this far. I think he just invited Mrs. Holton up there to talk to her, and now she thinks he had amorous intentions instead of business ones and he can't get rid of her. She strikes me as the sort who'd be hard to dissuade. She's a very pushy woman, and Dawson's very rich. It may be that she's chasing him, instead of the reverse."

"He never said that."

"Did you give him a chance to say anything?" Antonia asked.

"It's safer if I don't," Barrie muttered. "I don't know if I want to risk giving Dawson a whole weekend to spend giving me hell."

"You could try. He might have had a change of heart."

"Not likely." There was a harsh laugh. "Well, I'll call him, and if he asks me again, I'll go, but only if there are plenty of people around, not just the widow."

"Call him up and tell him that."

"I don't know…"

"He's not an ogre. He's just a man."

"Sure." She sounded unconvinced.

"Barrie, you're not a coward. Save him."

"Imagine, the iceman needing saving." She hesitated. "Who told you they called him that?"

"Just about everybody I know. He doesn't date.

The widow is the first woman he's been seen with in years." Antonia's voice softened. "Curious, isn't it?"

It was, but Barrie didn't dare mention why. She had some ideas about it, and she wondered if she had enough courage to go to Sheridan and find out the truth.

"Maybe I'll go," Barrie said.

"Maybe you should," Antonia agreed, and shortly afterward, she hung up, giving Barrie plenty to think about.

Powell came to find her after she'd gotten off the phone, smiling at her warmly. "You look pretty in pink," he remarked.

She smiled back. "Thanks."

He sat down beside her on the sofa and pulled her close. "What's wrong?"

"The widow Holton is giving Dawson a hard time."

"Good," Powell said.

She glared at him. "You might have the decency to feel sorry for the poor man. You were her target once, I believe."

"Until you stepped in and saved me, you sweet woman," he replied, and bent to kiss her warmly.

"There isn't anybody to save Dawson unless Barrie will."

"He can fight his own dragons. Or should I say dragonettes?" he mused thoughtfully.

"Aren't you still after that strip of land, too?"

"Oh, I gave up on it when we got married," he

said easily. "I had an idea that she wanted more than money for it, and you were jealous enough of her already."

"I like that!" she muttered.

"You never had anything to worry about," he said. "She wasn't my type. But, I had an idea she'd make mischief if I kept trying to get those few acres, so I let the idea go. And I'll tell you something else," he added with a chuckle. "I don't think Dawson Rutherford's going to get that strip, either. She may string him along to see if she can get him interested in a more permanent arrangement, but unless he wants to propose…"

"Maybe he does," she said.

He shook his head. "I don't like him," he said, "but he's not a fool. She isn't his type of woman. She likes to give orders, not take them. He's too strong willed to suit her for long. More than likely, it's because she can't get him that she wants him."

"I hope so," she replied. "I'd hate to see him trapped into marriage. I think Barrie cares a lot more for him than she'll admit."

He drew her close. "They'll work out their own problems. Do you realize how this household has changed since you married me?"

She smiled. "Yes. Maggie is a whole new person."

"So am I. So are you. So is your father and Mrs. Bates," he added. "And now we've got a baby on the way as well, and Maggie's actually looking forward to it. I tell you, we've got the world."

She nestled close to him and closed her eyes. "The whole world," she agreed huskily.

Seven months later, Nelson Charles Long was born in the Bighorn community hospital. It had been a quick, easy birth, and Powell had been with Antonia every step of the way. Maggie was allowed in with her dad to see the baby while Antonia fed him.

"He looks like you, Dad," Maggie said.

"He looks like Antonia," he protested. "*You* look like me," he added.

Maggie beamed. There was a whole new relationship between Maggie and her father. She wasn't threatened by the baby at all, not when she was so well loved by both parents. The cold, empty past was truly behind her now, just as it had finally been laid to rest by her parents.

Antonia had asked Powell finally what Sally had written in the letter she'd sent back, so many years ago. Sally had told him very little about it, he recalled, except he recalled one line she'd quoted from some author he couldn't quite remember: *Take what you want, says God, and pay for it.* The letter was to the effect that Sally had discovered the painful truth of that old proverb, and she was sorry.

Too late, of course. Much too late.

Sally had been forgiven, and the joy Antonia felt with Powell and Maggie grew by the day. She, too, had learned a hard lesson from the experience, that one had to stand and fight sometimes. She would

teach that lesson to Maggie, she thought as she looked
adoringly up at her proud husband; and to the child
she held in her arms.

* * * * *

Matt Caldwell:
Texas Tycoon

DIANA PALMER

Chapter One

The man on the hill sat on his horse with elegance and grace, and the young woman found herself staring at him. He was obviously overseeing the roundup, which the man at her side had brought her to view. This ranch was small by Texas standards, but around Jacobsville, it was big enough to put its owner in the top ten in size.

"Dusty, isn't it?" Ed Caldwell asked with a chuckle, oblivious to the distant mounted rider, who was behind him and out of his line of sight. "I'm glad I work for the corporation and not here. I like my air cool and unpolluted."

Leslie Murry smiled. She wasn't pretty. She had a plain, rather ordinary sort of face with blond hair that had a natural wave, and gray eyes. Her one good feature besides her slender figure was a pretty bow mouth. She had a quiet, almost reclusive demeanor these days. But she hadn't always been like that. In her early teens, Leslie had been flamboyant and outgoing, a live wire of a girl whose friends had laughed at her exploits. Now, at twenty-three, she was as sedate as a matron. The change in her was shocking to people who'd once known her. She knew Ed Caldwell from college in Houston. He'd graduated in her sophomore year, and she'd quit the following semester to go to work as a paralegal for his father's law firm in Houston. Things had gotten too complicated there, and Ed had come to the rescue once again. In fact, Ed was the reason she'd just been hired as an executive assistant by the mammoth Caldwell firm. His cousin owned it.

She'd never met Mather Gilbert Caldwell, or Matt as he was known locally. People said he was a nice, easygoing man who loved an underdog. In fact, Ed said it frequently himself. They were down here for roundup so that Ed could introduce Leslie to the head of the corporation. But so far, all they'd seen was dust and cattle and hardworking cowboys.

"Wait here," Ed said. "I'm going to ride over and find Matt. Be right back." He urged his horse into a trot and held on for dear life. Leslie had to bite her lip to conceal a smile at the way he rode. It was painfully obvious that he was much more at home behind the wheel of a car. But she wouldn't have been so rude as to have mentioned it, because Ed was the only friend she had these days. He was, in fact, the only person around who knew about her past.

While she was watching him, the man on horseback on the hill behind them was watching her. She sat on a horse with style, and she had a figure that would have attracted a connoisseur of women—which the man on horseback was. Impulsively he spurred his horse into a gallop and came down the rise behind her. She didn't hear him until he reined in and the harsh sound of the horse snorting had her whirling in the saddle.

The man was wearing working clothes, like the other cowboys, but all comparisons ended there. He wasn't ragged or missing a tooth or unshaven. He was oddly intimidating, even in the way he sat the horse, with one hand on the reins and the other on his powerful denim-clad thigh.

Matt Caldwell met her gray eyes with his dark ones and noted that she wasn't the beauty he'd expected, despite her elegance of carriage and that perfect figure. "Ed brought you, I gather," he said curtly.

She'd almost guessed from his appearance that his voice would be deep and gravelly, but not that it would cut like a knife. Her hands tightened on the reins. "I...yes, he...he brought me."

The stammer was unexpected. Ed's usual sort of girl was brash and brassy, much more sophisticated than this shrinking violet here. He liked to show off Matt's ranch and impress the girls. Usually it didn't bother Matt, but he'd had a frustrating day and he was out of humor. He scowled. "Interested in cattle ranching, are you?" he drawled with ice dripping from every syllable. "We could always get you a rope and let you try your hand, if you'd like."

She felt as if every muscle in her body had gone taut. "I...came to meet Ed's cousin," she managed. "He's rich." The man's dark eyes flashed and she flushed. She couldn't believe she'd made such a remark to a stranger. "I mean," she corrected, "he owns the company where Ed works. Where I work," she added. She could have bitten her tongue for her artless mangling of a straightforward subject, but the man rattled her.

Something kindled in the man's dark eyes under the jutting brow; something not very nice at all. He leaned forward and his eyes narrowed. "Why are you really out here with Ed?" he asked.

She swallowed. He had her hypnotized, like a cobra with a rabbit. Those eyes...those very dark, unyielding eyes...!

"It's not your business, is it?" she asked finally, furious at her lack of cohesive thought and this man's assumption that he had the right to interrogate her.

He didn't say a word. Instead, he just looked at her.

"Please," she bit off, hunching her shoulders uncomfortably. "You're making me nervous!"

"You came to meet the boss, didn't you?" he asked in a velvety smooth tone. "Didn't anyone tell you that he's no marshmallow?"

She swallowed. "They say he's a very nice, pleasant man," she returned a little belligerently. "Something I'll bet nobody in his right mind would dream of saying about you!" she added with her first burst of spirit in years.

His eyebrows lifted. "How do you know I'm not nice and pleasant?" he asked, chuckling suddenly.

"You're like a cobra," she said uneasily.

He studied her for a few seconds before he nudged his horse in the side with a huge dusty boot and eased so close to her that she actually shivered. He hadn't been impressed with the young woman who stammered and stuttered with nerves, but a spirited woman was a totally new proposition. He liked a woman who wasn't intimidated by his bad mood.

His hand went across her hip to catch the back of her saddle and he looked into her eyes from an unnervingly close distance. "If I'm a cobra, then what does that make you, cupcake?" he drawled with deliberate sensuality, so close that she caught the faint smoky scent of his breath, the hint of spicy cologne that clung to his lean, tanned face. "A soft, furry little bunny?"

She was so shaken by the proximity of him that she tried desperately to get away, pulling so hard on the reins that her mount unexpectedly reared and she went down on the ground, hard, hitting her injured left hip and her shoulder as she fell into the thick grass.

A shocked sound came from the man, who vaulted out of the saddle and was beside her as she tried to sit up. He reached for her a little roughly, shaken by her panic. Women didn't usually try to back away from him; especially ordinary ones like this. She fell far short of his usual companions.

She fought his hands, her eyes huge and overly bright, panic in the very air around her. "No…!" she cried out helplessly.

He froze in place, withdrawing his lean hand from her arm, and stared at her with scowling curiosity.

"Leslie!" came a shout from a few yards away. Ed bounced up as quickly as he could manage it without being unseated. He fumbled his way off the horse and knelt beside her, holding out his arm so that she could catch it and pull herself up.

"I'm sorry," she said, refusing to look at the man who was responsible for her tumble. "I jerked the reins. I didn't mean to."

"Are you all right?" Ed asked, concerned.

She nodded. "Sure." But she was shaking, and both men could see it.

Ed glanced over her head at the taller, darker, leaner man who stood with his horse's reins in his hand, staring at the girl.

"Uh, have you two introduced yourselves?" he asked awkwardly.

Matt was torn by conflicting emotions, the strongest of which was bridled fury at the woman's panicky attitude. She acted as if he had plans to assault her, when he'd only been trying to help her up. He was angry and it cost him his temper. "The next time you bring a certifiable lunatic to my ranch, give me some advance warning," the tall man sniped at Ed. He moved as curtly as he spoke, swinging abruptly into the saddle to glare down at them. "You'd better take her home," he told Ed. "She's a damned walking liability around animals."

"But she rides very well, usually," Ed protested. "Okay, then," he added when the other man glowered at him. He forced a smile. "I'll see you later."

The tall man jerked his hat down over his eyes, wheeled the horse without another word and rode back up on the rise where he'd been sitting earlier.

"Whew!" Ed laughed, sweeping back his light brown hair uneasily. "I haven't seen him in a mood like that for years. I can't imagine what set him off. He's usually the soul of courtesy, especially when someone's hurt."

Leslie brushed off her jeans and looked up at her friend morosely. "He rode right up to me," she said unsteadily, "and leaned across me to talk with a hand on the saddle. I just...panicked. I'm sorry. I guess he's some sort of foreman here. I hope you don't get in trouble with your cousin because of it."

"That *was* my cousin, Leslie," he said heavily.

She stared at him vacantly. "That was Matt Caldwell?"

He nodded.

She let out a long breath. "Oh, boy. What a nice way to start a new job, by alienating the man at the head of the whole food chain."

"He doesn't know about you," he began.

Her eyes flashed. "And you're not to tell him," she returned firmly. "I mean it! I will not have my past paraded out again. I came down here to get away from reporters and movie producers, and that's what I'm going to do. I've had my hair cut, bought new clothes, gotten contact lenses. I've done everything I can think of so I won't be recognized. I'm not going to have it all dragged up again. It's been six years," she added miserably. "Why can't people just leave it alone?"

"The newsman was just following a lead," he said gently. "One of the men who attacked you was arrested for drunk driving and someone connected the name to your mother's case. His father is some high city official in Houston. It was inevitable that the press would dig up his son's involvement in your mother's case in an election year."

"Yes, I know, and that's what prompted the producer to think it would make a great TV movie of the week." She ground her teeth together. "That's just what we all need. And I thought it was all over. How silly of me," she said in a defeated tone. "I wish I were rich and famous," she added. "Then maybe I could buy myself some peace and privacy." She glanced up where the tall man sat silently watching the herding below. "I made some stupid remarks to your cousin, too, not knowing who he really was. I guess he'll be down in personnel first thing Monday to have me fired."

"Over my dead body," he said. "I may be only a lowly cousin, but I do own stock in the corporation. If he fires you, I'll fight for you."

"Would you really, for me?" she asked solemnly.

He ruffled her short blond hair. "You're my pal," he said. "I've had a pretty bad blow of my own. I don't want to get serious about anybody ever again. But I like having you around."

She smiled sadly. "I'm glad you can act that way about me. I can't really bear to be..." She swallowed. "I don't like men close to me, in any physical way. The therapist said I might be able to change that someday, with the right man. I don't know. It's been so long..."

"Don't sit and worry," he said. "Come on. I'll take you back to town and buy you a nice vanilla ice-cream cone. How's that?"

She smiled at him. "Thanks, Ed."

He shrugged. "Just another example of my sterling character." He glanced up toward the rise and away again. "He's just not himself today," he said. "Let's go."

Matt Caldwell watched his visitors bounce away on their respective horses with a resentment and fury he hadn't experienced in years. The little blond icicle had made him feel like a lecher. As if she could have

appealed to him, a man who had movie stars chasing
after him! He let out a rough sigh and pulled a much-
used cigar from his pocket and stuck it in his teeth.
He didn't light it. He was trying to give up the bad
habit, but it was slow going. This cigar had been just
recently the target of his secretary's newest weapon
in her campaign to save him from nicotine. The end
was still damp, in fact, despite the fact that he'd only
arrived here from his office in town about an hour
ago. He took it out of his mouth with a sigh, eyed it
sadly and put it away. He'd threatened to fire her and
she'd threatened to quit. She was a nice woman, married with two cute little kids. He couldn't let her
leave him. Better the cigar than good help, he decided.

He let his eyes turn again toward the couple growing smaller in the distance. What an odd girlfriend
Ed had latched onto this time. Of course, she'd let
Ed touch her. She'd flinched away from Matt as if
he was contagious. The more he thought about it, the
madder he got. He turned his horse toward the bawling cattle in the distance. Working might take the
edge off his temper.

Ed took Leslie to her small apartment at a local
boardinghouse and left her at the front door with an
apology.

"You don't think he'll fire me?" she asked in a
plaintive tone.

He shook his head. "No," he assured her. "I've

already told you that I won't let him. Now stop worrying. Okay?''

She managed a smile. "Thanks again, Ed."

He shrugged. "No problem. See you Monday."

She watched him get into his sports car and roar away before she went inside to her lonely room at the top corner of the house, facing the street. She'd made an enemy today, without meaning to. She hoped it wasn't going to adversely affect her life. There was no going back now.

Monday morning, Leslie was at her desk five minutes early in an attempt to make a good impression. She liked Connie and Jackie, the other two women who shared administrative duties for the vice president of marketing and research. Leslie's job was more routine. She kept up with the various shipments of cattle from one location to another, and maintained the herd records. It was exacting, but she had a head for figures and she enjoyed it.

Her immediate boss was Ed, so it was really a peachy job. They had an entire building in downtown Jacobsville, a beautiful old Victorian mansion, which Matt had painstakingly renovated to use as his corporation's headquarters. There were two floors of offices, and a canteen for coffee breaks where the kitchen and dining room once had been.

Matt wasn't in his office much of the time. He did a lot of traveling, because aside from his business interests, he sat on boards of directors of other businesses and even on the board of trustees of at least one college. He had business meetings in all sorts of places. Once he'd even gone to South America to see about investing in a growing cattle market there, but he'd come home angry and disillusioned when he saw the slash and burn method of pasture creation that had already killed a substantial portion of rain forest. He wanted no part of that, so he turned to Australia instead and bought another huge ranching tract in the Northern Territory there.

Ed told her about these fascinating exploits, and Leslie listened with her eyes wide. It was a world she'd never known. She and her mother, at the best of times, had been poor before the tragedy that separated them. Now, even with Leslie's job and the good salary she made, it still meant budgeting to the bone so that she could afford even a taxi to work and pay rent on the small apartment where she lived. There wasn't much left over for travel. She envied Matt being able to get on a plane—his own private jet, in fact—and go anywhere in the world he liked. It was a glimpse inside a world she'd never know.

"I guess he goes out a lot," she murmured once when Ed had told her that his cousin was away in New York for a cattlemen's banquet.

"With women?" Ed chuckled. "He beats them off with a stick. Matt's one of the most hunted bachelors in south Texas, but he never seems to get serious about any one woman. They're just accessories to him, pretty things to take on the town. You know," he added with a faint smile, "I don't think he really likes women very much. He was kind to a couple of local girls who needed a shoulder to cry on, but that was as far as it went, and they weren't the sort of women to chase him. He's like this because he had a rough time as a child."

"How?" she asked.

"His mother gave him away when he was six."

Her intake of breath was audible. "Why?"

"She had a new boyfriend who didn't like kids," he said bluntly. "He wouldn't take Matt, so she gave him to my dad. He was raised with me. That's why we're so close."

"What about his father?" she asked.

"We...don't talk about his father."

"Ed!"

He grimaced. "This can't go any further," he said.

"Okay."

"We don't think his mother knew who his father was," he confided. "There were so many men in her life around that time."

"But her husband..."

"What husband?" he asked.

She averted her eyes. "Sorry. I assumed that she was married."

"Not Beth," he mused. "She didn't want ties. She didn't want Matt, but her parents had a screaming fit when she mentioned an abortion. They wanted him terribly, planned for him, made room for him in their house, took Beth and him in the minute he was born."

"But you said your father raised him."

"Matt has had a pretty bad break all around. Our grandparents were killed in a car wreck, and then just a few months later, their house burned down," he added. "There was some gossip that it was intentional to collect on insurance, but nothing was ever proven. Matt was outside with Beth, in the yard, early that morning when it happened. She'd taken him out to see the roses, a pretty strange and unusual thing for her. Lucky for Matt, though, because he'd have been in the house, and would have died. The insurance settlement was enough for Beth to treat herself to some new clothes and a car. She left Matt with my dad and took off with the first man who came along." His eyes were full of remembered outrage on Matt's behalf. "Grandfather left a few shares of stock in a ranch to him, along with a small trust that couldn't be touched until Matt was twenty-one. That's the only thing that kept Beth from getting her hands on it. When he inherited it, he seemed to have an instinct for making money. He never looked back."

"What happened to his mother?" she asked.

"We heard that she died a few years ago. Matt never speaks of her."

"Poor little boy," she said aloud.

"Don't make that mistake," he said at once. "Matt doesn't need pity."

"I guess not. But it's a shame that he had to grow up so alone."

"You'd know about that."

She smiled sadly. "I guess so. My dad died years ago. Mama supported us the best way she could. She wasn't very intelligent, but she was pretty. She used what she had." Her eyes were briefly haunted. "I haven't gotten over what she did. Isn't it horrible, that in a few seconds you can destroy your own life and several other peoples' like that? And what was it all for? Jealousy, when there wasn't even a reason for it. He didn't care about me—he just wanted to have a good time with an innocent girl, him and his drunk friends." She shivered at the memory. "Mama thought she loved him. But that jealous rage didn't get him back. He died."

"I agree that she shouldn't have shot him, but it's hard to defend what he and his friends were doing to you at the time, Leslie."

She nodded. "I know," she said simply. "Sometimes kids get the short end of the stick, and it's up to them to do better with their future."

All the same, she wished that she'd had a normal upbringing, like so many other kids had.

After their conversation, she felt sorry for Matt Caldwell and wished that they'd started off better. She shouldn't have overreacted. But it was curious that he'd been so offensive to her, when Ed said that he was the soul of courtesy around women. Perhaps he'd just had a bad day.

* * *

Later in the week, Matt was back, and Leslie began to realize how much trouble she'd landed herself in from their first encounter.

He walked into Ed's office while Ed was out at a meeting, and the ice in his eyes didn't begin to melt as he watched Leslie typing away at the computer. She hadn't seen him, and he studied her with profound, if prejudiced, curiosity. She was thin and not much above average height, with short blond hair that curled toward her face. Nice skin, but she was much too pale. He remembered her eyes most of all, wide and full of distaste as he came close. It amazed him that there was a woman on the planet who could find his money repulsive, even if he didn't appeal to her himself. It was new and unpleasant to discover a woman who didn't want him. He'd never been repulsed by a woman in his life. It left him feeling inadequate. Worse, it brought back memories of the woman who'd rejected him, who'd given him away at the age of six because she didn't want him.

She felt his eyes on her and lifted her head. Gray eyes widened and stared as her hands remained suspended just over the black keyboard.

He was wearing a vested gray suit. It looked very expensive, and his eyes were dark and cutting. He had a cigar in his hand, but it wasn't lit. She hoped he wasn't going to try to smoke it in the confined space, because she was allergic to tobacco smoke.

"So you're Ed's," he murmured in that deep, cutting tone.

"Ed's assistant," she agreed. "Mr. Caldwell…"

"What did you do to land the job?" he continued with a faintly mocking smile. "And how often?"

She wasn't getting what he implied. She blinked, still staring. "I beg your pardon?"

"Why did Ed bring you in here above ten other more qualified applicants?" he persisted.

"Oh, that." She hesitated. She couldn't tell him the real reason, so she told him enough of the truth to distract him. "I have the equivalent of an associate in arts degree in business and I worked as a paralegal for his father for four years in a law office," she said. "I might not have the bachelor's degree that was preferred, but I have experience. Or so Ed assured me," she added, looking worried.

"Why didn't you finish college?" he persisted.

She swallowed. "I had…some personal problems at the time."

"You still have some personal problems, Miss Murry," he replied lazily, but his eyes were cold and alert in a lean, hard face. "You can put me at the top of the list. I had other plans for the position you're holding. So you'd better be as good as Ed says you are."

"I'll give value for money, Mr. Caldwell," she assured him. "I work for my living. I don't expect free rides."

"Don't you?"

"No, I don't."

He lifted the cigar to his mouth, looked at the wet tip, sighed and slipped it back down to dangle, unlit in his fingers.

"Do you smoke?" she asked, having noted the action.

"I try to," he murmured.

Just as he spoke, a handsome woman in her forties with blond hair in a neat bun and wearing a navy-and-white suit, walked down the hall toward him.

He glared at her as she paused in the open door of Ed's office. "I need you to sign these, Mr. Caldwell. And Mr. Bailey is waiting in your office to speak to you about that committee you want him on."

"Thanks, Edna."

Edna Jones smiled. "Good day, Miss Murry. Keeping busy, are you?"

"Yes, ma'am, thank you," Leslie replied with a genuine smile.

"Don't let him light that thing," Edna continued, gesturing toward the cigar dangling in Matt's fingers. "If you need one of these—" she held up a small water pistol "—I'll see that you get one." She smiled at a fuming Matt. "You'll be glad to know that I've already passed them out to the girls in the other executive offices, Mr. Caldwell. You can count on all of us to help you quit smoking."

Matt glared at her. She chuckled like a woman twenty years younger, waved to Leslie, and stalked off back to the office. Matt actually started to make a comical lunge after her, but caught himself in time. It wouldn't do to show weakness to the enemy.

He gave Leslie a cool glance, ignoring the faint amusement in her gray eyes. With a curt nod, he followed Edna down the hall, the damp, expensive cigar still dangling from his lean fingers.

Chapter Two

From her first day on the job, Leslie was aware of Matt's dislike and disapproval of her. He piled the work on Ed, so that it would inevitably drift down to Leslie. A lot of it was really unnecessary, like having her type up old herd records from ten years ago, which had never been converted to computer files. He said it was so that he could check progress on the progeny of his earlier herd sires, but even Ed muttered when Leslie showed him what she was expected to do.

"We have secretaries to do this sort of thing," Ed grumbled as he stared at the yellowed pages on her desk. "I need you for other projects."

"Tell him," Leslie suggested.

He shook his head. "Not in the mood he's been in lately," he said with a rueful smile. "He isn't himself."

"Did you know that his secretary is armed?" she asked suddenly. "She carries a water pistol around with her."

Ed chuckled. "Matt asked her to help him stop smoking cigars. Not that he usually did it inside the building," he was quick to add. "But Mrs. Jones feels that if you can't light a cigar, you can't smoke it. She bought a water pistol for herself and armed the other secretaries, too. If Matt even lifts a cigar to his mouth in the executive offices, they shoot him."

"Dangerous ladies," she commented.

"You bet. I've seen…"

"Nothing to do?" purred a soft, deep voice from behind Ed. The piercing dark eyes didn't match the bantering tone.

"Sorry, Matt," Ed said immediately. "I was just passing the time of day with Leslie. Can I do anything for you?"

"I need an update on that lot of cattle we placed with Ballenger," he said. He stared at Leslie with narrowed eyes. "Your job, I believe?"

She swallowed and nodded, jerking her fingers on the keyboard so that she opened the wrong file and had to push the right buttons to close it again. Normally she wasn't a nervous person, but he made her ill at ease, standing over her without speaking. Ed seemed to be a little twitchy, himself, because he moved back to his own office the minute the phone rang, placing himself out of the line of fire with an apologetic look that Leslie didn't see.

"I thought you were experienced with computers," Matt drawled mockingly as he paused beside her to look over her shoulder.

The feel of his powerful body so close behind her made every muscle tense. Her fingers froze on the keyboard, and she was barely breathing.

With a murmured curse, Matt stepped back to the side of the desk, fighting the most intense emotions he'd ever felt. He stuck his hands deep into the pockets of his slacks and glared at her.

She relaxed, but only enough to be able to pull up the file he wanted and print it for him.

He took it out of the printer tray when it was finished and gave it a slow perusal. He muttered something, and tossed the first page down on Leslie's desk.

"Half these words are misspelled," he said curtly.

She looked at it on the computer screen and nodded. "Yes, they are, Mr. Caldwell. I'm sorry, but I didn't type it."

Of course she hadn't typed it, it was ten years old, but something inside him wanted to hold her accountable for it.

He moved away from the desk as he read the rest of the pages. "You can do this file—and the others—over," he murmured as he skimmed. "The whole damned thing's illiterate."

She knew that there were hundreds of records in this particular batch of files, and that it would take days, not minutes or hours, to complete the work. But he owned the place, so he could set the rules. She pursed her lips and glanced at him speculatively. Now that he was physically out of range, she felt safe again. "Your wish is my command, boss," she murmured dryly, surprising a quick glance from him. "Shall I just put aside all of Ed's typing and devote the next few months to this?"

Her change of attitude from nervous kid to sassy woman caught him off guard. "I didn't put a time limit on it," Matt said curtly. "I only said, do it!"

"Oh, yes, sir," she agreed at once, and smiled vacantly.

He drew in a short breath and glared down at her. "You're remarkably eager to please, Miss Murry. Or is it just because I'm the boss?"

"I always try to do what I'm asked to do, Mr. Caldwell," she assured him. "Well, almost always," she amended. "Within reason."

He moved back toward the desk. As he leaned over to put down the papers she'd printed for him, he saw her visibly tense. She was the most confounding woman he'd ever known, a total mystery.

"What would you define as 'within reason'?" he drawled, holding her eyes.

She looked hunted. Amazing, that she'd been jovial and uninhibited just seconds before. Her stiff expression made him feel oddly guilty. He turned away. "Ed! Have you got my Angus file?" he called to his cousin through the open door to Ed's private office.

Ed was off the phone and he had a file folder in his hands. "Yes, sorry. I wanted to check the latest growth figures and projected weight gain ratios. I meant to put it back on your desk and I got busy."

Matt studied the figures quietly and then nodded. "That's acceptable. The Ballenger brothers do a good job."

"They're expanding, did you know?" Ed chuckled. "Nice to see them prospering."

"Yes, it is. They've worked hard enough in their lives to warrant a little prosperity."

While he spoke, Leslie was watching him covertly. She thought about the six-year-old boy whose mother had given him away, and it wrung her heart. Her own childhood had been no picnic, but Matt's upbringing had been so much worse.

He felt those soft gray eyes on his face, and his own gaze jerked down to meet them. She flushed and looked away.

He wondered what she'd been thinking to produce such a reaction. She couldn't have possibly made it plainer that she felt no physical attraction to him, so why the wide-eyed stare? It puzzled him. So many things about her puzzled him. She was neat and attractively dressed, but those clothes would have suited a dowager far better than a young woman. While he didn't encourage short skirts and low-cut blouses, Leslie was covered from head to toe; long dress, long sleeves, high neck buttoned right up to her throat.

"Need anything else?" Ed asked abruptly, hoping to ward off more trouble.

Matt's powerful shoulders shrugged. "Not for the moment." He glanced once more at Leslie. "Don't forget those files I want updated."

After he walked out, Ed stared after him for a minute, frowning. "What files?"

She explained it to him.

"But those are outdated," Ed murmured thoughtfully. "And he never looks at them. I don't understand why he has to have them corrected at all."

She leaned forward. "Because it will irritate me and make me work harder!" she said in a stage whisper. "God forbid that I should have time to twiddle my thumbs."

His eyebrows arched. "He isn't vindictive."

"That's what you think." She picked up the file Matt had left and grimaced as she put it back in the filing cabinet. "I'll start on those when I've finished answering your mail. Do you suppose he wants me to stay over after work to do them? He'd have to pay me overtime." She grinned impishly, a reminder of the woman she'd once been. "Wouldn't that make his day?"

"Let me ask him," Ed volunteered. "Just do your usual job for now."

"Okay. Thanks, Ed."

He shrugged. "What are friends for?" he murmured with a smile.

The office was a great place to work. Leslie had a ball watching the other women in the executive offices lie in wait for Matt. His secretary caught him trying to light a cigar out on the balcony, and she let him have it from behind a potted tree with the water pistol. He laid the cigar down on Bessie David's desk and she "accidentally" dropped it into his half-full coffee cup that he'd set down next to it. He held it up, dripping, with an accusing look at Bessie.

"You told me to do it, sir," Bessie reminded him.

He dropped the sodden cigar back in the coffee and left it behind. Leslie, having seen the whole thing, ducked into the rest room to laugh. It amazed her that Matt was so easygoing and friendly to his other employees. To Leslie, he was all bristle and venom. She wondered what he'd do if she let loose with a water pistol. She chuckled, imagining herself tearing up Main Street in Jacobsville ahead of a cursing Matt Caldwell. It was such a pity that she'd changed so much. Before tragedy had touched her young life, she would have been very attracted to the tall, lean cattleman.

A few days later, he came into Ed's office dangling a cigar from his fingers. Leslie, despite her amusement at the antics of the other secretaries, didn't say a word at the sight of the unlit cigar.

"I want to see the proposal the Cattlemen's Association drafted about brucellosis testing."

She stared at him. "Sir?"

He stared back. She was getting easier on his eyes, and he didn't like his reactions to her. She was repulsed by him. He couldn't get past that because it destroyed his pride. "Ed told me he had a copy of it," he elaborated. "It came in the mail yesterday."

"Okay." She knew where the mail was kept. Ed tried to ignore it, leaving it in the In box until Leslie dumped it on his desk in front of him and refused to leave until he dealt with it. This usually happened at the end of the week, when it had piled up and overflowed into the Out box.

She rummaged through the box and produced a thick letter from the Cattlemen's Association, unopened. She carried it back through and handed it to Matt.

He'd been watching her walk with curious intensity. She was limping. He couldn't see her legs, because she was wearing loose knit slacks with a tunic that flowed to her thighs as she walked. Very obviously, she wasn't going to do anything to call attention to her figure.

"You're limping," he said. "Did you see a doctor after that fall you took at my ranch?"

"No need to," she said at once. "It was only a bruise. I'm sore, that's all."

He picked up the receiver of the phone on her desk and pressed the intercom button. "Edna," he said abruptly, "set Miss Murry up with Lou Coltrain as soon as possible. She took a spill from a horse at my place a few days ago and she's still limping. I want her X-rayed."

"No!" Leslie protested.

"Let her know when you've made the appointment. Thanks," he told his secretary and hung up. His dark eyes met Leslie's pale ones squarely. "You're going," he said flatly.

She hated doctors. Oh, how she hated them! The doctor at the emergency room in Houston, an older man retired from regular practice, had made her feel cheap and dirty as he examined her and made cold remarks about tramps who got men killed. She'd never gotten over the double trauma of her experience and that harsh lecture, despite the therapists' attempts to soften the memory.

She clenched her teeth and glared at Matt. "I said I'm not hurt!"

"You work here. I'm the boss. You get examined. Period."

She wanted to quit. She wished she could. She had no place else to go. Houston was out of the question. She was too afraid that she'd be up to her ears in reporters, despite her physical camouflage, the minute she set foot in the city.

She drew a sharp, angry breath.

Her attitude puzzled him. "Don't you want to make sure the injury won't make that limp permanent?" he asked suddenly.

She lifted her chin proudly. "Mr. Caldwell, I had an…accident…when I was seventeen and that leg suffered some bone damage." She refused to think about how it had happened. "I'll always have a slight limp, and it's not from the horse throwing me."

He didn't seem to breathe for several seconds. "All the more reason for an examination," he replied. "You like to live dangerously, I gather. You've got no business on a horse."

"Ed said the horse was gentle. It was my fault I got thrown. I jerked the reins."

His eyes narrowed. "Yes, I remember. You were trying to get away from me. Apparently you think I have something contagious."

She could see the pride in his eyes that made him resent her. "It wasn't that," she said. She averted her gaze to the wall. "It's just that I don't like to be touched."

"Ed touches you."

She didn't know how to tell him without telling him everything. She couldn't bear having him know about her sordid past. She raised turbulent gray eyes to his dark ones. "I don't like to be touched by strangers," she amended quickly. "Ed and I have known each other for years," she said finally. "It's…different with him."

His eyes narrowed. He searched over her thin face. "It must be," he said flatly.

His mocking smile touched a nerve. "You're like a steamroller, aren't you?" she asked abruptly. "You assume that because you're wealthy and powerful, there isn't a woman alive who can resist you!''

He didn't like that assumption. His eyes began to glitter. ''You shouldn't listen to gossip,'' he said, his voice deadly quiet. ''She was a spoiled little debutante who thought Daddy should be able to buy her any man she wanted. When she discovered that he couldn't, she came to work for a friend of mine and spent a couple of weeks pursuing me around Jacobsville. I went home one night and found her piled up in my bed wearing a sheet and nothing else. I threw her out, but then she told everyone that I'd assaulted her. She had a field day with me in court until my housekeeper, Tolbert, was called to tell the truth about what happened. The fact that she lost the case should tell you what the jury thought of her accusations.''

''The jury?'' she asked huskily. Besides his problems with his mother, she hadn't known about any incident in his past that might predispose him even further to distrusting women.

His thin lips drew up in a travesty of a smile. ''She had me arrested and prosecuted for criminal assault,'' he returned. ''I became famous locally—the one black mark in an otherwise unremarkable past. She had the misfortune to try the same trick later on an oilman up in Houston. He called me to testify in his behalf. When he won the case, he had her prosecuted for fraud and extortion, and won. She went to jail.''

She felt sick. He'd had his own dealings with the

press. She was sorry for him. It must have been a real ordeal after what he'd already suffered in his young life. It also explained why he wasn't married. Marriage involved trust. She doubted he was capable of it any longer. Certainly it explained the hostility he showed toward Leslie. He might think she was pretending to be repulsed by him because she was playing some deep game for profit, perhaps with some public embarrassment in mind. He might even think she was setting him up for another assault charge.

"Maybe you think that I'm like that," she said after a minute, studying him quietly. "But I'm not."

"Then why act like I'm going to attack you whenever I come within five feet of you?" he asked coldly.

She studied her fingers on the desk before her, their short fingernails neatly trimmed, with a coat of colorless sheen. Nothing flashy, she thought, and that was true of her life lately. She didn't have an answer for him.

"Is Ed your lover?" he persisted coldly.

She didn't flinch. "Ask him."

He rolled the unlit cigar in his long fingers as he watched her. "You are one enormous puzzle," he mused.

"Not really. I'm very ordinary." She looked up. "I don't like doctors, especially male ones…"

"Lou's a woman," he replied. "She and her husband are both physicians. They have a little boy."

"Oh." A woman. That would make things easier. But she didn't want to be examined. They could probably tell from X rays how breaks occurred, and she didn't know if she could trust a local doctor not to talk about it.

"It isn't up to you," he said suddenly. "You work for me. You had an accident on my ranch." He smiled mirthlessly. "I have to cover my bets. You might decide later on to file suit for medical benefits."

She searched his eyes. She couldn't really blame him for feeling like that. "Okay," she said. "I'll let her examine me."

"No comment?"

She shrugged. "Mr. Caldwell, I work hard for my paycheck. I always have. You don't know me, so I don't blame you for expecting the worst. But I don't want a free ride through life."

One of his eyebrows jerked. "I've heard that one before."

She smiled sadly. "I suppose you have." She touched her keyboard absently. "This Dr. Coltrain, is she the company doctor?"

"Yes."

She gnawed on her lower lip. "What she finds out, it is confidential, isn't it?" she added worriedly, looking up at him.

He didn't reply for a minute. The hand dangling the cigar twirled it around. "Yes," he said. "It's confidential. You're making me curious, Miss Murry. Do you have secrets?''

"We all have secrets," she said solemnly. "Some are darker than others."

He flicked a thumbnail against the cigar. "What's yours? Did you shoot your lover?"

She didn't dare show a reaction to that. Her face felt as if it would crack if she moved.

He stuck the cigar in his pocket. "Edna will let you know when you're to go see Lou," he said abruptly, with a glance at his watch. He held up the letter. "Tell Ed I've got this. I'll talk to him about it later."

"Yes, sir."

He resisted the impulse to look back at her. The more he discovered about his newest employee, the more intrigued he became. She made him restless. He wished he knew why.

There was no way to get out of the doctor's appointment. Leslie spoke briefly with Dr. Coltrain before she was sent to the hospital for a set of X rays. An hour later, she was back in Lou's office, watching the older woman pore somberly over the films against a lighted board on the wall.

Lou looked worried when she examined the X ray of the leg. "There's no damage from the fall, except for some bruising," she concluded. Her dark eyes met Leslie's squarely. "These old breaks aren't consistent with a fall, however."

Leslie ground her teeth together. She didn't say anything.

Lou moved back around her desk and sat down, indicating that Leslie should sit in the chair in front of the desk after she got off the examining table.

"You don't want to talk about it," Lou said gently. "I won't press you. You do know that the bones weren't properly set at the time, don't you? The improper alignment is unfortunate, because that limp isn't going to go away. I really should send you to an orthopedic surgeon."

"You can send me," Leslie replied, "but I won't go."

Lou rested her folded hands on her desk over the calendar blotter with its scribbled surface. "You don't know me well enough to confide in me. You'll learn, after you've been in Jacobsville a while, that I can be trusted. I don't talk about my patients to anyone, not even my husband. Matt won't hear anything from me."

Leslie remained silent. It was impossible to go over it again with a stranger. It had been hard enough to elaborate on her past to the therapist, who'd been shocked, to put it mildly.

The older woman sighed. "All right, I won't pressure you. But if you ever need anyone to talk to, I'll be here."

Leslie looked up. "Thank you," she said sincerely.

"You're not Matt's favorite person, are you?" Lou asked abruptly.

Leslie laughed without mirth. "No, I'm not. I think he'll find a way to fire me eventually. He doesn't like women much."

"Matt likes everybody as a rule," Lou said. "And he's always being pursued by women. They love him. He's kind to people he likes. He offered to marry Kitty Carson when she quit working for Dr. Drew Morris. She didn't do it, of course, she was crazy for Drew and vice versa. They're happily married now." She hesitated, but Leslie didn't speak. "He's a dish—rich, handsome, sexy, and usually the easiest man on earth to get along with."

"He's a bulldozer," Leslie said flatly. "He can't seem to talk to people unless he's standing on them." She folded her arms over her chest and looked uncomfortable.

So that's it, Lou thought, wondering if the young woman realized what her body language was giving away. Lou knew instantly that someone had caused those breaks in the younger woman's leg; very probably a man. She had reason to know.

"You don't like people to touch you," Lou said.

Leslie shifted in the chair. "No."

Lou's perceptive eyes went over the concealing garments Leslie wore, but she didn't say another word. She stood up, smiling gently. "There's no damage from the recent fall," she said gently. "But come back if the pain gets any worse."

Leslie frowned. "How did you know I was in pain?"

"Matt said you winced every time you got out of your chair."

Leslie's heart skipped. "I didn't realize he noticed."

"He's perceptive."

Lou prescribed an over-the-counter medication to take for the pain and advised her to come back if she didn't improve. Leslie agreed and went out of the office in an absentminded stupor, wondering what else Matt Caldwell had learned from her just by observation. It was a little unnerving.

When she went back to the office, it wasn't ten minutes before Matt was standing in the doorway.

"Well?" he asked.

"I'm fine," she assured him. "Just a few bruises. And believe me, I have no intention of suing you."

He didn't react visibly. "Plenty have." He was irritated. Lou wouldn't tell him anything, except that his new employee was as closemouthed as a clam. He knew that already.

"Tell Ed I'll be out of the office for a couple of days," he said.

"Yes, sir."

He gave her a last look, turned and walked back out. It wasn't until Matt was out of sight that Leslie began to relax.

Chapter Three

The nightmares came back that night. Leslie had
even expected them, because of the visit to Dr. Lou
Coltrain and the hospital's X-ray department. Having
to wear high heeled shoes to work hadn't done her
damaged leg any good, either. Along with the night-
mare that left her sweating and panting, her leg was
killing her. She went to the bathroom and downed
two aspirin, hoping they were going to do the trick.
She decided that she was going to have to give up
fashion and wear flats again.

Matt noticed, of course, when he returned to the
office three days later. His eyes narrowed as he
watched her walk across the floor of her small office.

"Lou could give you something to take for the
pain," he said abruptly.

She glanced at him as she pulled a file out of the metal cabinet. "Yes, she could, Mr. Caldwell, but do you really want a comatose secretary in Ed's office? Painkillers put me to sleep."

"Pain makes for inefficiency."

She nodded. "I know that. I have a bottle of aspirin in my purse," she assured him. "And the pain isn't so bad that I can't remember how to spell. It's just a few bruises. They'll heal. Dr. Coltrain said so."

He stared at her through narrowed, cold eyes. "You shouldn't be limping after a week. I want you to see Lou again…"

"I've limped for six years, Mr. Caldwell," she said serenely. Her eyes kindled. "If you don't like the limp, perhaps you shouldn't stand and watch me walk."

His eyebrows arched. "Can't the doctors do anything to correct it?"

She glared at him. "I hate doctors!"

The vehemence of her statement took him aback. She meant it, too. Her face flushed, her eyes sparkled with temper. It was such a difference from her usual expression that he found himself captivated. When she was animated, she was pretty.

"They're not all bad," he replied finally.

"There's only so much you can do with a shattered bone," she said and then bit her lip. She hadn't meant to tell him that.

The question was in his eyes, on his lips, but it

never made it past them. Just as he started to ask, Ed came out of his office and spotted him.

"Matt! Welcome back," he said, extending a hand. "I just had a call from Bill Payton. He wanted to know if you were coming to the banquet Saturday night. They've got a live band scheduled."

"Sure," Matt said absently. "Tell him to reserve two tickets for me. Are you going?"

"I thought I would. I'll bring Leslie along." He smiled at her. "It's the annual Jacobsville Cattlemen's Association banquet. We have speeches, but if you survive them, and the rubber chicken, you get to dance."

"Her leg isn't going to let her do much dancing," Matt said solemnly.

Ed's eyebrows lifted. "You'd be surprised," he said. "She loves Latin dances." He grinned at Leslie. "So does Matt here. You wouldn't believe what he can do with a mambo or a rhumba, to say nothing of the tango. He dated a dance instructor for several months, and he's a natural anyway."

Matt didn't reply. He was watching the play of expressions on Leslie's face and wondering about that leg. Maybe Ed knew the truth of it, and he could worm it out of him.

"You can ride in with us," Matt said absently. "I'll hire Jack Bailey's stretch limo and give your secretary a thrill."

"It'll give me a thrill, too," Ed assured him.

"Thanks, Matt. I hate trying to find a parking space at the country club when there's a party."

"That makes two of us."

One of the secretaries motioned to Matt that he had a phone call. He left and Ed departed right behind him for a meeting. Leslie wondered how she was going to endure an evening of dancing without ending up close to Matt Caldwell, who already resented her standoffish attitude. It would be an ordeal, she supposed, and wondered if she could develop a convenient headache on Saturday afternoon.

Leslie only had one really nice dress that was appropriate to wear to the function at the country club. The gown was a long sheath of shimmery silver fabric, suspended from her creamy shoulders by two little spaghetti straps. With it, she wore a silver-and-rhinestone clip in her short blond hair and neat little silver slippers with only a hint of a heel.

Ed sighed at the picture she made when the limousine pulled up in front of the boardinghouse where she was staying. She met him on the porch, a small purse clenched in damp hands, all aflutter at the thought of her first evening out since she was seventeen. She was terribly nervous.

"Is the dress okay?" she asked at once.

Ed smiled, taking in her soft oval face with its faint blush of lipstick and rouge, which was the only makeup she ever wore. Her gray eyes had naturally thick black lashes, which never needed mascara.

"You look fine," he assured her.

"You're not bad in a tux yourself," she murmured with a grin.

"Don't let Matt see how nervous you are," he said as they approached the car. "Somebody phoned and set him off just as we left my house. Carolyn was almost in tears."

"Carolyn?" she asked.

"His latest trophy girlfriend," he murmured. "She's from one of the best families in Houston, staying with her aunt so she'd be on hand for to-night's festivities. She's been relentlessly pursuing Matt for months. Some of us think she's gaining ground."

"She's beautiful, I guess?" she asked.

"Absolutely. In a way, she reminds me of Franny."

Franny had been Ed's fiancée, shot to death in a foiled bank robbery about the time Leslie had been catapulted into sordid fame. It had given them something in common that drew them together as friends.

"That must be rough," Leslie said sympathetically.

He glanced at her curiously as they approached the car. "Haven't you ever been in love?"

She shrugged, tugging the small faux fur cape closer around her shoulders. "I was a late bloomer." She swallowed hard. "What happened to me turned me right off men."

"I'm not surprised."

He waited while the chauffeur, also wearing a tuxedo, opened the door of the black super-stretch limousine for them. Leslie climbed in, followed by Ed, and the door closed them in with Matt and the most beautiful blond woman Leslie had ever seen. The other woman was wearing a simple black sheath dress with a short skirt and enough diamonds to open a jewelry store. No point in asking if they were real, Leslie thought, considering the look of that dress and the very real sable coat wrapped around it.

"You remember my cousin, Ed," Matt drawled, lounging back in the leather seat across from Ed and Leslie. Small yellow lights made it possible for them to see each other in the incredibly spacious interior. "This is his secretary, Miss Murry. Carolyn Engles," he added, nodding toward the woman at his side.

Murmured acknowledgments followed his introduction. Leslie's fascinated eyes went from the bar to the phones to the individual controls on the airconditioning and heating systems. It was like a luxury apartment on wheels, she thought, and tried not to let her amusement show.

"Haven't you ever been in a limousine before?" Matt asked with a mocking smile.

"Actually, no," she replied with deliberate courtesy. "It's quite a treat. Thank you."

He seemed disconcerted by her reply. He averted his head and studied Ed. His next words showed he'd forgotten her. "Tomorrow morning, first thing, I want you to pull back every penny of support we're giving Marcus Boles. Nobody, and I mean nobody, involves me in a shady land deal like that!''

''It amazes me that we didn't see through him from the start,'' Ed agreed. ''The whole campaign was just a diversion, to give the real candidate someone to shoot down. He'll look like a hero, and Boles will take the fall manfully. I understand he's being handsomely paid for his disgrace. Presumably the cash is worth his reputation and social standing.''

''He's got land in South America. I hear he's going over there to live. Just as well,'' Matt added coldly. ''If he's lucky, he might make it to the airport tomorrow before I catch up with him.''

The threat of violence lay over him like an invisible mantle. Leslie shivered. Of the four people in that car, she knew firsthand how vicious and brutal physical violence could be. Her memories were hazy, confused, but in the nightmares she had constantly, they were all too vivid.

''Do calm down, darling,'' Carolyn told Matt gently. ''You're upsetting Ms. Marley.''

''Murry,'' Ed corrected before Leslie could. ''Strange, Carolyn, I don't remember your memory being so poor.''

Carolyn cleared her throat. ''It's a lovely night, at least,'' she said, changing the subject. ''No rain and a beautiful moon.''

''So it is,'' Ed drawled.

Matt gave him a cool look, which Ed met with a vacant smile. Leslie was amused by the way Ed

could look so innocent. She knew him far too well
to be fooled.

Matt, meanwhile, was drinking in the sight of Leslie in that formfitting dress that just matched her
eyes. She had skin like marble, and he wondered if
it was as soft to the touch as it seemed. She wasn't
conventionally pretty, but there was a quality about
her that made him weak in the knees. He was driven
to protect her, without knowing why he felt that way
about a stranger. It irritated him as much as the
phone call he'd fielded earlier.

"Where are you from, Ms. Murbery?" Carolyn
asked.

"Miss Murry," Leslie corrected, beating Ed to the
punch. "I'm from a little town north of Houston."

"A true Texan," Ed agreed with a grin in her
direction.

"What town?" Matt asked.

"I'm sure you won't have heard of it," Leslie said
confidently. "Our only claim to fame was a radio
station in a building shaped like a ten-gallon hat.
Very much off the beaten path."

"Did your parents own a ranch?" he persisted.

She shook her head. "My father was a crop
duster."

"A what?" Carolyn asked with a blank face.

"A pilot who sprays pesticides from the air in a
small airplane," Leslie replied. "He was killed…on
the job."

"Pesticides," Matt muttered darkly. "Just what the groundwater table needs to—"

"Matt, can we forget politics for just one night?" Ed asked. "I'd like to enjoy my evening."

Matt gave him a measured glare with one eye narrowed menacingly. But he relaxed all at once and leaned back in his seat, to put a lazy arm around Carolyn and let her snuggle close to him. His dark eyes seemed to mock Leslie as if comparing her revulsion to Carolyn's frank delight in his physical presence.

She let him win this round with an amused smile. Once, she might have enjoyed his presence just as much as his date was reveling in now. But she had more reason than most to fear men.

The country club, in its sprawling clubhouse on a man-made lake, was a beautiful building with graceful arches and fountains. It did Jacobsville proud. But, as Ed had intimated, there wasn't a single parking spot available. Matt had the pager number of the driver and could summon the limousine whenever it was needed. He herded his charges out of the car and into the building, where the reception committee made them welcome.

There was a live band, a very good one, playing assorted tunes, most of which resembled bossa nova rhythms. The only time that Leslie really felt alive was when she could close her eyes and listen to music; any sort of music—classical, opera, country-

western or gospel. Music had been her escape as a
child from a world too bitter sometimes to stomach.
She couldn't play an instrument, but she could dance.
That was the one thing she and her mother had
shared, a love of dancing. In fact, Marie had taught
her every dance step she knew, and she knew a lot.
Marie had taught dancing for a year or so and had
shared her expertise with her daughter. How ironic
it was that Leslie's love of dance had been stifled
forever by the events of her seventeenth year.

"Fill a plate," Ed coaxed, motioning her to the
small china dishes on the buffet table. "You could
use a little more meat on those bird bones."

She grinned at him. "I'm not skinny."

"Yes, you are," he replied, and he wasn't kidding.
"Come on, forget your troubles and enjoy yourself.
Tonight, there is no tomorrow. Eat, drink and be
merry."

For tomorrow, you die, came the finish to that ad-
monishing verse, she recalled darkly. But she didn't
say it. She put some cheese straws and finger sand-
wiches on a plate and opted for soda water instead
of a drink.

Ed found them two chairs on the rim of the dance
floor, where they could hear the band and watch the
dancing.

The band had a lovely dark-haired singer with a
hauntingly beautiful voice. She was playing a guitar
and singing songs from the sixties, with a rhythm
that made Leslie's heart jump. The smile on her face,

the sparkle in her gray eyes as she listened to the talented performer, made her come alive.

From across the room, Matt noted the abrupt change in Leslie. She loved music. She loved dancing, too, he could tell. His strong fingers contracted around his own plate.

"Shall we sit with the Devores, darling?" Carolyn asked, indicating a well-dressed couple on the opposite side of the ballroom.

"I thought we'd stick with my cousin," he said carelessly. "He's not used to this sort of thing."

"He seems very much at home," Carolyn corrected, reluctantly following in Matt's wake. "It's his date who looks out of place. Good heavens, she's tapping her toe! How gauche!"

"Weren't you ever twenty-three?" he asked with a bite in his voice. "Or were you born so damned sophisticated that nothing touched you?"

She actually gasped. Matt had never spoken to her that way.

"Excuse me," he said gruffly, having realized his mistake. "I'm still upset by Boles."

"So...so I noticed," she stammered, and almost dropped her plate. This was a Matt Caldwell she'd never seen before. His usual smile and easygoing attitude were conspicuous for their absence tonight. Boles must really have upset him!

Matt sat down on the other side of Leslie, his eyes darkening as he saw the life abruptly drain out of her. Her body tensed. Her fingers on her plate went white.

"Here, Carolyn, trade places with me," Matt said suddenly, and with a forced smile. "This chair's too low for me."

"I don't think mine's much higher, darling, but I'll do it," Carolyn said in a docile tone.

Leslie relaxed. She smiled shyly at the other woman and then turned her attention back to the woman on the stage.

"Isn't she marvelous?" Carolyn asked. "She's from the Yucatán."

"Not only talented, but pretty as well," Ed agreed. "I love that beat."

"Oh, so do I," Leslie said breathlessly, nibbling a finger sandwich but with her whole attention on the band and the singer.

Matt found himself watching her, amused and touched by her uninhibited joy in the music. It had occurred to him that not much affected her in the office. Here, she was unsure of herself and nervous. Perhaps she even felt out of place. But when the band was playing and the vocalist was singing, she was a different person. He got a glimpse of the way she had been, perhaps, before whatever blows of fate had made her so uneasy around him. He was intrigued by her, and not solely because she wounded his ego. She was a complex person.

Ed noticed Matt's steady gaze on Leslie, and he wanted to drag his cousin aside and tell him the whole miserable story. Matt was curious about Leslie, and he was a bulldozer when he wanted something. He'd run roughshod right over her to get his answers, and Leslie would retreat into the shell her experiences had built around her. She was just coming into the sunlight, and here was Matt driving her back into shadow. Why couldn't Matt be content with Carolyn's adoration? Most women flocked around him; Leslie didn't. He was sure that was the main attraction she held for his cousin. But Matt, pursuing her interest, could set her back years. He had no idea what sort of damage he could do to her fragile emotions.

The singer finished her song, and the audience applauded. She introduced the members of the band and the next number, a beautiful, rhythmic feast called "Brazil." It was Leslie's very favorite piece of music, and she could dance to it, despite her leg. She longed, ached, for someone to take her on the dance floor and let her show those stiff, inhibited people how to fly to that poignant rhythm!

Watching her, Matt saw the hunger in her eyes. Ed couldn't do those steps, but he could. Without a word, he handed Carolyn his empty plate and got to his feet.

Before Leslie had a chance to hesitate or refuse outright, he pulled her gently out of her seat and onto the dance floor.

His dark eyes met her shocked pale ones as he

caught her waist in one lean, strong hand and took her left hand quite reverently into his right one.

"I won't make any sudden turns," he assured her. He nodded once, curtly, to mark the rhythm.

And then he did something remarkable.

Leslie caught her breath as she recognized his ability. She forgot to be afraid of him. She forgot that she was nervous to be held by a man. She was caught up in the rhythm and the delight of having a partner who knew how to dance to perfection the intricate steps that accompanied the Latin beat.

"You're good," Matt mused, smiling with genuine pleasure as they measured their quick steps to the rhythm.

"So are you." She smiled back.

"If your leg gives you trouble, let me know and I'll get you off the floor. Okay?"

"Okay."

"Then let's go!"

He moved her across the floor with the skill of a professional dancer and she followed him with such perfection that other dancers stopped and got out of the way, moving to the sidelines to watch what had become pure entertainment.

Matt and Leslie, enjoying the music and their own interpretation of it, were blind to the other guests, to the smiling members of the band, to everything except the glittering excitement of the dance. They moved as if they were bound by invisible strings, each to the other, with perfectly matching steps.

As the music finally wound down, Matt drew her in close against his lean frame and tilted her down in an elegant, but painful, finish.

The applause was thunderous. Matt drew Leslie upright again and noticed how pale and drawn her face was.

"Too much too soon," he murmured. "Come on. Off you go."

He didn't move closer. Instead, he held out his arm and let her come to him, let her catch hold of it where the muscle was thickest. She clung with both hands, hating herself for doing something so incredibly stupid. But, oh, it had been fun! It was worth the pain.

She didn't realize she'd spoken aloud until Matt eased her down into her chair again.

"Do you have any aspirin in that tiny thing?" Matt asked, indicating the small string purse on her arm.

She grimaced.

"Of course not." He turned, scanning the audience. "Back in a jiffy."

He moved off in the general direction of the punch bowl while Ed caught Leslie's hand in his. "That was great," he enthused. "Just great! I didn't know you could dance like that."

"Neither did I," she murmured shyly.

"Quite an exhibition," Carolyn agreed coolly. "But silly to do something so obviously painful. Now Matt will spend the rest of the night blaming himself and trying to find aspirin, I suppose." She got up and marched off with her barely touched plate and Matt's empty one.

"Well, she's in a snit," Ed observed. "She can't dance like that."

"I shouldn't have done it," Leslie murmured. "But it was so much fun, Ed! I felt alive, really alive!"

"You looked it. Nice to see your eyes light up again."

She made a face at him. "I've spoiled Carolyn's evening."

"Fair trade," he murmured dryly, "she spoiled mine the minute she got into the limousine and complained that I smelled like a sweets shop."

"You smell very nice," she replied.

He smiled. "Thanks."

Matt was suddenly coming back toward them, with Lou Coltrain by the arm. It looked as if she were being forcibly escorted across the floor and Ed had to hide the grin he couldn't help.

"Well," Lou huffed, staring at Matt before she lowered her gaze to Leslie. "I thought you were dying, considering the way he appropriated me and dragged me over here!"

"I don't have any aspirin," Leslie said uneasily. "I'm sorry…"

"There's nothing to be sorry about," Lou said instantly. She patted Leslie's hand gently. "But you've had some pretty bad bruising and this isn't the sort of exercise I'd recommend. Shattered bones are

never as strong, even when they're set properly—and
yours were not.''

Embarrassed, Leslie bit her lower lip.

''You'll be okay,'' Lou promised with a gentle
smile. ''In fact, exercise is good for the muscles that
support that bone—it makes it stronger. But don't do
this again for a couple of weeks, at least. Here. I
always carry aspirin!''

She handed Leslie a small metal container of aspirin and Matt produced another cup of soda water
and stood over her, unsmiling, while she took two of
the aspirins and swallowed them.

''Thanks,'' she told Lou. ''I really appreciate it.''

''You come and see me Monday,'' Lou instructed,
her dark eyes full of authority. ''I'll write you a prescription for something that will make your life easier. Not narcotics,'' she added with a smile. ''Anti-
inflammatories. They'll make a big difference in the
way you get around.''

''You're a nice doctor,'' she told Lou solemnly.

Lou's eyes narrowed. ''I gather that you've known
some who weren't.''

''One, at least,'' she said in a cold tone. She
smiled at Lou. ''You've changed my mind about
doctors.''

''That's one point for me. I'll rush right over and
tell Copper,'' she added, smiling as she caught her
redheaded husband's eyes across the room. ''He'll
be impressed!''

''Not much impresses the other Doctor Coltrain,''

Matt told her after Lou was out of earshot. "Lou did."

"Not until he knew she had a whole closetful of Lionel electric trains," Ed commented with a chuckle.

"Their son has a lot to look forward to when he grows up," Matt mused. He glanced beside Leslie. "Where's Carolyn?"

"She left in a huff," Ed said.

"I'll go find her. Sure you'll be okay?" he asked Leslie with quiet concern.

She nodded. "Thanks for the aspirin. They really help."

He nodded. His dark eyes slid over her drawn face and then away as he went in search of his date.

"I've spoiled his evening, too, I guess," she said wistfully.

"You can't take credit for that," Ed told her. "I've hardly ever seen Matt having so much fun as he was when he was dancing with you. Most of the women around here can only do a two-step. You're a miracle on the dance floor."

"I love to dance," she sighed. "I always did. Mama was so light on her feet." Her eyes twinkled with fond memories. "I used to love to watch her when I was little and she danced with Daddy. She was so pretty, so full of life." The light went out of her eyes. "She thought I'd encouraged Mike, and the others, too," she said dully. "She…shot him and the bullet went through him, into my leg…"

"So that's how your leg got in that shape."

She glanced at him, hardly aware of what she'd been saying. She nodded. "The doctor in the emergency room was sure it was all my fault. That's why my leg wasn't properly set. He removed the bullet and not much else. It wasn't until afterward that another doctor put a cast on. Later, I began to limp. But there was no money for any other doctor visits by then. Mama was in jail and I was all alone. If it hadn't been for my best friend Jessica's family, I wouldn't even have had a home. They took me in despite the gossip and I got to finish school."

"I'll never know how you managed that," Ed said. "Going to school every day with the trial making headlines week by week."

"It was tough," she agreed. "But it made me tough, too. Fire tempers steel, don't they say? I'm tempered."

"Yes, you are."

She smiled at him. "Thanks for bringing me. It was wonderful."

"Tell Matt that. It might change him."

"Oh, he's not so bad, I think," she replied. "He dances like an angel."

He stared toward the punch bowl, where Matt was glancing toward him and Leslie. The dark face was harder than stone and Ed felt a tingle of apprehension when Matt left Carolyn and started walking toward them. He didn't like that easygoing stride of Matt's. The only time Matt moved that slowly was when he was homicidally angry.

Chapter Four

Leslie knew by the look in Matt's eyes that he was furious. She thought his anger must be directed toward her, although she couldn't remember anything she'd done to deserve it. As he approached them, he had his cellular phone out and was pushing a number into it. He said something, then closed it and put it back in his pocket.

"I'm sorry, but we have to leave," he said, every syllable dripping ice. "It seems that Carolyn has developed a vicious headache."

"It's all right," Leslie said, and even smiled as relief swept over her that she hadn't put that expression on his handsome face. "I wouldn't have been able to dance again." Her eyes met Matt's shyly. "I really enjoyed it."

He didn't reply. His eyes were narrow and not very friendly. "Ed, will you go out front and watch for the car? I've just phoned the driver."

"Sure." He hesitated noticeably for a moment before he left.

Matt stood looking down at Leslie with an intensity that made her uncomfortable. "You make yourself out to be a broken stick," he said quietly. "But you're not what you appear to be, are you? I get the feeling that you used to be quite a dancer before that leg slowed you down."

She was puzzled. "I learned how from my mother," she said honestly. "I used to dance with her."

He laughed curtly. "Pull the other one," he said. He was thinking about her pretended revulsion, the way she constantly backed off when he came near her. Then, tonight, the carefully planned capitulation. It was an old trick that had been used on him before—backing away so that he'd give chase. He was surprised that he hadn't realized it sooner. He wondered how far she'd let him go. He was going to find out.

She blinked and frowned. "I beg your pardon?" she asked, genuinely puzzled.

"Never mind," he said with a parody of a smile. "Ed should be outside with the driver by now. Shall we go?"

He reached out a lean hand and pulled her to her feet abruptly. Her face was very pale at the hint of domination not only in his eyes, but the hold he had on her. It was hard not to panic. It reminded her of another man who had used domination; only that time she had no knowledge of how to get away. Now she did. She turned her arm quickly and pushed it down against his thumb, the weakest spot in his hold, freeing herself instantly as the self-defense instructor had taught her.

Matt was surprised. "Where did you learn that? From your mother?" he drawled.

"No. From my Tae Kwon Do instructor in Houston," she returned. "Despite my bad leg, I can take care of myself."

"Oh, I'd bet on that." His dark eyes narrowed and glittered faintly. "You're not what you seem, Miss Murry. I'm going to make it my business to find out the truth about you."

She blanched. She didn't want him digging into her past. She'd run from it, hidden from it, for years. Would she have to run some more, just when she felt secure?

He saw her frightened expression and felt even more certain that he'd almost been taken for the ride of his life. Hadn't his experience with women taught him how to recognize deceit? He thought of his mother and his heart went cold. Leslie even had a look of her, with that blond hair. He took her by the upper arm and pulled her along with him, noticing that she moved uncomfortably and tugged at his hold.

"Please," she said tightly. "Slow down. It hurts."

He stopped at once, realizing that he was forcing her to a pace that made walking painful. He'd forgotten about her disability, as if it were part of her act. He let out an angry breath.

"The damaged leg is real," he said, almost to himself. "But what else is?"

She met his angry eyes. "Mr. Caldwell, whatever I am, I'm no threat to you," she said quietly. "I really don't like being touched, but I enjoyed dancing with you. I haven't danced...in years."

He studied her wan face, oblivious to the music of the band, and the murmur of movement around them. "Sometimes," he murmured, "you seem very familiar to me, as if I've seen you before." He was thinking about his mother, and how she'd betrayed him and hurt him all those years ago.

Leslie didn't know that, though. Her teeth clenched as she tried not to let her fear show. Probably he had seen her before, just like the whole country had, her face in the tabloid papers as it had appeared the night they took her out of her mother's bloodstained apartment on a stretcher, her leg bleeding profusely, her sobs audible. But then her hair had been dark, and she'd been wearing glasses. Could he really recognize her?

"Maybe I just have that kind of face." She grimaced and shifted her weight. "Could we go, please?" she asked on a moan. "My leg really is killing me."

He didn't move for an instant. Then he bent suddenly and lifted her in his strong arms and carried her through the amused crowd toward the door.

"Mr....Mr. Caldwell," she protested, stiffening. She'd never been picked up and carried by a man in her entire life. She studied his strong profile with fascinated curiosity, too entranced to feel the usual fear. Having danced with him, she was able to accept his physical closeness. He felt very strong and he smelled of some spicy, very exotic cologne. She had the oddest urge to touch his wavy black hair just over his broad forehead, where it looked thickest.

He glanced down into her fascinated eyes and one of his dark eyebrows rose in a silent question.

"You're...very strong, aren't you?" she asked hesitantly.

The tone of her voice touched something deep inside him. He searched her eyes and the tension was suddenly thick as his gaze fell to her soft bow of a mouth and lingered there, even as his pace slowed slightly.

Her hand clutched the lapel of his tuxedo as her own gaze fell to his mouth. She'd never wanted to be kissed like this before. When she'd been kissed during that horrible encounter, it had been repulsive—a wet, invading, lustful kiss that made her want to throw up.

It wouldn't be like that with Matt. She knew instinctively that he was well versed in the art of lovemaking, and that he would be gentle with a woman.

His mouth was sensual, wide and chiseled. Her own mouth tingled as she wondered visibly what it would feel like to let him kiss her.

He read that curiosity with pinpoint accuracy and his sharp intake of breath brought her curious eyes up to meet his.

"Careful," he cautioned, his voice deeper than usual. "Curiosity killed the cat."

Her eyes asked a question she couldn't form with her lips.

"You fell off a horse avoiding any contact with me," he reminded her quietly. "Now you look as if you'd do anything to have my mouth on yours. Why?"

"I don't know," she whispered, her hand contracting on the lapel of his jacket. "I like being close to you," she confessed, surprised. "It's funny. I haven't wanted to be close to a man like this before."

He stopped dead in his tracks. There was a faint vibration in the hard arms holding her. His eyes lanced into hers. His breath became audible. The arm under her back contracted, bringing her breasts hard against him as he stood there on the steps of the building, totally oblivious to everything except the ache that was consuming him.

Leslie's body shivered with its first real taste of desire. She laughed shakily at the new and wonderful sensations she was feeling. Her breasts felt suddenly heavy. They ached.

"Is this what it feels like?" she murmured.

"What?" he asked huskily.

She met his gaze. "Desire."

He actually shuddered. His arms contracted. His lips parted as he looked at her mouth and knew that he couldn't help taking it. She smelled of roses, like the tiny pink fairy roses that grew in masses around the front door of his ranch house. She wanted him. His head began to spin. He bent his dark head and bit at her lower lip with a sensuous whisper.

"Open your mouth, Leslie," he whispered, and his hard mouth suddenly went down insistently on hers.

But before he could even savor the feel of her soft lips, the sound of high heels approaching jerked his head up. Leslie was trembling against him, shocked and a little frightened, and completely entranced by the unexpected contact with his beautiful mouth.

Matt's dark eyes blazed down into hers. "No more games. I'm taking you home with me," he said huskily.

She started to speak, to protest, when Carolyn came striding angrily out the door.

"Does she have to be carried?" the older woman asked Matt with dripping sarcasm. "Funny, she was dancing eagerly enough a few minutes ago!"

"She has a bad leg," Matt said, regaining his control. "Here's the car."

The limousine drew up at the curb and Ed got out, frowning when he saw Leslie in Matt's arms.

"Are you all right?" he asked as he approached them.

"She shouldn't have danced," Matt said stiffly as he moved the rest of the way down the steps to deposit her inside the car on the leather-covered seat. "She made her leg worse."

Carolyn was livid. She slid in and moved to the other side of Leslie with a gaze that could have curdled milk. "One dance and we have to leave," she said furiously.

Matt moved into the car beside Ed and slammed the door. "I thought we were leaving because you had a headache," he snapped at Carolyn, his usual control quite evidently gone. He was in a foul mood. Desire was frustrating him. He glanced at Leslie and thought how good she was at manipulation. She had him almost doubled over with need. She was probably laughing her head off silently. Well, she was going to pay for that.

Carolyn, watching his eyes on Leslie, made an angry sound in her throat and stared out the window.

To Ed's surprise and dismay, they dropped him off at his home first. He tried to argue, but Matt wasn't having that. He told Ed he'd see him at the office Monday and closed the door on his protests.

Carolyn was deposited next. Matt walked her to her door, but he moved back before she could claim a good-night kiss. The way she slammed her door was audible even inside the closed limousine.

Leslie bit her lower lip as Matt climbed back into the car with her. In the lighted interior, she could see the expression on his face as he studied her slender body covetously.

"This isn't the way to my apartment," she ventured nervously a few minutes later, hoping he hadn't meant what he said just before they got into the limousine.

"No, it isn't, is it?" he replied dangerously.

Even as he spoke, the limousine pulled up at the door to his ranch house. He helped Leslie out and spoke briefly to the driver before dismissing him. Then he swung a frightened Leslie up into his arms and carried her toward the front door.

"Mr. Caldwell..." she began.

"Matt," he corrected, not looking at her.

"I want to go home," she tried again.

"You will. Eventually."

"But you sent the car away."

"I have six cars," he informed her as he shifted his light burden to produce his keys from the pocket of his slacks and insert one in the lock. The door swung open. "I'll drive you home when the time comes."

"I'm very tired." Her voice sounded breathless and high-pitched.

"Then I know just the place for you." He closed the door and carried her down a long, dimly lit hallway to a room near the back of the house. He leaned down to open the door and once they were through it, he kicked it shut with his foot.

Seconds later, Leslie was in the middle of a huge

king-size bed, sprawled on the beige-brown-and-black comforter that covered it and Matt was removing her wrap.

It went flying onto a chair, along with his jacket and tie. He unbuttoned his shirt and slid down onto the bed beside her, his hands on either side of her face as he poised just above her.

The position brought back terrible, nightmarish memories. She stiffened all over. Her face went pale. Her eyes dilated so much that the gray of them was eclipsed by black.

Matt ignored her expression. He looked down the length of her in the clinging silver dress, his eyes lingering on the thrust of her small breasts. One of his big hands came up to trace around the prominent hard nipple that pointed through the fabric.

The touch shocked Leslie, because she didn't find it revolting or unpleasant. She shivered a little. Her eyes, wide and frightened, and a little curious, met his.

His strong fingers brushed lazily over the nipple and around the contours of her breast as if the feel of her fascinated him.

"Do you mind?" he asked with faint insolence, and slipped one of the spaghetti straps down her arm, moving her just enough that he could pull the bodice away from her perfect little breast.

Leslie couldn't believe what was happening. Men were repulsive to her. She hated the thought of intimacy. But Matt Caldwell was looking at her bare breast and she was letting him, with no thought of resistance. She hadn't even had anything to drink.

He searched her face as his warm fingers traced her breast. He read the pleasure she was feeling in her soft eyes. "You feel like sun-touched marble to my hand," he said quietly. "Your skin is beautiful." His gaze traveled down her body. "Your breasts are perfect."

She was shivering again. Her hands clenched beside her head as she watched him touch her, like an observer, like in a dream.

He smiled with faint mockery when he saw her expression. "Haven't you done this before?"

"No," she said, and she actually sounded serious.

He discounted that at once. She was far too calm and submissive for an inexperienced woman.

One dark eyebrow lifted. "Twenty-three and still a virgin?"

How had he known that? "Well...yes." Technically she certainly was. Emotionally, too. Despite what had been done to her, she'd been spared rape, if only by seconds, when her mother came home unexpectedly.

Matt was absorbed in touching her body. His forefinger traced around the hard nipple, and he watched her body lift to follow it when he lifted his hand.

"Do you like it?" he asked softly.

She was watching him intensely. "Yes." She sounded as if it surprised her that she liked what he was doing.

With easy self-confidence, he pulled her up just a little and pushed the other strap down her arm, baring her completely to his eyes. She was perfect, like a warm statue in beautifully smooth marble. He'd never seen breasts like hers. She aroused him profoundly.

He held her by the upper part of her rib cage, his thumbs edging onto her breasts to caress them tenderly while he watched the expressions chase each other across her face. The silence in the bedroom was broken only by the sound of cars far in the distance and the sound of some mournful night bird outside the window. Closer was the rasp of her own breathing and her heart beating in her ears. She should be fighting for her life, screaming, running, escaping. She'd avoided this sort of situation successfully for six years. Why didn't she want to avoid Matt's hands?

Matt touched her almost reverently, his eyes on her hard nipples. With a faint groan, he bent his dark head and his mouth touched the soft curve of her breast.

She gasped and stiffened. His head lifted immediately. He looked at her and realized that she wasn't trying to get away. Her eyes were full of shocked pleasure and curiosity.

"Another first?" he asked with faint arrogance and a calculating smile that didn't really register in her whirling mind.

She nodded, swallowing. Her body, as if it was

ignoring her brain, moved sensuously on the bed.
She'd never dreamed that she could let a man touch
her like this, that she could enjoy letting him touch
her, after her one horrible experience with intimacy.

He put his mouth over her nipple and suckled her
so insistently that she cried out, drowning in a veritable flood of shocked pleasure.

The little cry aroused Matt unexpectedly, and he
was rougher with her than he meant to be, his mouth
suddenly demanding on her soft flesh. He tasted her
hungrily for several long seconds until he forced his
mind to remember why he shouldn't let himself go
in headfirst. He wanted her almost beyond bearing,
but he wasn't going to let her make a fool of him.

He lifted his head and studied her flushed face
clinically. She was enjoying it, but she needn't think
he was going to let her take possession of him with
that pretty body. He knew now that he could have
her. She was willing to give in. For a price, he added.

She opened her eyes and lay there watching him
with wide, soft, curious eyes. She thought she had
him in her pocket, he mused. But she was all too
acquiescent. That, he thought amusedly, was a gross
miscalculation on her part. It was her nervous retreat
that challenged him, not the sort of easy conquest
with which he was already too familiar.

Abruptly he sat up, pulling her with him, and slid
the straps of her evening dress back up onto her
shoulders.

She watched him silently, still shocked by his ardor and puzzled at her unexpected response to it.

He got to his feet and rebuttoned his shirt, reaching for his snap-on tie and then his jacket. He studied her there, sitting dazed on the edge of his bed, and his dark eyes narrowed. He smiled, but it wasn't a pleasant smile.

"You're not bad," he murmured lazily. "But the fascinated virgin bit turns me right off. I like experience."

She blinked. She was still trying to make her mind work again.

"I assume that your other would-be lovers liked that wide-eyed, first-time look?"

Other lovers. Had he guessed about her past? Her eyes registered the fear.

He saw it. He was vaguely sorry that she wasn't what she pretended to be. He was all but jaded when it came to pursuing women. He hated the coy behavior, the teasing, the manipulation that eventually ended in his bedroom. He was considered a great catch by single women, rich and handsome and experienced in sensual techniques. But he always made his position clear at the outset. He didn't want marriage. That didn't really matter to most of the women in his life. A diamond here, an exotic vacation there, and they seemed satisfied for as long as it lasted. Not that there were many affairs. He was tired of the game. In fact, he'd never been more tired of it than he was right now. His whole expression was one of disgust.

Leslie saw it in his eyes and wished she could curl up into a ball and hide under the bed. His cold scrutiny made her feel cheap, just as that doctor had, just as the media had, just as her mother had...

He couldn't have explained why that expression on her face made him feel guilty. But it did.

He turned away from her. "Come on," he said, picking up her wrap and purse and tossing them to her. "I'll run you home."

She didn't look at him as she followed him down the length of the hall. It was longer than she realized, and even before they got to the front door, her leg was throbbing. Dancing had been damaging enough, without the jerk of his hand as they left the ballroom. But she ground her teeth together and didn't let her growing discomfort show in her face. He wasn't going to make her feel any worse than she already did by accusing her of putting on an act for sympathy. She went past him out the door he was holding open, avoiding his eyes. She wondered how things could have gone so terribly wrong.

The spacious garage was full of cars. He got out the silver Mercedes and opened the door to let her climb inside, onto the leather-covered passenger seat. He closed her door with something of a snap. Her fingers fumbled the seat belt into its catch and she hoped he wouldn't want to elaborate on what he'd already said.

She stared out the window at the dark silhouettes of buildings and trees as he drove along the back roads that eventually led into Jacobsville. She was sick about the way she'd acted. He probably thought she was the easiest woman alive. The only thing she didn't understand was why he didn't take advantage of it. The obvious reason made her even more uncomfortable. Didn't they say that some men didn't want what came easily? It was probably true. He'd been in pursuit as long as she was backing away from him. What irony, to spend years being afraid of men, running crazily from even the most platonic involvement, to find herself capable of torrid desire with the one man in the world who didn't want her!

He felt her tension. It was all too apparent that she was disappointed that he hadn't played the game to its finish.

"Is that what Ed gets when he takes you home?" he drawled.

Her nails bit into her small evening bag. Her teeth clenched. She wasn't going to dignify that remark with a reply.

He shrugged and paused to turn onto the main highway. "Don't take it so hard," he said lazily. "I'm a little too sophisticated to fall for it, but there are a few rich single ranchers around Jacobsville. Cy Parks comes to mind. He's hell on the nerves, but he is a widower." He glanced at her averted face. "On second thought, he's had enough tragedy in his life. I wouldn't wish you on him.''

She couldn't even manage to speak, she was so choked up with hurt. Why, she wondered, did everything she wanted in life turn on her and tear her to pieces? It was like tracking cougars with a toy gun. Just when she seemed to find peace and purpose, her life became nothing but torment. As if her tattered pride wasn't enough, she was in terrible pain. She shifted in the seat, hoping that a change of position would help. It didn't.

''How did that bone get shattered?'' he asked conversationally.

''Don't you know?'' she asked on a harsh laugh. If he'd seen the story about her, as she suspected, he was only playing a cruel game—the sort of game he'd already accused her of playing!

He glanced at her with a scowl. ''And how would I know?'' he wondered aloud.

She frowned. Maybe he hadn't read anything at all! He might be fishing for answers.

She swallowed, gripping her purse tightly.

He swung the Mercedes into the driveway of her boardinghouse and pulled up at the steps, with the engine still running. He turned to her. ''How *would* I know?'' he asked again, his voice determined.

''You seem to think you're an expert on everything else about me,'' she replied evasively.

His chin lifted as he studied her through narrowed

eyes. "There are several ways a bone can be shattered," he said quietly. "One way is from a bullet."

She didn't feel as if she were still breathing. She sat like a statue, watching him deliberate.

"What do you know about bullets?" she asked shortly.

"My unit was called up during Operation Desert Storm," he told her. "I served with an infantry unit. I know quite a lot about bullets. And what they do to bone," he added. "Which brings me to the obvious question. Who shot you?"

"I didn't say...I was shot," she managed.

His intense gaze held her like invisible ropes. "But you were, weren't you?" he asked with shrewd scrutiny. His lips tugged into a cold smile. "As to who did it, I'd bet on one of your former lovers. Did he catch you with somebody else, or did you tease him the way you teased me tonight and then refuse him?" He gave her another contemptuous look. "Not that you refused. You didn't exactly play hard to get."

Her ego went right down to her shoes. He was painting her over with evil colors. She bit her lower lip. It was unpleasant enough to have her memories, but to have this man making her out to be some sort of nymphomaniac was painful beyond words. Her first real taste of tender intimacy had been with him, tonight, and he made it sound dirty and cheap.

She unfastened her seat belt and got out of the car with as much dignity as she could muster. Her leg was incredibly painful. All she wanted was her bed, her heating pad and some more aspirins. And to get away from her tormenter.

Matt switched off the engine and moved around the car, irritated by the way she limped.

"I'll take you to the door…!"

She flinched when he came close. She backed away from him, actually shivering when she remembered shamefully what she'd let him do to her. Her eyes clouded with unshed angry tears, with outraged virtue.

"More games?" he asked tersely. He hadn't liked having her back away again after the way she'd been in his bedroom.

"I don't…play games," she replied, hating the hiccup of a sob that revealed how upset she really was. She clutched her wrap and her purse to her chest, accusing eyes glaring at him. "And you can go to hell!"

He scowled at the way she looked, barely hearing the words. She was white in the face and her whole body seemed rigid, as if she really was upset.

She turned and walked away, wincing inwardly with every excruciating step, to the front porch. But her face didn't show one trace of her discomfort. She held her head high. She still had her pride, she thought through a wave of pain.

Matt watched her go into the boardinghouse with more mixed, confused emotions than he'd ever felt.

He remembered vividly that curious "Don't you know?" when he'd asked who shot her.

He got back into the Mercedes and sat staring through the windshield for a long moment before he started it. Miss Murry was one puzzle he intended to solve, and if it cost him a fortune in detective fees, he was going to do it.

Chapter Five

Leslie cried for what seemed hours. The aspirin didn't help the leg pain at all. There was no medicine known to man that she could take for her wounded ego. Matt had swept the floor with her, played with her, laughed at her naiveté and made her out to be little better than a prostitute. He was like that emergency room doctor so long ago who'd made her ashamed of her body. It was a pity that her first real desire for a man's touch had made her an object of contempt to the man himself.

Well, she told herself as she wiped angrily at the tears, she'd never make that mistake again. Matt Caldwell could go right where she'd told him to!

The phone rang and she hesitated to answer it. But it might be Ed. She picked up the receiver.

"We had a good laugh about you," Carolyn told her outright. "I guess you'll think twice before you throw yourself at him again! He said you were so easy that you disgusted him...!"

Almost shaking with humiliation, she put the receiver down with a slam and then unplugged the phone. It was so close to what Matt had already said that there was no reason not to believe her. Carolyn's harsh arrogance was just what she needed to make the miserable evening complete.

The pain, combined with the humiliation, kept her awake until almost daylight. She missed breakfast, not to mention church, and when she did finally open her eyes, it was to a kind of pain she hadn't experienced since the night she was shot.

She shifted, wincing, and then moaned as the movement caused another searing wave of discomfort up her leg. The knock on her door barely got through to her. "Come in," she said in a husky, exhausted tone.

The door opened and there was Matt Caldwell, unshaven and with dark circles under his eyes.

Carolyn's words came back to haunt her. She grabbed the first thing that came to hand, a plastic bottle of spring water she kept by the bed, and flung it furiously across the room at him. It missed his head, and Ed's, by a quarter of an inch.

"No, thanks," Ed said, moving in front of Matt. "I don't want any water."

Her face was lined with pain, white with it. She glared at Matt's hard, angry face with eyes that would have looked perfectly natural over a cocked pistol.

"I couldn't get you on the phone, and I was worried," Ed said gently, approaching her side of the double bed she occupied. He noticed the unplugged telephone on her bedside table. "Now I know why I couldn't get you on the phone." He studied her drawn face. "How bad is it?"

She could barely breathe. "Bad," she said huskily, thinking what an understatement that word was.

He took her thick white chenille bathrobe from the chair beside the bed. "Come on. We're going to drive you to the emergency room. Matt can phone Lou Coltrain and have her meet us there."

It was an indication of the pain that she didn't argue. She got out of bed, aware of the picture she must make in the thick flannel pajamas that covered every inch of her up to her chin. Matt was probably shocked, she thought as she let Ed stuff her into the robe. He probably expected her to be naked under the covers, conforming to the image he had of her nymphomania!

He hadn't said a word. He just stood there, by the door, grimly watching Ed get her ready—until she tried to walk, and folded up.

Ed swung her up in his arms, stopping Matt's instinctive quick movement toward her. Ed knew for a fact that she'd scream the house down if his cousin so much as touched her. He didn't know what had gone on the night before, but judging by the way Matt and Leslie looked, it had been both humiliating and embarrassing.

"I can carry her," he told Matt. "Let's go."

Matt glimpsed her contorted features and didn't hesitate. He led the way down the hall and right out the front door.

"My purse," she said huskily. "My insurance card…"

"That can be taken care of later," Matt said stiffly. He opened the back door of the Mercedes and waited while Ed slid her onto the seat.

She leaned back with her eyes closed, almost sick from the pain.

"She should never have gotten on the dance floor," Matt said through his teeth as they started toward town. "And then I jerked her up out of her chair. It's my fault."

Ed didn't reply. He glanced over the seat at Leslie with concern in his whole expression. He hoped she hadn't done any major damage to herself with that exhibition the night before.

Lou Coltrain was waiting in the emergency room as Ed carried Leslie inside the building. She motioned him down the hall to a room and closed the door behind Matt as soon as he entered.

She examined the leg carefully, asking questions that Leslie was barely able to answer. "I want

X rays,'' she said. ''But I'll give you something for pain first.''

''Thank you,'' Leslie choked, fighting tears.

Lou smoothed her wild hair. ''You poor little thing,'' she said softly. ''Cry if you want to. It must hurt like hell.''

She went out to get the injection, and tears poured down Leslie's face because of that tender concern. She hardly ever cried. She was tough. She could take anything—near-rape, bullet wounds, notoriety, her mother's trial, the refusal of her parent to even speak to her...

''There, there,'' Ed said. He produced a handkerchief and blotted the tears, smiling down at her. ''Dr. Lou is going to make it all better.''

''For God's sake...!'' Matt bit off angry words and walked out of the room. It was unbearable that he'd hurt her like that. Unbearable! And then to have to watch Ed comforting her...!

''I hate him,'' Leslie choked when he was gone. She actually shivered. ''He laughed about it,'' she whispered, blind to Ed's curious scowl. ''She said they both laughed about it, that he was disgusted.''

''She?''

''Carolyn.'' The tears were hot in her eyes, cold on her cheeks. ''I hate him!''

Lou came back with the injection and gave it, waiting for it to take effect. She glanced at Ed. ''You might want to wait outside. I'm taking her down to

X ray myself. I'll come and get you when we've done some tests.''

"Okay."

He went out and joined Matt in the waiting room. The older man's face was drawn, tormented. He barely glanced at Ed before he turned his attention to the trees outside the window. It was a dismal gray day, with rain threatening. It matched his mood.

Ed leaned against the wall beside him with a frown. "She said Carolyn phoned her last night," he began. "I suppose that's why the phone was unplugged."

It was Matt's turn to look puzzled. "What?"

"Leslie said Carolyn told her the two of you were laughing at her," he murmured. "She didn't say what about."

Matt's face hardened visibly. He rammed his hands into his pockets and his eyes were terrible to look into.

"Don't hurt Leslie," Ed said suddenly, his voice quiet but full of venom. "She hasn't had an easy life. Don't make things hard on her. She has no place else to go."

Matt glanced at him, disliking the implied threat as much as the fact that Ed knew far more about Leslie than he did. Were they lovers? Old lovers, perhaps?

"She keeps secrets," he said. "She was shot. Who did it?"

Ed lifted both eyebrows. "Who said she was

shot?'' he asked innocently, doing it so well that he actually fooled his cousin.

Matt hesitated. ''Nobody. I assumed...well, how else does a bone get shattered?''

''By a blow, by a bad fall, in a car wreck...'' Ed trailed off, leaving Matt with something to think about.

''Yes. Of course.'' The older man sighed. ''Dancing put her in this shape. I didn't realize just how fragile she was. She doesn't exactly shout her problems to the world.''

''She was always like that,'' Ed replied.

Matt turned to face him. ''How did you meet her?''

''She and I were in college together,'' Ed told him. ''We used to date occasionally. She trusts me,'' he added.

Matt was turning what he knew about Leslie over in his mind. If the pieces had been part of a puzzle, none of them would fit. When they first met, she avoided his touch like the plague. Last night, she'd enjoyed his advances. She'd been nervous and shy at their first meeting. Later, at the office, she'd been gregarious, almost playful. Last night, she'd been a completely different woman on the dance floor. Then, when he'd taken her home with him, she'd been hungry, sensuous, tender. Nothing about her made any sense.

''Don't trust her too far,'' Matt advised the other

man. "She's too secretive to suit me. I thinks she's hiding something…maybe something pretty bad."

Ed didn't dare react. He pursed his lips and smiled. "Leslie's never hurt anyone in her life," he remarked. "And before you get the wrong idea about her, you'd better know that she has a real fear of men."

Matt laughed. "Oh, that's a good one," he said mockingly. "You should have seen her last night when we were alone."

Ed's eyes narrowed. "What do you mean?"

"I mean she's easy," Matt said with a contemptuous smile.

Ed's eyes began to glitter. He called his cousin a name that made Matt's eyebrows arch.

"Easy. My God!" Ed ground out.

Matt was puzzled by the other man's inexplicable behavior. Probably he was jealous. His cell phone began to trill, diverting him. He answered it. He recognized Carolyn's voice immediately and moved away, so that Ed couldn't hear what he said. Ed was certainly acting strange lately.

"I thought you were coming over to ride with me this afternoon," Carolyn said cheerfully. "Where are you?"

"At the hospital," he said absently, his eyes on Ed's retreating back going through the emergency room doors. "What did you say to Leslie last night?"

"What do you mean?"

"When you phoned her!" Matt prompted.

Carolyn sounded vague. "Well, I wanted to see if she was better," she replied. "She seemed to be in a lot of pain after the dance."

"What else did you say?"

Carolyn laughed. "Oh, I see. I'm being accused of something underhanded, is that it? Really, Matt, I thought you could see through that phony vulnerability of hers. What did she tell you I said?"

He shrugged. "Never mind. I must have misunderstood."

"You certainly did," she assured him firmly. "I wouldn't call someone in pain to upset them. I thought you knew me better than that."

"I do." He was seething. So now it seemed that Miss Murry was making up lies about Carolyn. Had it been to get even with him, for not giving in to her wiles? Or was she trying to turn his cousin against him?

"What about that horseback ride? And what are you doing at the hospital?" she added suddenly.

"I'm with Ed, visiting one of his friends," he said. "Better put the horseback ride off until next weekend. I'll phone you."

He hung up. His eyes darkened with anger. He wanted the Murry woman out of his company, out of his life. She was going to be nothing but trouble.

He repocketed the phone and went outside to wait for Ed and Leslie.

* * *

A good half hour later, Ed came out of the emergency room with his hands in his pockets, looking worried.

"They're keeping her overnight," he said curtly.

"For a sore leg?" Matt asked with mild sarcasm.

Ed scowled. "One of the bones shifted and it's pressing on a nerve," he replied. "Lou says it won't get any better until it's fixed. They're sending for an orthopedic man from Houston. He'll be in this afternoon."

"Who's going to pay for that?" Matt asked coldly.

"Since you ask, I am," Ed returned, not intimidated even by those glittery eyes.

"It's your money," the older man replied. He let out a breath. "What caused the bone to separate?"

"Why ask a question when you already know the answer?" Ed wanted to know. "I'm going to stay with her. She's frightened."

He was fairly certain that even if Leslie could fake pain, she couldn't fake an X ray. Somewhere in the back of his mind he found guilt lurking. If he hadn't pulled her onto the dance floor, and if he hadn't jerked her to her feet...

He turned away and walked out of the building without another word. Leslie was Ed's business. He kept telling himself that. But all the way home, his conscience stabbed at him. She couldn't help being what she was. Even so, he hadn't meant to hurt her. He remembered the tears, genuine tears, boiling out of her eyes when Lou had touched her hair so gently. She acted as if she'd never had tenderness in her life.

He drove himself home and tried to concentrate on briefing himself for a director's meeting the next day. But long before bedtime, he gave it up and drank himself into uneasy sleep.

The orthopedic man examined the X rays and seconded Lou's opinion that immediate surgery was required. But Leslie didn't want the surgery. She refused to talk about it. The minute the doctors and Ed left the room, she struggled out of bed and hobbled to the closet to pull her pajamas and robe and shoes out of it.

In the hall, Matt came upon Ed and Lou and a tall, distinguished stranger in an expensive suit.

"You two look like stormy weather," he mused. "What's wrong?"

"Leslie won't have the operation," Ed muttered worriedly. "Dr. Santos flew all the way from Houston to do the surgery, and she won't hear of it."

"Maybe she doesn't think she needs it," Matt said.

Lou glanced at him. "You have no idea what sort of pain she's in," she said, impatient with him. "One of the bone fragments, the one that shifted, is pressing right on a nerve."

"The bones should have been properly aligned at the time the accident occurred," the visiting orthopedic surgeon agreed. "It was criminally irresponsible of the attending physician to do nothing more than bandage the leg. A cast wasn't even used until afterward!''

That sounded negligent to Matt, too. He frowned. "Did she say why not?"

Lou sighed angrily. "She won't talk about it. She won't listen to any of us. Eventually she'll have to. But in the meantime, the pain is going to drive her insane.''

Matt glanced from one set face to the other and walked past them to Leslie's room.

She was wearing her flannel pajamas and reaching for the robe when Matt walked in. She gave him a glare hot enough to boil water.

"Well, at least you won't be trying to talk me into an operation I don't want," she muttered as she struggled to get from the closet to the bed.

"Why won't I?"

She arched both eyebrows expressively. "I'm the enemy.''

He stood at the foot of the bed, watching her get into the robe. Her leg was at an awkward angle, and her face was pinched. He could imagine the sort of pain she was already experiencing.

"Suit yourself about the operation," he replied with forced indifference, folding his arms across his chest. "But don't expect me to have someone carry you back and forth around the office. If you want to make a martyr of yourself, be my guest.''

She stopped fiddling with the belt of the robe and stared at him quietly, puzzled.

"Some people enjoy making themselves objects of pity to people around them," he continued deliberately.

"I don't want pity!" she snapped.

"Really?"

She wrapped the belt around her fingers and stared at it. "I'll have to be in a cast."

"No doubt."

"My insurance hasn't taken effect yet, either," she said with averted eyes. "Once it's in force, I can have the operation." She looked back at him coldly. "I'm not going to let Ed pay for it, in case you wondered, and I don't care if he can afford it!"

He had to fight back a stirring of admiration for her independent stance. It could be part of the pose, he realized, but it sounded pretty genuine. His blue eyes narrowed. "I'll pay for it," he said, surprising both of them. "It can come out of your weekly check."

Her teeth clenched. "I know how much this sort of thing costs. That's why I've never had it done before. I'd never be able to pay it back in my lifetime."

His eyes fell to her body. "We could work something out," he murmured.

She flushed. "No, we couldn't!"

She stood up, barely able to stand the pain, despite the painkillers they'd given her. She hobbled over to the chair, where her shoes were placed, and eased her feet into them.

"Where are you going?" he asked conversationally.

"Home," she said, and started past him.

He caught her up in his arms like a fallen package and carried her right back to the bed, dumping her on it gently. His arms made a cage as he looked down at her flushed face. "Don't be stupid," he said in a voice that went right through her. "You're no good to yourself or anyone else in this condition. You have no choice."

Her lips trembled as she fought to control the tears. She would be helpless, vulnerable. Besides, that surgeon reminded her of the man at the emergency room in Houston. He brought back unbearable shame.

The unshed tears fascinated Matt. She fascinated him. He didn't want to care about what happened to her, but he did.

He reached down and smoothed a long forefinger over her wet lashes. "Do you have family?" he asked unexpectedly.

She thought of her mother, in prison, and felt sick to her very soul. "No," she whispered starkly.

"Are both your parents dead?"

"Yes," she said at once.

"No brothers, sisters?"

She shook her head.

He frowned, as if her situation disturbed him. In fact, it did. She looked vulnerable and fragile and completely lost. He didn't understand why he cared so much for her well-being. Perhaps it was guilt because he'd lured her into a kind of dancing she wasn't really able to do anymore.

"I want to go home," she said harshly.

"Afterward," he replied.

She remembered him saying that before, in almost the same way, and she averted her face in shame.

He could have bitten his tongue for that. He shouldn't bait her when she was in such a condition. It was hitting below the belt.

He drew in a long breath. "Leave it to Ed to pick up strays, and make me responsible for them!" he muttered, angry because of her vulnerability and his unwanted response to it.

She didn't say a word, but her lower lip trembled and she turned her face away from him. Beside her hip, her hand was clenched so tightly that the knuckles were white.

He shot away from the bed, his eyes furious. "You're having the damned operation," he informed her flatly. "Once you're healthy and whole again, you won't need Ed to prop you up. You can work for your living like every other woman."

She didn't answer him. She didn't look at him. She wanted to get better so that she could kick the hell out of him.

"Did you hear me?" he asked in a dangerously soft tone.

She jerked her head to acknowledge the question but she didn't speak.

He let out an angry breath. "I'll tell the others."

He left her lying there and announced her decision to the three people in the hall.

"How did you manage that?" Ed asked when Lou and Dr. Santos went back in to talk to Leslie.

"I made her mad," Matt replied. "Sympathy doesn't work."

"No, it doesn't," Ed replied quietly. "I don't think she's had much of it in her whole life."

"What happened to her parents?" he wanted to know.

Ed was careful about the reply. "Her father misjudged the position of some electrical wires and flew right into them. He was electrocuted."

He frowned darkly. "And her mother?"

"They were both in love with the same man," Ed said evasively. "He died, and Leslie and her mother still aren't on speaking terms."

Matt turned away, jingling the change in his pocket restlessly. "How did he die?"

"Violently," Ed told him. "It was a long time ago. But I don't think Leslie will ever get over it."

Which was true, but it sounded as if Leslie was still in love with the dead man—which was exactly what Ed wanted. He was going to save her from Matt, whatever it took. She was a good friend. He didn't want her life destroyed because Matt was on the prowl for a new conquest. Leslie deserved something better than to be one of Matt's ex-girlfriends.

Matt glanced at his cousin with a puzzling expression. "When will they operate?"

"Tomorrow morning," Ed said. "I'll be late getting to work. I'm going to be here while it's going on."

Matt nodded. He glanced down the hall toward the door of Leslie's room. He hesitated for a moment before he turned and went out of the building without another comment.

Later, Ed questioned her about what Matt had said to her.

"He said that I was finding excuses because I wanted people to feel sorry for me," she said angrily. "And I do not have a martyr complex!"

Ed chuckled. "I know that."

"I can't believe you're related to someone like that," she said furiously. "He's horrible!"

"He's had a rough life. Something you can identify with," he added gently.

"I think he and his latest girlfriend deserve each other," she murmured.

"Carolyn phoned while he was here. I don't know what was said, but I'd bet my bottom dollar she denied saying anything to upset you."

"Would you expect her to admit it?" she asked. She laid back against the pillow, glad that the injection they'd given her was taking effect. "I guess I'll be clumping around your office in a cast for weeks, if he doesn't find some excuse to fire me in the meantime.''

"There is company policy in such matters," he said easily. "He'd have to have my permission to fire you, and he won't get it.''

"I'm impressed," she said, and managed a wan smile.

"So you should be," he chuckled. He searched her eyes. "Leslie, why didn't the doctor set those bones when it happened?''

She studied the ceiling. "He said the whole thing was my fault and that I deserved all my wounds. He called me a vicious little tramp who caused decent men to be murdered." Her eyes closed. "Nothing ever hurt so much.''

"I can imagine!''

"I never went to a doctor again," she continued. "It wasn't just the things he said to me, you know. There was the expense, too. I had no insurance and no money. Mama had to have a public defender and I worked while I finished high school to help pay my way at my friend's house. The pain was bad, but eventually I got used to it, and the limp." She turned quiet eyes to Ed's face. "It would be sort of nice to be able to walk normally again. And I will pay back whatever it costs, if you and your cousin will be patient.''

He winced. "Nobody's worried about the cost.''

"He is," she informed him evenly. "And he's

right. I don't want to be a financial burden on anyone, not even him.''

"We'll talk about all this later," he said gently.
"Right now, I just want you to get better."

She sighed. "Will I? I wonder."

"Miracles happen all the time," he told her.
"You're overdue for one."

"I'd settle gladly for the ability to walk normally," she said at once, and she smiled.

Chapter Six

The operation was over by lunchtime the following day. Ed stayed until Leslie was out of the recovery room and out of danger, lying still and pale in the bed in the private room with the private nurse he'd hired to stay with her for the first couple of days. He'd spoken to both Lou Coltrain and the visiting orthopedic surgeon, who assured him that Miss Murry would find life much less painful from now on. Modern surgery had progressed to the point that procedures once considered impossible were now routine.

He went back to work feeling light and cheerful. Matt stopped him in the hall.

"Well?" he asked abruptly.

Ed grinned from ear to ear. "She's going to be fine. Dr. Santos said that in six weeks, when she comes out of that cast, she'll be able to dance in a contest."

Matt nodded. "Good."

Ed answered a question Matt had about one of their accounts and then, assuming that Matt didn't want anything else at the moment, he went back to his office. He had a temporary secretary, a pretty little redhead who had a bright personality and good dictation skills.

Surprisingly, Matt followed him into his office and closed the door. "Tell me how that bone was shattered," he said abruptly.

Ed sat down and leaned forward with his forearms on his cluttered desk. "That's Leslie's business, Matt," he replied. "I wouldn't tell you, even if I knew," he added, lying through his teeth with deliberate calm.

He sighed irritably. "She's a puzzle. A real puzzle."

"She's a sweet girl who's had a lot of hard knocks," Ed told him. "But regardless of what you think you know about her, she isn't 'easy.' Don't make the mistake of classing her with your usual sort of woman. You'll regret it."

Matt studied the younger man curiously and his eyes narrowed. "What do you mean, I think she's 'easy'?" he asked, bristling.

"Forgotten already? That's what you said about her."

Matt felt uncomfortable at the words that he'd spoken with such assurance to Leslie. He glanced at Ed irritably. "Miss Murry obviously means something to you. If you're so fond of her, why haven't you married her?"

Ed smoothed back his hair. "She kept me from blowing my brains out when my fiancée was gunned down in a bank robbery in Houston," he said. "I actually had the pistol loaded. She took it away from me."

Matt's eyes narrowed. "You never told me you were that despondent."

"You wouldn't have understood," came the reply. "Women were always a dime a dozen to you, Matt. You've never really been in love."

Matt's face, for once, didn't conceal his bitterness. "I wouldn't give any woman that sort of power over me," he said in clipped tones. "Women are devious, Ed. They'll smile at you until they get what they want, then they'll walk right over you to the next sucker. I've seen too many good men brought down by women they loved."

"There are bad men, too," Ed pointed out.

Matt shrugged. "I'm not arguing with that." He smiled. "I would have done what I could for you, though," he added. "We have our disagreements, but we're closer than most cousins are."

Ed nodded. "Yes, we are."

"You really are fond of Miss Murry, aren't you?"

"In a big brotherly sort of way," Ed affirmed. "She trusts me. If you knew her, you'd understand how difficult it is for her to trust a man."

"I think she's pulling the wool over your eyes," Matt told him. "You be careful. She's down on her luck, and you're rich."

Ed's face contorted briefly. "Good God, Matt, you haven't got a clue what she's really like."

"Neither have you," Matt commented with a cold smile. "But I know things about her that you don't. Let's leave it at that."

Ed hated his own impotence. "I want to keep her in my office."

"How do you expect her to come to work in a cast?" he asked frankly.

Ed leaned back in his chair and grinned. "The same way I did five years ago, when I had that skiing accident and broke my ankle. People work with broken bones all the time. And she doesn't type with her feet."

Matt shrugged. Miss Murry had him completely confused. "Suit yourself," he said finally. "Just keep her out of my way."

That shouldn't be difficult, Ed thought ruefully. Matt certainly wasn't on Leslie's list of favorite people. He wondered what the days ahead would bring. It would be like storing dynamite with lighted candles.

* * *

Leslie was out of the hospital in three days and back at work in a week. The company had paid for her surgery, to her surprise and Ed's. She knew that Matt had only done that out of guilt. Well, he needn't flay himself over what happened. She didn't really blame him. She had loved dancing with him. She refused to think of how that evening had ended. Some memories were best forgotten.

She hobbled into Ed's office with the use of crutches and plopped herself down behind her desk on her first day back on the job.

"How did you get here?" Ed asked with a surprised smile. "You can't drive, can you?"

"No, but one of the girls in my rooming house works in downtown Jacobsville and we're going to become a carpool three days a week. I'm paying my share of the gas and on her days off, I'll get a taxi to work," she added.

"I'm glad you're back," he said with genuine fondness.

"Oh, sure you are," she said with a teasing glance. "I heard all about Karla Smith when the girls from Mr. Caldwell's office came to see me. I understand she has a flaming crush on you."

Ed chuckled. "So they say. Poor girl."

She made a face. "You can't live in the past."

"Tell yourself that."

She put her crutches on the floor beside the desk, and swiveled back in her desk chair. "It's going to be a little difficult for me to get back and forth to your office," she said. "Can you dictate letters in here?"

"Of course."

She looked around the office with pleasure. "I'm glad I got to come back," she murmured. "I thought Mr. Caldwell might find an excuse to let me go."

"I'm Mr. Caldwell, too," he pointed out. "Matt's bark is worse than his bite. He won't fire you."

She grimaced. "Don't let me cause trouble between you," she said with genuine concern. "I'd rather quit…"

"No, you won't," he interrupted. He ruffled her short hair with a playful grin. "I like having you around. Besides, you spell better than the other women."

Her eyes lit up as she looked at him. She smiled back. "Thanks, boss."

Matt opened the door in time to encounter the affectionate looks they exchanged and his face hardened as he slammed it behind him.

They both jumped.

"Jehosophat, Matt!" Ed burst out, catching his breath. "Don't do that!"

"Don't play games with your secretary on my time," Matt returned. His cold dark eyes went to Leslie, whose own eyes went cold at sight of him. "Back at work, I see, Miss Murry."

"All the better to pay you back for my hospital stay, sir," she returned with a smile that bordered on insolence.

He bit back a sharp reply and turned to Ed, ignoring her. "I want you to take Nell Hobbs out to lunch and find out how she's going to vote on the zoning proposal. If they zone that land adjoining my ranch as recreational, I'm going to spend my life in court."

"If she votes for it, she'll be the only one," Ed assured him. "I spoke to the other commissioners myself."

He seemed to relax a little. "Okay. In that case, you can run over to Houlihan's dealership and drive my new Jaguar over here. It came in this morning."

Ed's eyes widened. "You're going to let me drive it?"

"Why not?" Matt asked with a warm smile, the sort Leslie knew she'd never see on that handsome face.

Ed chuckled. "Then, thanks. I'll be back shortly!" He started down the hall at a dead run. "Leslie, we'll do those letters after lunch!"

"Sure," she said. "I can spend the day updating those old herd records." She glanced at Matt to let him know she hadn't forgotten his instructions from before her operation.

He put his hands in the pockets of his slacks and his blue eyes searched her gray ones intently. Deliberately he let his gaze fall to her soft mouth. He remembered the feel of it clinging to his parted lips, hungry and moaning…

His teeth clenched. He couldn't think about that.

"The herd records can wait," he said tersely. "My secretary is home with a sick child, so you can work for me for the rest of the day. Ed can let Miss Smith handle his urgent stuff today."

She hesitated visibly. "Yes, sir," she said in a wooden voice.

"I have to talk to Henderson about one of the new accounts. I'll meet you in my office in thirty minutes."

"Yes, sir."

They were watching each other like opponents in a match when Matt made an angry sound under his breath and walked out.

Leslie spent a few minutes sorting the mail and looking over it. A little over a half hour went by before she realized it. A sound caught her attention and she looked up to find an impatient Matt Caldwell standing in the doorway.

"Sorry. I lost track of the time," she said quickly, putting the opened mail aside. She reached for her crutches and got up out of her chair, reaching for her pad and pen when she was ready to go. She looked up at Matt, who seemed taller than ever. "I'm ready when you are, boss," she said courteously.

"Don't call me boss," he said flatly.

"Okay, Mr. Caldwell," she returned.

He glared at her, but she gave him a bland look and even managed a smile. He wanted to throw things.

He turned, leaving her to follow him down the

long hall to his executive office, which had a bay window overlooking downtown Jacobsville. His desk was solid oak, huge, covered with equipment and papers of all sorts. There was a kid leather-covered chair behind the desk and two equally impressive wing chairs, and a sofa, all done in burgundy. The carpet was a deep, rich beige. The curtains were plaid, picking up the burgundy in the furniture and adding it to autumn hues. There was a framed portrait of someone who looked vaguely like Matt over the mantel of the fireplace, in which gas logs rested. There were two chairs and a table near the fireplace, probably where Matt and some visitor would share a pot of coffee or a drink. There was a bar against one wall with a mirror behind it, giving an added air of spacious comfort to the high-ceilinged room. The windows were tall ones, unused because the Victorian house that contained the offices had central heating.

Matt watched her studying her surroundings covertly. He closed the door behind them and motioned her into a chair facing the desk. She eased down into it and put her crutches beside her. She was still a little uncomfortable, but aspirin was enough to contain the pain these days. She looked forward to having the cast off, to walking normally again.

She put the pad on her lap and maneuvered the leg in the cast so that it was as comfortable as she could get it.

Matt was leaning back in his chair with his booted

feet on the desk and his eyes narrow and watchful as he sketched her slender body in the flowing beige pantsuit she was wearing with a patterned scarf tucked in the neck of the jacket. The outside seam in the left leg of her slacks had been snipped to allow for the cast. Otherwise, she was covered from head to toe, just as she had been from the first time he saw her. Odd, that he hadn't really noticed that before. It wasn't a new habit dating from the night he'd touched her so intimately, either.

"How's the leg?" he asked curtly.

"Healing, thank you," she replied. "I've already spoken to the bookkeeper about pulling out a quarter of my check weekly..."

He leaned forward so abruptly that it sounded like a gunshot when his booted feet hit the floor.

"I'll take that up with bookkeeping," he said sharply. "You've overstepped your authority, Miss Murry. Don't do it again."

She shifted in the chair, moving the ungainly cast, and assumed a calm expression. "I'm sorry, Mr. Caldwell."

Her voice was serene but her hands were shaking on the pad and pen. He averted his eyes and got to his feet, glaring out the window.

She waited patiently with her eyes on the blank pad, wondering when he was going to start dictation.

"You told Ed that Carolyn phoned you the night before we took you to the emergency room and made some cruel remarks." He remembered what Ed had related about that conversation and it made him unusually thoughtful. He turned and caught her surprised expression. "Carolyn denies saying anything to upset you."

Her expression didn't change. She didn't care what he thought of her anymore. She didn't say a word in her defense.

His dark eyebrows met over the bridge of his nose. "Well?"

"What would you like me to say?"

"You might try apologizing," he told her coldly, trying to smoke her out. "Carolyn was very upset to have such a charge made against her. I don't like having her upset," he added deliberately and stood looking down his nose at her, waiting for her to react to the challenge.

Her fingers tightened around the pencil. It was going to be worse than she ever dreamed, trying to work with him. He couldn't fire her, Ed had said, but that didn't mean he couldn't make her quit. If he made things difficult enough for her, she wouldn't be able to stay.

All at once, it didn't seem worth the effort. She was tired, worn-out, and Carolyn had hurt her, not the reverse. She was sick to death of trying to live from one day to the next with the weight of the past bearing down on her more each day. Being tormented by Matt Caldwell on top of all that was the last straw.

She reached for her crutches and stood up, pad and all.

"Where do you think you're going?" Matt demanded, surprised that she was giving up without an argument.

She went toward the door. He got in front of her, an easy enough task when every step she took required extreme effort.

She looked up at him with the eyes of a trapped animal, resigned and resentful and without life. "Ed said you couldn't fire me without his consent," she said quietly. "But you can hound me until I quit, can't you?"

He didn't speak. His face was rigid. "Would you give up so easily?" he asked, baiting her. "Where will you go?"

Her gaze dropped to the floor. Idly she noticed that one of her flat-heeled shoes had a smudge of mud on it. She should clean it off.

"I said, where will you go?" Matt persisted.

She met his cold eyes. "Surely in all of Texas, there's more than one secretarial position available," she said. "Please move. You're blocking the door."

He did move, but not in the way she'd expected. He took the crutches away from her and propped them against the bookshelf by the door. His hands went on either side of her head, trapping her in front of him. His dark eyes held a faint glitter as he studied her wan face, her soft mouth.

"Don't," she managed tightly.

He moved closer. He smelled of spice and after-shave and coffee. His breath was warm where it brushed her forehead. She could feel the warmth of his tall, fit body, and she remembered reluctantly how it had felt to let him hold her and touch her in his bedroom.

He was remembering those same things, but not with pleasure. He hated the attraction he felt for this woman, whom he didn't, couldn't trust.

"You don't like being touched, you said," he reminded her with deliberate sarcasm as his lean hand suddenly smoothed over her breast and settled there provocatively.

Her indrawn breath was audible. She looked up at him with all her hidden vulnerabilities exposed. "Please don't do this," she whispered. "I'm no threat to Ed, or to you, either. Just…let me go. I'll vanish."

She probably would, and that wounded him. He was making her life miserable. Why did this woman arouse such bitter feelings in him, when he was the soul of kindness to most people with problems—especially physical problems, like hers.

"Ed won't like it," he said tersely.

"Ed doesn't have to know anything," she said dully. "You can tell him whatever you like."

"Is he your lover?"

"No."

"Why not? You don't mind if he touches you."

"He doesn't. Not…the way you do."

Her strained voice made him question his own cruelty. He lifted his hand away from her body and tilted her chin up so that he could see her eyes. They were turbulent, misty.

"How many poor fools have you played the innocent with, Miss Murry?" he asked coldly.

She saw the lines in his face, many more than his age should have caused. She saw the coldness in his eyes, the bitterness of too many betrayals, too many loveless years.

Unexpectedly she reached up and touched his hair, smoothing it back as Lou had smoothed hers back in an act of silent compassion.

It made him furious. His body pressed down completely against hers, holding her prisoner. His hips twisted in a crude, rough motion that was instantly arousing.

She tried to twist away and he groaned huskily, giving her a worldly smile when she realized that her attempt at escape had failed and made the situation even worse.

Her face colored. It was like that night. It was the way Mike had behaved, twisting his body against her innocent one and laughing at her embarrassment. He'd said things, done things to her in front of his friends that still made her want to gag.

Matt's hand fell to her hip and contracted as he used one of his long legs to nudge hers apart. She was stiff against him, frozen with painful memories of another man, another encounter, that had begun just this way. She'd thought she loved Mike until he made her an object of lustful ridicule, making fun of her innocence as he anticipated its delights for the enjoyment of his laughing friends, grouped around them as he forcibly stripped the clothes away from her body. He laughed at her small breasts, at her slender figure, and all the while he touched her insolently and made jokes about her most intimate places.

She was years in the past, reliving the torment, the shame, that had seen her spread-eagled on the wood floor with Mike's drug-crazed friends each holding one of her shaking limbs still while Mike lowered his nude body onto hers and roughly parted her legs...

Matt realized belatedly that Leslie was frozen in place like a statue with a white face and eyes that didn't even see him. He could hear her heartbeat, quick and frantic. Her whole body shook, but not with pleasure or anticipation.

Frowning, he let her go and stepped back. She shivered again, convulsively. Mike had backed away, too, to the sound of a firecracker popping loudly. But it hadn't been a firecracker. It had been a bullet. It went right through him, into Leslie's leg. He looked surprised. Leslie remembered his blue eyes as the life visibly went out of them, leaving them fixed and blank just before he fell heavily on her. There had been such a tiny hole in his back, compared to the one in his chest. Her mother was screaming, trying to fire again, trying to kill her. Leslie had seduced her own lover, she wanted to kill them both, and she was glad Mike was dead. Leslie would be dead, too!

Leslie remembered lying there naked on the floor, with a shattered leg and blood pouring from it so rapidly that she knew she was going to bleed to death before help arrived…

"Leslie?" Matt asked sharply.

He became a white blur as she slid down the wall into oblivion.

When she came to, Ed was bending over her with a look of anguished concern. He had a damp towel pressed to her forehead. She looked at him dizzily.

"Ed?" she murmured.

"Yes. How are you?"

She blinked and looked around. She was lying on the big burgundy leather couch in Matt's office. "What happened?" she asked numbly. "Did I faint?"

"Apparently," Ed said heavily. "You came back to work too soon. I shouldn't have agreed."

"But I'm all right," she insisted, pulling herself up. She felt nauseous. She had to swallow repeatedly before she was able to move again.

She took a slow breath and smiled at him. "I'm still a little weak, I guess, and I didn't have any breakfast."

"Idiot," he said, smiling.

She smiled back. "I'm okay. Hand me my crutches, will you?"

He got them from where they were propped against the wall, and she had a glimpse of Matt standing there as if he'd been carved from stone. She took the crutches from Ed and got them under her arms.

"Would you drive me home?" she asked Ed. "I think maybe I will take one more day off, if that's all right?"

"That's all right," Ed assured her. He looked across the room. "Right, Matt?"

Matt nodded, a curt jerk of his head. He gave her one last look and went out the door.

The relief Leslie felt almost knocked her legs from under her. She remembered what had happened, but she wasn't about to tell Ed. She wasn't going to cause a breach between him and the older cousin he adored. She, who had no family left in the world except the mother who hated her, had more respect for family than most people.

She let Ed take her home, and she didn't think about what had happened in Matt's office. She knew that every time she saw him from now on, she'd relive those last few horrible minutes in her mother's apartment when she was seventeen. If she'd had any-place else to go, she'd leave. But she was trapped, for the moment, at the mercy of a man who had none, a victim of a past she couldn't even talk about.

* * *

Ed went back to the office determined to have it out with Matt. He knew instinctively that Leslie's collapse was caused by something the other man did or said, and he was going to stop the treatment Matt was giving her before it was too late.

It was anticlimactic when he got into Matt's office, with his speech rehearsed and ready, only to find it empty.

"He said he was going up to Victoria to see a man about some property, Mr. Caldwell," one of the secretaries commented. "Left in a hurry, too, in that brand-new red Jaguar. We hear you got to drive it over from Houlihan's."

"Yes, I did," he replied, forcing a cheerful smile. "It goes like the wind."

"We noticed," she murmured dryly. "He was flying when he turned the corner. I hope he slows down. It would be a pity if he wrecked it when he'd only just gotten it."

"So it would," Ed replied. He went back to his own office, curious about Matt's odd behavior but rather relieved that the showdown wouldn't have to be faced right away.

Chapter Seven

Matt was doing almost a hundred miles an hour on the long highway that led to Victoria. He couldn't get Leslie's face out of his mind. That hadn't been anger or even fear in her gray eyes. It went beyond those emotions. She had been terrified; not of him, but of something she could see that he couldn't. Her tortured gaze had hurt him in a vulnerable spot he didn't know he had. When she fainted, he hated himself. He'd never thought of himself as a particularly cruel man, but he was with Leslie. He couldn't understand the hostility she roused in him. She was fragile, for all her independence and strength of will. Fragile. Vulnerable. Tender.

He remembered the touch of her soft fingers

smoothing back his hair and he groaned out loud with self-hatred. He'd been tormenting her, and she'd seen right through the harsh words to the pain that lay underneath them. In return for his insensitivity, she'd reached up and touched him with genuine compassion. He'd rewarded that exquisite tenderness with treatment he wouldn't have offered to a hardened prostitute.

He realized that the speed he was going exceeded the limit by a factor of two and took his foot off the pedal. He didn't even know where the hell he was going. He was running for cover, he supposed, and laughed coldly at his own reaction to Leslie's fainting spell. All his life he'd been kind to stray animals and people down on their luck. He'd followed up that record by torturing a crippled young woman who felt sorry for him. Next, he supposed, he'd be kicking lame dogs down steps.

He pulled off on the side of the highway, into a lay-by, and stopped the car, resting his head on the steering wheel. He didn't recognize himself since Leslie Murry had walked into his life. She brought out monstrous qualities in him. He was ashamed of the way he'd treated her. She was a sweet woman who always seemed surprised when people did kind things for her. On the other hand, Matt's antagonism and hostility didn't seem to surprise her. Was that what she'd had the most of in her life? Had people been so cruel to her that now she expected and accepted cruelty as her lot in life?

He leaned back in the seat and stared at the flat horizon. His mother's desertion and his recent notoriety had soured him on the whole female sex. His mother was an old wound. The assault suit had made him bitter, yet again, despite the fact that he'd avenged himself on the perpetrator. But he remembered her coy, sweet personality very well. She'd pretended innocence and helplessness and when the disguise had come off, he'd found himself the object of vicious public humiliation. His name had been cleared, but the anger and resentment had remained.

But none of that excused his recent behavior. He'd overreacted with Leslie. He was sorry and ashamed for making her suffer for something that wasn't her fault. He took a long breath and put the car in gear. Well, he couldn't run away. He might as well go back to work. Ed would probably be waiting with blood in his eye, and he wouldn't blame him. He deserved a little discomfort.

Ed did read him the riot act, and he took it. He couldn't deny that he'd been unfair to Leslie. He wished he could understand what it was about her that raised the devil in him.

"If you genuinely don't like her," Ed concluded, "can't you just ignore her?"

"Probably," Matt said without meeting his cousin's accusing eyes.

"Then would you? Matt, she needs this job," he continued solemnly.

Matt studied him sharply. "Why does she need it?" he asked. "And why doesn't she have anyplace to go?"

"I can't tell you. I gave my word."

"Is she in some sort of trouble with the law?"

Ed laughed softly. "Leslie?"

"Never mind." He moved back toward the door. He stopped and turned as he reached it. "When she fainted, she said something."

"What?" Ed asked curiously.

"She said, 'Mike, don't.'" He didn't blink. "Who's Mike?"

"A dead man," Ed replied. "Years dead."

"The man she and her mother competed for."

"That's right," Ed said. "If you mention his name in front of her, I'll walk out the door with her, and I won't come back. Ever."

That was serious business to Ed, he realized. He frowned thoughtfully. "Did she love him?"

"She thought she did," Ed replied. His eyes went cold. "He destroyed her life."

"How?"

Ed didn't reply. He folded his hands on the desk and just stared at Matt.

The older man let out an irritated breath. "Has it occurred to you that all this secrecy is only complicating matters?"

"It's occurred. But if you want answers, you'll have to ask Leslie. I don't break promises."

Matt muttered to himself as he opened the door

and went out. Ed stared after him worriedly. He hoped he'd done the right thing. He was trying to protect Leslie, but for all he knew, he might just have made matters worse. Matt didn't like mysteries. God forbid that he should try to force Leslie to talk about something she only wanted to forget. He was also worried about Matt's potential reaction to the old scandal. How would he feel if he knew how notorious Leslie really was, if he knew that her mother was serving a sentence for murder?

Ed was worried enough to talk to Leslie about it that evening when he stopped by to see how she was.

"I don't want him to know," she said when Ed questioned her. "Ever."

"What if he starts digging and finds out by himself?" Ed asked bluntly. "He'll read everyone's point of view except yours, and even if he reads every tabloid that ran the story, he still won't know the truth of what happened."

"I don't care what he thinks," she lied. "Anyway, it doesn't matter now."

"Why not?"

"Because I'm not coming back to work," she said evenly, avoiding his shocked gaze. "They need a typist at the Jacobsville sewing plant. I applied this afternoon and they accepted me."

"How did you get there?" he asked.

"Cabs run even in Jacobsville, Ed, and I'm not totally penniless." She lifted her head proudly. "I'll pay your cousin back the price of my operation, however long it takes. But I won't take one more day of the sort of treatment I've been getting from him. I'm sorry if he hates women, but I'm not going to become a scapegoat. I've had enough misery.''

"I'll agree there," he said. "But I wish you'd reconsider. I had a long talk with him…''

"You didn't tell him?" she exclaimed, horrified.

"No, I didn't tell him," he replied. "But I think you should."

"It's none of his business," she said through her teeth. "I don't owe him an explanation."

"I know it doesn't seem like it, Leslie," he began, "but he's not a bad man." He frowned, searching for a way to explain it to her. "I don't pretend to understand why you set him off, but I'm sure he realizes that he's being unfair."

"He can be unfair as long as he likes, but I'm not giving him any more free shots at me. I mean it, Ed. I'm not coming back."

He leaned forward, feeling defeated. "Well, I'll be around if you need me. You're still my best friend."

She reached out and touched his hand where it rested on his knee. "You're mine, too. I don't know how I'd have managed if it hadn't been for you and your father."

He smiled. "You'd have found a way. Whatever you're lacking, it isn't courage."

She sighed, looking down at her hand resting on his. "I don't know if that's true anymore," she confessed. "I'm so tired of fighting. I thought I could come to Jacobsville and get my life in order, get some peace. And the first man I run headlong into is a male chauvinist with a grudge against the whole female sex. I feel like I've been through the ringer backward."

"What did he say to you today?" he asked.

She blotted out the physical insult. "The usual things, most vividly the way I'd upset Carolyn by lying about her phone call."

"Some lie!" he muttered.

"He believes her."

"I can't imagine why. I used to think he was intelligent."

"He is, or he wouldn't be a millionaire." She got up. "Now go home, Ed. I've got to get some rest so I can be bright and cheerful my first day at my new job."

He winced. "I wanted things to be better than this for you."

She laughed gently. "And just think what a terrible world we'd have if we always got what we think we want."

He had to admit that she had a point. "That sewing plant isn't a very good place to work," he added worriedly.

"It's only temporary," she assured him.

He grimaced. "Well, if you need me, you know where I am."

She smiled. "Thanks."

*   *   *

He went home and ate supper and was watching the news when Matt knocked at the door just before opening it and walking in. And why not, Ed thought, when Matt had been raised here, just as he had. He grinned at his cousin as he came into the living room and sprawled over an easy chair.

"How does the Jag drive?" he asked.

"Like an airplane on the ground," he chuckled. He stared at the television screen for a minute. "How's Leslie?"

He grimaced. "She's got a new job."

Matt went very still. "What?"

"She said she doesn't want to work for me anymore. She got a job at the sewing plant, typing. I tried to talk her out of it. She won't budge." He glanced at Matt apologetically. "She knew I wouldn't let you fire her. She said you'd made sure she wanted to quit." He shrugged. "I guess you did. I've known Leslie for six years. I've never known her to faint."

Matt's dark eyes slid to the television screen and seemed to be glued there for a time. The garment company paid minimum wage. He doubted she'd have enough left over after her rent and grocery bill to pay for the medicine she had to take for pain. He couldn't remember a time in his life when he'd been so ashamed of himself. She wasn't going to like working in that plant. He knew the manager, a penny-pinching social climber who didn't believe in holidays, sick days, or paid vacation. He'd work her to death for her pittance and complain because she couldn't do more.

Matt's mouth thinned. He'd landed Leslie in hell with his bad temper and unreasonable prejudice.

Matt got up from the chair and walked out the door without a goodbye. Ed went back to the news without much real enthusiasm. Matt had what he wanted. He didn't look very pleased with it, though.

After a long night fraught with even more nightmares, Leslie got up early and took a cab to the manufacturing company, hobbling in on her crutches to the personnel office where Judy Blakely, the personnel manager, was waiting with her usual kind smile.

"Nice to see you, Miss Murry!"

"Nice to see you, too," she replied. "I'm looking forward to my new job."

Mrs. Blakely looked worried and reticent. She folded her hands in a tight clasp on her desk. "Oh, I don't know how to tell you this," she wailed. She grimaced. "Miss Murry, the girl you were hired to replace just came back a few minutes ago and begged me to let her keep her job. It seems she has serious family problems and can't do without her salary. I'm so sorry. If we had anything else open, even on the floor, I'd offer it to you temporarily. But we just don't."

The poor woman looked as if the situation tormented her. Leslie smiled gently. "Don't worry,

Mrs. Blakely, I'll find something else," she assured the older woman. "It's not the end of the world."

"I'd be furious," she said, her eyes wrinkled up with worry. "And you're being so nice…I feel like a dog!"

"You can't help it that things worked out like this." Leslie got to her feet a little heavily, still smiling. "Could you call me a cab?"

"Certainly! And we'll pay for it, too," she said firmly. "Honestly, I feel so awful!"

"It's all right. Sometimes we have setbacks that really turn into opportunities, you know."

Mrs. Blakely studied her intently. "You're such a positive person. I wish I was. I always seem to dwell on the negative."

"You might as well be optimistic, I always think," Leslie told her. "It doesn't cost extra."

Mrs. Blakely chuckled. "No, it doesn't, does it?" She phoned the cab and apologized again as Leslie went outside to wait for it.

She felt desolate, but she wasn't going to make that poor woman feel worse than she already did.

She was tired and sleepy. She wished the cab would come. She eased down onto the bench the company had placed out front for its employees, so they'd have a place to sit during their breaks. It was hard and uncomfortable, but much better than standing.

She wondered what she would do now. She had no prospects, no place to go. The only alternative was to look for something else or go back to Ed, and the latter choice wasn't a choice at all. She could never look Matt Caldwell in the face again without remembering how he'd treated her.

The sun glinted off the windshield of an approaching car, and she recognized Matt's new red Jaguar at once. She stood up, clutching her purse, stiff and defensive as he parked the car and got out to approach her.

He stopped an arm's length away. He looked as tired and worn-out as she did. His eyes were heavily lined. His black, wavy hair was disheveled. He put his hands on his hips and looked at her with pure malice.

She stared back with something approaching hatred.

"Oh, what the hell," he muttered, adding something about being hanged for sheep as well as lambs.

He bent and swooped her up in his arms and started walking toward the Jaguar. She hit him with her purse.

"Stop that," he muttered. "You'll make me drop you. Considering the weight of that damned cast, you'd probably sink halfway through the planet."

"You put me down!" she raged, and hit him again. "I won't go as far as the street with you!"

He paused beside the passenger door of the Jag and searched her hostile eyes. "I hate secrets," he said.

"I can't imagine you have any, with Carolyn shouting them to all and sundry!"

His eyes fell to her mouth. "I didn't tell Carolyn that you were easy," he said in a voice so tender that it made her want to cry.

Her lips trembled as she tried valiantly not to.

He made a husky sound and his mouth settled right on her misty eyes, closing them with soft, tender kisses.

She bawled.

He took a long breath and opened the passenger door, shifting her as he slid her into the low-slung vehicle. "I've noticed that about you," he murmured as he fastened her seat belt.

"Noticed...what?" she sobbed, sniffling.

He pulled a handkerchief out of his dress slacks and put it in her hands. "You react very oddly to tenderness."

He closed the door on her surprised expression and fetched her crutches before he went around to get in behind the wheel. He paused to fasten his own seat belt and give her a quick scrutiny before he started the powerful engine and pulled out into the road.

"How did you know I was here?" she asked when the tears stopped.

"Ed told me."

"Why?"

He shrugged. "Beats me. I guess he thought I might be interested."

"Fat chance!"

He chuckled. It was the first time she'd heard him laugh naturally, without mockery or sarcasm. He shifted gears. "You don't know the guy who owns that little enterprise," he said conversationally, "but the plant is a sweatshop."

"That isn't funny."

"Do you think I'm joking?" he replied. "He likes to lure illegal immigrants in here with promises of big salaries and health benefits, and then when he's got them where he wants them, he threatens them with the immigration service if they don't work hard and accept the pittance he pays. We've all tried to get his operation closed down, but he's slippery as an eel." He glanced at her with narrowed dark eyes. "I'm not going to let you sell yourself into that just to get away from me."

"Let me?" She rose immediately to the challenge, eyes flashing. "You don't tell me what to do!"

He grinned. "That's better."

She hit her hand against the cast, furious. "Where are you taking me?"

"Home."

"You're going the wrong way."

"My home."

"No," she said icily. "Not again. Not ever again!"

He shifted gears, accelerated, and shifted again. He loved the smoothness of the engine, the ride. He loved the speed. He wondered if Leslie had loved fast cars before her disillusionment.

He glanced at her set features. "When your leg heals, I'll let you drive it."

"No, thanks," she almost choked.

"Don't you like cars?"

She pushed back her hair. "I can't drive," she said absently.

"What?"

"Look out, you're going to run us off the road!" she squealed.

He righted the car with a muffled curse and downshifted. "Everybody drives, for God's sake!"

"Not me," she said flatly.

"Why?"

She folded her arms over her breasts. "I just never wanted to."

More secrets. He was becoming accustomed to the idea that she never shared anything about her private life except, possibly, with Ed. He wanted her to open up, to trust him, to tell him what had happened to her. Then he laughed to himself at his own presumption. He'd been her mortal enemy since the first time he'd laid eyes on her, and he expected her to trust him?

"What are you laughing at?" she demanded.

He glanced at her as he slowed to turn into the ranch driveway. "I'll tell you one day. Are you hungry?"

"I'm sleepy."

He grimaced. "Let me see if I can guess why."

She glared at him. His own eyes had dark circles. "You haven't slept, either."

"Misery loves company."

"You started it!"

"Yes, I did!" he flashed back at her, eyes blazing. "Every time I look at you, I want to throw you down on the most convenient flat surface and ravish you! How's that for blunt honesty?"

She stiffened, wide-eyed, and gaped at him. He pulled up at his front door and cut off the engine. He turned in his seat and looked at her as if he resented her intensely. At the moment, he did.

His dark eyes narrowed. They were steady, intimidating. She glared into them.

But after a minute, the anger went out of him. He looked at her, really looked, and he saw things he hadn't noticed before. Her hair was dark just at her scalp. She was far too thin. Her eyes had dark circles so prominent that it looked as if she had two black eyes. There were harsh lines beside her mouth. She might pretend to be cheerful around Ed, but she wasn't. It was an act.

"Take a picture," she choked.

He sighed. "You really are fragile," he remarked quietly. "You give as good as you get, but all your vulnerabilities come out when you've got your back to the wall."

"I don't need psychoanalysis, but thanks for the thought," she said shortly.

He reached out, noticing how she shrank from his

touch. It didn't bother him now. He knew that it was tenderness that frightened her with him, not ardor. He touched her hair at her temple and brushed it back gently, staring curiously at the darkness that was more prevalent then.

"You're a brunette," he remarked. "Why do you color your hair?"

"I wanted to be a blonde," she replied instantly, trying to withdraw further against the door.

"You keep secrets, Leslie," he said, and for once he was serious, not sarcastic. "At your age, it's unusual. You're young and until that leg started to act up, you were even relatively healthy. You should be carefree. Your life is an adventure that's only just beginning."

She laughed hollowly. "I wouldn't wish my life even on you," she said.

He raised an eyebrow. "Your worst enemy," he concluded for her.

"That's right."

"Why?"

She averted her eyes to the windshield. She was tired, so tired. The day that had begun with such promise had ended in disappointment and more misery.

"I want to go home," she said heavily.

"Not until I get some answers out of you…!"

"You have no right!" she exploded, her voice breaking on the words. "You have no right, no right…!"

"Leslie!"

He caught her by the nape of the neck and pulled her face into his throat, holding her there even as she struggled. He smoothed her hair, her back, whispering to her, his voice tender, coaxing.

"What did I ever do to deserve you?" she sobbed. "I've never willingly hurt another human being in my life, and look where it got me! Years of running and hiding and never feeling safe…!"

He heard the words without understanding them, soothing her while she cried brokenly. It hurt him to hear her cry. Nothing had ever hurt so much.

He dried the tears and kissed her swollen, red eyes tenderly, moving to her temples, her nose, her cheeks, her chin and, finally, her soft mouth. But it wasn't passion that drove him now. It was concern.

"Hush, sweetheart," he whispered. "It's all right. It's all right!"

She must be dotty, she thought, if she was hearing endearments from Attila the Hun here. She sniffed and wiped her eyes again, finally getting control of herself. She sat up and he let her, his arm over the back of her seat, his eyes watchful and quiet.

She took a steadying breath and slumped in the seat, exhausted.

"Please take me home," she asked wearily.

He hesitated, but only for a minute. "If that's what you really want."

She nodded. He started the car and turned it around.

* * *

He helped her to the front door of the boarding-house, visibly reluctant to leave her.

"You shouldn't be alone in this condition," he said flatly. "I'll phone Ed and have him come over to see you."

"I don't need..." she protested.

His eyes flared. "The hell you don't! You need someone you can talk to. Obviously it isn't going to be your worst enemy, but then Ed knows all about you, doesn't he? You don't have secrets from him!"

He seemed to mind. She searched his angry face and wondered what he'd say if he knew those secrets. She gave him a lackluster smile.

"Some secrets are better kept," she said heavily. "Thanks for the ride."

"Leslie."

She hesitated, looking back at him.

His face looked harder than ever. "Were you raped?"

Chapter Eight

The words cut like a knife. She actually felt them. Her sad eyes met his dark, searching ones.

"Not quite," she replied tersely.

As understatements went, it was a master stroke. She watched the blood drain out of his face, and knew he was remembering, as she was, their last encounter, in his office, when she'd fainted.

He couldn't speak. He tried to, but the words choked him. He winced and turned away, striding back to the sports car. Leslie watched him go with a curious emptiness, as if she had no more feelings to bruise. Perhaps this kind detachment would last for a while, and she could have one day without the mental anguish that usually accompanied her, waking and sleeping.

She turned mechanically and went slowly into the house on her crutches, and down the hall to her small apartment. She had a feeling that she wouldn't see much of Matt Caldwell from now on. At last she knew how to deflect his pursuit. All it took was the truth—or as much of it as she felt comfortable letting him know.

Ed phoned to check on her later in the day and promised to come and see her the next evening. He did, arriving with a bag full of the Chinese take-out dishes she loved. While they were eating it, he mentioned that her job was still open.

"Miss Smith wouldn't enjoy hearing that," she teased lightly.

"Oh, Karla's working for Matt now."

She stared down at the wooden chopsticks in her hand. "Is she?"

"For some reason, he doesn't feel comfortable asking you to come back, so he sent me to do it," he replied. "He realizes that he's made your working environment miserable, and he's sorry. He wants you to come back and work for me."

She stared at him hard. "What did you tell him?"

"What I always tell him, that if he wants to know anything about you, he can ask you." He ate a forkful of soft noodles and took a sip of the strong coffee she'd brewed before he continued. "I gather he's realized that something pretty drastic happened to you."

"Did he say anything about it to you?"

"No." He lifted his gaze to meet hers. "He did go to the roadhouse out on the Victoria highway last night and wreck the bar."

"Why would he do something like that?" she asked, stunned by the thought of the straitlaced Mather Caldwell throwing things around.

"He was pretty drunk at the time," Ed confessed. "I had to bail him out of jail this morning. That was one for the books, let me tell you. The whole damned police department was standing around staring at him openmouthed when we left. He was only ever in trouble once, a woman accused him of assault—and he was cleared. His housekeeper testified that she'd been there the whole time and she and Matt had sent the baggage packing. But he's never treed a bar before."

She remembered the stark question he'd asked her and how she'd responded. She didn't understand why her past should matter to Matt. In fact, she didn't want to understand. He still didn't know the whole of it, and she was frightened of how he'd react if he knew. That wonderful tenderness he'd given her in the Jaguar had been actually painful, a bitter taste of what a man's love would be like. It was something she'd never experienced, and she'd better remember that Matt was the enemy. He'd felt sorry for her. He certainly wasn't in love with her. He wanted her, that was all. But despite her surprising response to his light caresses, complete physical intimacy was something she wasn't sure she was capable of responding to. The memories of Mike's vicious fondling made her sick. She couldn't live with them.

"Stop doing that to yourself," Ed muttered, dragging her back to the present. "You can't change the past. You have to walk straight into the future without flinching. It's the only way, to meet things head-on."

"Where did you learn that?" she asked.

"Actually I heard a televised sermon that caught my attention. That's what the minister said, that you have to go boldly forward and meet trouble head-on, not try to run away from it or hide." He pursed his lips. "I'd never heard it put quite that way before. It really made me think."

She sipped coffee with a sad face. "I've always tried to run. I've had to run." She lifted her eyes to his. "You know what they would have done to me if I'd stayed in Houston."

"Yes, I do, and I don't blame you for getting out while you could," Ed assured her. "But there's something I have to tell you now. And you're not going to like it."

"Don't tell me," she said with black humor, "someone from the local newspaper recognized me and wants an interview."

"Worse," he returned. "A reporter from Houston is down here asking questions. I think he's traced you."

She put her head in her hands. "Wonderful. Well, at least I'm no longer an employee of the Caldwell group, so it won't embarrass your cousin when I'm exposed."

"I haven't finished. Nobody will talk to him," he added with a grin. "In fact, he actually got into Matt's office yesterday when his secretary wasn't looking. He was only in there for a few minutes, and nobody knows what was said. But he came back out headfirst and, from what I hear, he ran out the door so fast that he left his briefcase behind with Matt cursing like a wounded sailor all the way down the hall. They said Matt had only just caught up with him at the curb when he ran across traffic and got away."

She hesitated. "When was this?"

"Yesterday." He smiled wryly. "It was a bad time to catch Matt. He'd already been into it with one of the county commissioners over a rezoning proposal we're trying to get passed, and his secretary had hidden in the bathroom to avoid him. That was how the reporter got in."

"You don't think he…told Matt?" she asked worriedly.

"No. I don't know what was said, of course, but he wasn't in there very long."

"But, the briefcase…"

"…was returned to him unopened," Ed said. "I know because I had to take it down to the front desk." He smiled, amused. "I understand he paid someone to pick it up for him."

"Thank God."

"It was apparently the last straw for Matt, though," he continued, "because it wasn't long after that when he said he was leaving for the day."

"How did you know he was in jail?"

He grimaced. "Carolyn phoned me. He'd come by her place first and apparently made inroads into a bottle of scotch. She hid the rest, after which he decided to go and get his own bottle." He shook his head. "That isn't like Matt. He may have a drink or two occasionally, but he isn't a drinker. This has shocked everybody in town."

"I guess so." She couldn't help but wonder if it had anything to do with the way he'd treated her. But if he'd gone to Carolyn, perhaps they'd had an argument and it was just one last problem on top of too many. "Was Carolyn mad at him?" she asked.

"Furious," he returned. "Absolutely seething. It seems they'd had a disagreement of major proportions, along with all the other conflicts of the day." He shook his head. "Matt didn't even come in to work today. I'll bet his head is splitting."

She didn't reply. She stared into her coffee with dead eyes. Everywhere she went, she caused trouble. Hiding, running—nothing seemed to help. She was only involving innocent people in her problems.

Ed hesitated when he saw her face. He didn't want

to make things even worse for her, but there was more news that he had to give her.

She saw that expression. "Go ahead," she invited. "One more thing is all I need right now, on top of being crippled and jobless."

"Your job is waiting," he assured her. "Whenever you want to come in."

"I won't do that to him," she said absently. "He's had enough."

His eyes became strangely watchful. "Feeling sorry for the enemy?" he asked gently.

"You can't help not liking people," she replied. "He likes most everybody except me. He's basically a kind person. I just rub him the wrong way."

He wasn't going to touch that line. "The same reporter who came here had gone to the prison to talk to your mother," he continued. "I was concerned, so I called the warden. It seems…she's had a heart attack."

Her heart jumped unpleasantly. "Will she live?"

"Yes," he assured her. "She's changed a lot in six years, Leslie," he added solemnly. "She's reconciled to serving her time. The warden says that she wanted to ask for you, but that she was too ashamed to let them contact you. She thinks you can't ever forgive what she said and did to you."

Her eyes misted, but she fought tears. Her mother had been eloquent at the time, with words and the pistol. She stared at her empty coffee cup. "I can forgive her. I just don't want to see her."

"She knows that," Ed replied.

She glanced at him. "Have you been to see her?"

He hesitated. Then he nodded. "She was doing very well until this reporter started digging up the past. He was the one who suggested the movie deal and got that bit started." He sighed angrily. "He's young and ambitious and he wants to make a name for himself. The world's full of people like that, who don't care what damage they do to other peoples' lives as long as they get what they want."

She was only vaguely listening. "My mother...did she ask you about me?"

"Yes."

"What did you tell her?" she wanted to know.

He put down his cup. "The truth. There really wasn't any way to dress it up." His eyes lifted. "She wanted you to know that she's sorry for what happened, especially for the way she treated you before and after the trial. She understands that you don't want to see her. She says she deserves it for destroying your life."

She stared into space with the pain of memory eating at her. "She was never satisfied with my father," she said quietly. "She wanted things he couldn't give her, pretty clothes and jewelry and nights on the town. All he knew how to do was fly a crop-dusting plane, and it didn't pay much..." Her eyes closed. "I saw him fly into the electrical wires, and go down," she whispered gruffly. "I saw him go down!" Her eyes began to glitter with feeling. "I knew he was dead before they ever got to him. I ran home. She was in the living room, playing music, dancing. She didn't care. I broke the record player and threw myself at her, screaming.''

Ed grimaced as she choked, paused, and fought for control. ''We were never close, especially after the funeral,'' she continued, ''but we were stuck with each other. Things went along fairly well. She got a job waiting tables and made good tips when she was working. She had trouble holding down a job because she slept so much. I got a part-time job typing when I was sixteen, to help out. Then when I'd just turned seventeen, Mike came into the restaurant and started flirting with her. He was so handsome, well-bred and had nice manners. In no time, he'd moved in with us. I was crazy about him, you know the way a young girl has crushes on older men. He teased me, too. But he had a drug habit that we didn't know about. She didn't like him teasing me, anyway, and she had a fight with him about it. The next day, he had some friends over and they all got high.'' She shivered. ''The rest you know.''

''Yes.'' He sighed, studying her wan face.

''All I wanted was for her to love me,'' she said dully. ''But she never did.''

''She said that,'' he replied. ''She's had a lot of time to live with her regrets.'' He leaned forward to search her eyes. ''Leslie, did you know that she had a drug habit?''

''She what?'' she exclaimed, startled.

"Had a drug habit," he repeated. "That's what she told me. It was an expensive habit, and your father got tired of trying to support it. He loved her, but he couldn't make the sort of money it took to keep her high. It wasn't clothes and jewelry and parties. It was drugs."

She felt as if she'd been slammed to the floor. She moved her hands over her face and pushed back her hair. "Oh, Lord!"

"She was still using when she walked in on Mike and his friends holding you down," he continued.

"How long had she been using drugs?" she asked.

"A good five years," he replied. "Starting with marijuana and working her way up to the hard stuff."

"I had no idea."

"And you didn't know that Mike was her dealer, either, apparently."

She gasped.

He nodded grimly. "She told me that when I went to see her, too. She still can't talk about it easily. Now that she has a good grip on reality, she sees what her life-style did to you. She had hoped that you might be married and happy by now. It hurt her deeply to realize that you don't even date."

"She'll know why, of course," she said bitterly.

"You sound so empty, Leslie."

"I am." She leaned back. "I don't care if the reporter finds me. It doesn't matter anymore. I'm so tired of running."

"Then stand and deliver," he replied, getting to

his feet. "Come back to work. Let your leg heal. Let your hair grow out and go back to its natural color. Start living."

"Can I, after so long?"

"Yes," he assured her. "We all go through periods of anguish, times when we think we can't face what lies ahead. But the only way to get past it is to go through it, straight through it. No detours, no camouflage, no running. You have to meet problems head-on, despite the pain."

She cocked her head and smiled at him with real affection. "Were you ever a football coach?"

He chuckled. "I hate contact sports."

"Me, too." She brushed her short hair back with her hands. "Okay. I'll give it a shot. But if your cousin gives me any more trouble..."

"I don't think Matt is going to cause you any more problems," he replied.

"Then, I'll see you on Thursday morning."

"Thursday? Tomorrow is just Wednesday..."

"Thursday," she said firmly. "I have plans for tomorrow."

And she did. She had the color taken out of her hair at a local beauty salon. She took her contact lenses to the local optometrist and got big-lensed, wire-framed glasses to wear. She bought clothes that looked professional without being explicit.

Then, Thursday morning, cast and crutches notwithstanding, she went back to work.

She'd been at her desk in Ed's office for half an hour when Matt came in. He barely glanced at her, obviously not recognizing the new secretary, and tapped on Ed's door, which was standing open.

"I'm going to fly to Houston for the sale," he told Ed. He sounded different. His deep voice held its usual authority, but there was an odd note in it. "I don't suppose you were able to convince her to come back...why are you shaking your head?"

Ed stood up with an exasperated sigh and pointed toward Leslie.

Matt scowled, turning on his heel. He looked at her, scowled harder, moved closer, peering into her upturned face.

She saw him matching his memory of her with the new reality. She wondered how she came off, but it was far too soon to get personal.

His eyes went over her short dark hair, over the feminine but professional beige suit she was wearing with a tidy patterned blouse, lingering on the glasses that she'd never worn before in his presence. His own face was heavily lined and he looked as if he'd had his own share of turmoil since she'd seen him last. Presumably he was still having problems with Carolyn.

"Good morning, Miss Murry," he murmured. His eyes didn't smile at her. He looked as if his face was painted on.

That was odd. No sarcasm, no mockery. No insolent sizing up. He was polite and courteous to a fault.

If that was the way he intended to play it...

"Good morning, Mr. Caldwell," she replied with equal courtesy.

He studied her for one long moment before he turned back to Ed. "I should be back by tonight. If I'm not, you'll have to meet with the county commission and the zoning committee."

"Oh, no," Ed groaned.

"Just tell them we're putting up a two-story brick office building on our own damned land, whether they like it or not," Matt told him, "and that we can accommodate them in court for as many years as it takes to get our way. I'm tired of trying to do business in a hundred-year-old house with frozen pipes that burst every winter."

"It won't sound as intimidating if I say it."

"Stand in front of a mirror and practice looking angry."

"Is that how you did it?" Ed murmured dryly.

"Only at first," he assured the other man, deadpan. "Just until I got the hang of it."

"I remember," Ed chuckled. "Even Dad wouldn't argue with you unless he felt he had a good case."

Matt shoved his hands into his pockets. "If you need me, you know the cell phone number."

"Sure."

Still he hesitated. He turned and glanced at Leslie, who was opening mail. The expression on his face

fascinated Ed, who'd known him most of his life. It
wasn't a look he recognized.

Matt started out the door and then paused to look
back at Leslie, staring at her until she lifted her eyes.

He searched them slowly, intently. He didn't
smile. He didn't speak. Her cheeks became flushed
and she looked away. He made an awkward movement with his shoulders and went out the door.

Ed joined her at her desk when Matt was out of
sight. "So far, so good," he remarked.

"I guess he really doesn't mind letting me stay,"
she murmured. Her hands were shaking because of
that long, searching look of Matt's. She clasped them
together so that Ed wouldn't notice and lifted her
face. "But what if that reporter comes back?"

He pursed his lips. "Odd, that. He left town yesterday. In a real hurry, too. The police escorted him
to the city limits and the sheriff drove behind him to
the county line."

She gaped at him.

He shrugged. "Jacobsville is a small, close-knit
community and you just became part of it. That
means," he added, looking almost as imposing as his
cousin, "that we don't let outsiders barge in and start
harassing our citizens. I understand there's an old
city law still on the books that makes it a crime for
anyone to stay in a local place of lodging unless he
or she is accompanied by at least two pieces of lug-
gage or a trunk." He grinned. "Seems the reporter
only had a briefcase. Tough."

"He might come back with a trunk and two suit-cases," she pointed out.

He shook his head. "It seems that they found another old law which makes it illegal for a man driving a rental car to park it anywhere inside the city limits. Strange, isn't it, that we'd have such an unusual ordinance."

Leslie felt the first ripple of humor that she'd experienced for weeks. She smiled. "My, my."

"Our police chief is related to the Caldwells," he explained. "So is the sheriff, one of the county commissioners, two volunteer firemen, a sheriff's deputy and a Texas Ranger who was born here and works out of Fort Worth." He chuckled. "The governor is our second cousin."

Her eyes widened. "No Washington connections?" she asked.

"Nothing major. The vice president is married to my aunt."

"Nothing major." She nodded. She let out her breath. "Well, I'm beginning to feel very safe."

"Good. You can stay as long as you like. Permanently, as far as I'm concerned."

She couldn't quite contain the pleasure it gave her to feel as if she belonged somewhere, a place where she was protected and nurtured and had friends. It was a first for her. Her eyes stung with moisture.

"Don't start crying," Ed said abruptly. "I can't stand it."

She swallowed and forced a watery smile to her

lips. "I wasn't going to," she assured him. She moved her shoulders. "Thanks," she said gruffly.

"Don't thank me," he told her. "Matt rounded up the law enforcement people and had them going through dusty volumes of ordinances to find a way to get that reporter out of here."

"Matt did?"

He held up a hand as she started to parade her misgivings about what he might have learned of her past. "He doesn't know why the man was here. It was enough that he was asking questions about you. You're an employee. We don't permit harassment."

"I see."

She didn't, but that was just as well. The look Ed had accidentally seen on Matt's face had him turning mental cartwheels. No need to forewarn Leslie. She wasn't ever going to have to worry about being hounded again, not if he knew Matt. And he didn't believe for one minute that his cousin was flying all the way to Houston for a cattle sale that he usually wouldn't be caught dead at. The foreman at his ranch handled that sort of thing, although Leslie didn't know. Ed was betting that Matt had another reason for going to Houston, and it was to find out who hired that reporter and sent him looking for Leslie. He felt sorry for the source of that problem. Matt in a temper was the most menacing human being he'd ever known. He didn't rage or shout and he usually didn't hit, but he had wealth and power and he knew how to use them.

He went back into his office, suddenly worried despite the reassurances he'd given Leslie. Matt didn't know why the reporter was digging around, but what if he found out? He would only be told what the public had been told, that Leslie's mother had shot her daughter and her live-in lover in a fit of jealous rage and that she was in prison. He might think, as others had, that Leslie had brought the whole sordid business on herself by having a wild party with Mike and his friends, and he wouldn't be sympathetic. More than likely, he'd come raging back home and throw Leslie out in the street. Furthermore, he'd have her escorted to the county line like the reporter who'd been following her.

He worried himself sick over the next few hours. He couldn't tell Leslie, when he might only be worrying for nothing. But the thought haunted him that Matt was every bit as dogged as a reporter when it came to ferreting out facts.

In the end, he phoned a hotel that Matt frequented when he was in Houston overnight and asked for his room. But when he was connected, it wasn't Matt who answered the phone.

"Carolyn?" Ed asked, puzzled. "Is Matt there?"

"Not right now," came the soft reply. "He had an appointment to see someone. I suppose he's forgotten that I'm waiting for him with this trolley full of food. I suppose it will be cold as ice by the time he turns up."

"Everything's all right, isn't it?"

"Why wouldn't it be?" she teased.

"Matt's been acting funny."

"Yes, I know. That Murry girl!" Her indrawn breath was audible. "Well, she's caused quite enough trouble. When Matt comes back, she'll be right out of that office, let me tell you! Do you have any idea what that reporter told Matt about her…?"

Ed hung up, sick. So not only did Matt know, but Carolyn knew, too. She'd savage Leslie, given the least opportunity. He had to do something. What?

Ed didn't expect Matt that evening, and he was right. Matt didn't come back in time for the county commission meeting, and Ed was forced to go in his place. He held his own, as Matt had instructed him to, and got what he wanted. Then he went home, sitting on pins and needles as he waited for someone to call him—either Leslie, in tears, or Matt, in a temper.

But the phone didn't ring. And when he went into work the next morning, Leslie was sitting calmly at her desk typing the letters he'd dictated to her just before they closed the day before.

"How did the meeting go?" she asked at once.

"Great," he replied. "Matt will be proud of me." He hesitated. "He, uh, isn't in yet, is he?"

"No. He hasn't phoned, either." She frowned. "You don't suppose anything went wrong with the plane, do you?"

She sounded worried. Come to think of it, she looked worried, too. He frowned. "He's been flying for a long time," he pointed out.

"Yes, but there was a bad storm last night." She hesitated. She didn't want to worry, but she couldn't help it. Despite the hard time he'd given her, Matt had been kind to her once or twice. He wasn't a bad person; he just didn't like her.

"If anything had happened, I'd have heard by now," he assured her. His lips pursed as he searched for the words. "He didn't go alone."

Her heart stopped in her chest. "Carolyn?"

He nodded curtly. He ran a hand through his hair. "He knows, Leslie. They both do."

She felt the life ebb out of her. But what had she expected, that Matt would wait to hear her side of the story? He was the enemy. He wouldn't for one second believe that she was the victim of the whole sick business. How could she blame him?

She turned off the word processor and moved her chair back, reaching for her purse. She felt more defeated than she ever had in her life. One bad break after another, she was thinking, as she got to her feet a little clumsily.

"Hand me my crutches, Ed, there's a dear," she said steadily.

"Oh, Leslie," he groaned.

She held her hand out and, reluctantly, he helped her get them in place.

"Where will you go?" he asked.

She shrugged. "It doesn't matter. Something will turn up."

"I can help."

She looked up at him with sad resignation. "You can't go against your own blood kin, Ed," she replied. "I'm the outsider here. And one way or another, I've already caused too much trouble. See you around, pal. Thanks for everything."

He sighed miserably. "Keep in touch, at least."

She smiled. "Certainly I'll do that. See you."

He watched her walk away with pure anguish. He wished he could make her stay, but even he wouldn't wish that on her. When Matt came home, he'd be out for blood. At least she'd be spared that confrontation.

Chapter Nine

Leslie didn't have a lot to pack, only a few clothes and personal items, like the photograph of her father that she always carried with her. She'd bought a bus ticket to San Antonio, one of the places nosy reporters from Houston might not think to look for her. She could get a job as a typist and find another place to live. It wouldn't be so bad.

She thought about Matt, and how he must feel, now that he knew the whole truth, or at least, the reporter's version of it. She was sure that he and Carolyn would have plenty to gossip about on the way back home. Carolyn would broadcast the scandal all over town. Even if Leslie stopped working for Matt, she would never live down the gossip. Leaving was her only option.

Running away. Again.

Her hands went to a tiny napkin she'd brought home from the dance that she and Ed had attended with Matt and Carolyn. Matt had been doodling on it with his pen just before he'd pulled Leslie out of her seat and out onto the dance floor. It was a silly sentimental piece of nonsense to keep. On a rare occasion or two, Matt had been tender with her. She wanted to remember those times. It was good to have had a little glimpse of what love might have been like, so that life didn't turn her completely bitter.

She folded her coat over a chair and looked around to make sure she wasn't missing anything. She wouldn't have time to look in the morning. The bus would leave at 6:00 a.m., with or without her. She clumped around the apartment with forced cheer, thinking that at least she'd have no knowing, pitying smiles in San Antonio.

Ed looked up as Matt exploded into the office, stopping in his tracks when he reached Leslie's empty desk. He stood there, staring, as if he couldn't believe what he was seeing.

With a sigh, Ed got up and joined him in the outer office, steeling himself for the ordeal. Matt was obviously upset.

"It's all right," he told Matt. "She's already gone. She said she was sorry for the trouble she'd caused, and that…"

"Gone?" Matt looked horrified. His face was like white stone.

Ed frowned, hesitating. "She said it would spare you the trouble of firing her," he began uneasily.

Matt still hadn't managed a coherent sentence. He ran his hand through his hair, disturbing its neat wave. He stuck his other hand into his pocket and went on staring at her desk as if he expected she might materialize out of thin air if he looked hard enough.

He turned to Ed. He stared at him, almost as if he didn't recognize him. "She's gone. Gone where?"

"She wouldn't tell me," he replied reluctantly.

Matt's eyes were black. He looked back at her desk and winced. He made a violent motion, pressed his lips together, and suddenly took a deep audible breath and with a furious scowl, he let out a barrage of nonstop curses that had even Ed gaping.

"…and I did *not* say she could leave!" he finished at the end.

Ed managed to meet those flashing eyes, but it wasn't easy. Braver men than he had run for cover when the boss lost his temper. "Now, Matt…"

"Don't you 'Now, Matt' me, dammit!" he raged. His fists were clenched at his sides and he looked as if he really wanted to hit something. Or someone. Ed took two steps backward.

Matt saw two of the secretaries standing frozen in the hall, as if they'd come running to find the source of the uproar and were now hoping against hope that it wouldn't notice them.

No such luck. "Get the hell back to work!" he shouted.

They actually ran.

Ed wanted to. "Matt," he tried again.

He was talking to thin air. Matt was down the hall and out the door before he could catch up. He did the only thing he could. He rushed back to his office to phone Leslie and warn her. He was so nervous that it took several tries and one wrong number to get her.

"He's on his way over there," Ed told her the minute she picked up the phone. "Get out."

"No."

"Leslie, I've never seen him like this," he pleaded. "You don't understand. He isn't himself."

"It's all right, Ed," she said calmly. "There's nothing more he can do to me."

"Leslie…!" he groaned.

The loud roar of an engine out front caught her attention. "Try not to worry," she told Ed, and put the receiver down on an even louder exclamation.

She got up, put her crutches in place and hobbled to open her door just as Matt started to knock on it. He paused there, his fist upraised, his eyes black in a face the color of rice.

She stood aside to let him in, with no sense of self-preservation left. She was as far down as she could get already.

He closed the door behind him with an ultracontrolled softness before he turned to look at her. She went back to her armchair and eased down into it, laying the crutches to one side. Her chin lifted and she just looked at him, resigned to more verbal abuse if not downright violence. She was already packed and almost beyond his reach. Let him do his worst.

Now that he was here, he didn't know what to do. He hadn't thought past finding her. He leaned back against the door and folded his arms over his chest.

She didn't flinch or avert her eyes. She stared right at him. "There was no need to come here," she said calmly. "You don't have to run me out of town. I already have my ticket. I'm leaving on the bus first thing in the morning." She lifted a hand. "Feel free to search if you think I've taken anything from the office."

He didn't respond. His chest rose and fell rhythmically, if a little heavily.

She smoothed her hand over the cast where it topped her kneecap. There was an itch and she couldn't get to it. What a mundane thing to think about, she told herself, when she was confronted with a homicidal man.

He was making her more nervous by the minute. She shifted in the chair, grimacing as the cast moved awkwardly and gave her a twinge of pain.

"Why are you here?" she asked impatiently, her eyes flashing at him through her lenses. "What else do you want, an apology...?"

"An apology? Dear God!"

It sounded like a plea for salvation. He moved, for the first time, going slowly across the room to the chair a few feet away from hers, next to the window. He eased himself down into it and crossed his long legs. He was still scowling, watching, waiting.

His eyes were appraising her now, not cutting into her or mocking her. They were dark and steady and turbulent.

Her eyes were dull and lackluster as she averted her face. Her grip on the arm of the chair was painful. "You know, don't you?"

"Yes."

She felt as if her whole body contracted. She watched a bird fly past the window and wished that she could fly away from her problems. "In a way, it's sort of a relief," she said wearily. "I'm so tired…of running."

His face tautened. His mouth made a thin line as he stared at her. "You'll never have to run again," he said flatly. "There isn't going to be any more harassment from that particular quarter."

She wasn't sure she was hearing right. Her face turned back to his. It was hard to meet those searching eyes, but she did. He looked pale, worn.

"Why aren't you gloating?" she asked harshly. "You were right about me all along, weren't you? I'm a little tramp who lures men in and teases them…!"

"Don't!" He actually flinched. He searched for

words and couldn't manage to find anything to say to her. His guilt was killing him. His conscience had him on a particularly nasty rack. He looked at her and saw years of torment and self-contempt, and he wanted to hit something.

That expression was easily read in his dark eyes. She leaned her head back against the chair and closed her eyes on the hatred she saw there.

"Everybody had a different idea of why I did it," she said evenly. "One of the bigger tabloids even interviewed a couple of psychiatrists who said I was getting even with my mother for my childhood. Another said it was latent nymphomania..."

"Hell!"

She felt dirty. She couldn't look at him. "I thought I loved him," she said, as if even after all the years, she still couldn't believe it had happened. "I had no idea, none at all, what he was really like. He made fun of my body, he and his friends. They stretched me out like a human sacrifice and discussed... my...assets." Her voice broke. He clenched his hand on the arm of the chair.

Matt's expression, had she seen it, would have silenced her. As it was, she was staring blankly out the window.

"They decided Mike should go first," she said in a husky, strained tone. "And then they drew cards to see which of the other three would go next. I prayed to die. But I couldn't. Mike was laughing at the way I begged him not to do it. I struggled and he had the others hold me down while he..."

A sound came from Matt's tight throat that shocked her into looking at him. She'd never seen such horror in a man's eyes.

"My mother came in before he had time to—" she swallowed "—get started. She was so angry that she lost control entirely. She grabbed the pistol Mike kept in the table drawer by the front door and she shot him. The bullet went through him and into my leg," she whispered, sickened by the memory. "I saw his face when the bullet hit him in the chest from behind. I actually saw the life drain out of him." She closed her eyes. "She kept shooting until one of the men got the pistol away from her. They ran for their lives, and left us there, like that. A neighbor called an ambulance and the police. I remember that one of them got a blanket from the bedroom and wrapped me up in it. They were all...so kind," she choked, tears filling her eyes. "So kind!"

He put his face in his hands. He couldn't bear what he was hearing. He remembered her face in his office when he'd laughed at her. He groaned harshly.

"The tabloids made it look as if I'd invited what happened," she said huskily. "I don't know how a seventeen-year-old virgin can ask grown men to get high on drugs and treat her with no respect. I thought I loved Mike, but even so, I never did anything consciously to make him treat me that way."

Matt couldn't look at her. Not yet. "People high

on drugs don't know what they're doing, as a rule,"
he said through his teeth.

"That's hard to believe," she said.

"It's the same thing as a man drinking too much
alcohol and having a blackout," he said, finally lifting his head. He stared at her with dark, lifeless eyes.
"Didn't I tell you once that secrets are dangerous?"

She nodded. She looked back out the window.
"Mine was too sordid to share," she said bitterly. "I
can't bear to be touched by men. By most men," she
qualified. "Ed knew all about me, so he never approached me, that way. But you," she added quietly,
"came at me like a bull in a pasture. You scared me
to death. Aggression always reminds me of...of
Mike."

He leaned forward with his head bowed. Even after what he'd learned in Houston already, he was
unprepared for the full impact of what had been done
to this vulnerable, fragile creature in front of him.
He'd let hurt pride turn him into a predator. He'd
approached her in ways that were guaranteed to bring
back terrible memories of that incident in her past.

"I wish I'd known," he said heavily.

"I don't blame you," she said simply. "You
couldn't have known."

His dark eyes came up glittering. "I could have,"
he contradicted flatly. "It was right under my nose.
The way you downplayed your figure, the way you
backed off when I came too close, the way
you...fainted—" he had to force the word out "—in

my office when I pinned you to the wall." He looked away. "I didn't see it because I didn't want to. I was paying you back," he said on a bitter laugh, "for having the gall not to fall into my arms when I pursued you."

She'd never imagined that she could feel sorry for Matt Caldwell. But she did. He was a decent man. Surely it would be difficult for him to face the treatment he'd given her, now that he knew the truth.

She smoothed her hands over her arms. It wasn't cold in the room, but she was chilled.

"You've never talked about it, have you?" he asked after a minute.

"Only to Ed, right after it happened," she replied. "He's been the best friend in the world to me. When those people started talking about making a television movie of what had happened, I just panicked. They were all over Houston looking for me. Ed offered me a way out and I took it. I was so scared," she whispered. "I thought I'd be safe here."

His fists clenched. "Safe." He made a mockery of the very word.

He got to his feet and moved to the window, avoiding her curious gaze.

"That reporter," she began hesitantly. "He told you about it when he was here, didn't he?"

He didn't reply for a minute. "Yes," he said finally. "He had clippings of the story." She probably knew which ones, he thought miserably, of her being carried out on a stretcher with blood all over her.

There was one of the dead man lying on the floor of the apartment, and one of her blond mother shocked and almost catatonic as policemen escorted her to the squad car.

"I didn't connect it when you told Ed you were going to Houston. I thought it was some cattle sale, just like you said," she remarked.

"The reporter ran, but he'd already said that he was working with some people in Hollywood trying to put together a television movie. He'd tried to talk to your mother, apparently, and after his visit, she had a heart attack. That didn't even slow him down. He tracked you here and had plans to interview you." He glanced at her. "He thought you'd be glad to cooperate for a percentage of the take."

She laughed hollowly.

"Yes, I know," he told her. "You're not mercenary. That's one of the few things I've learned about you since you've been here."

"At least you found one thing about me that you like," she told him.

His face closed up completely. "There are a lot of things I like about you, but I've had some pretty hard knocks from women in my life."

"Ed told me."

"It's funny," he said, but he didn't look amused. "I've never been able to come to terms with my mother's actions—until I met you. You've helped me a lot—and I've been acting like a bear with a thorn in its paw. I've mistreated you."

She searched his lean, hard face quietly. He was so handsome. Her heart jumped every time she met his eyes. "Why did you treat me that way?" she asked.

He stuck his hand into his pocket. "I wanted you," he said flatly.

"Oh."

She wasn't looking at him, but he saw her fingers curl into the arm of the chair. "I know. You probably aren't capable of desire after what was done to you. Perhaps it's poetic justice that my money and position won't get me the one thing in the world I really want."

"I don't think I could sleep with someone," she agreed evenly. "Even the thought of it is...disgusting."

He could imagine that it was, and he cursed that man silently until he ran out of words.

"You liked kissing me."

She nodded, surprised. "Yes, I did."

"And being touched," he prompted, smiling gently at the memory of her reaction—astonishing now, considering her past.

She studied her lap. A button on her dress was loose. She'd have to stitch it. She lifted her eyes. "Yes," she said. "I enjoyed that, too, at first."

His face hardened as he remembered what he'd said to her then. He turned away, his back rigid. He'd made so damned many mistakes with this woman that he didn't know how he was going to make amends. There was probably no way to do it. But he could protect her from any more misery, and he was going to.

He rammed his hands into his pockets and turned. "I went to see that reporter in Houston. I can promise you that he won't be bothering you again, and there won't be any more talk of a motion picture. I went to see your mother, too," he added.

She hadn't expected that. She closed her eyes. She caught her lower lip in her teeth and bit it right through. The taste of blood steeled her as she waited for the explosion.

"Don't!"

She opened her eyes with a jerk. His face was dark and lined, like the downwardly slanted brows above his black eyes. She pulled a tissue from the box on the table beside her and dabbed at the blood on her lip. It was such a beautiful color, she thought irrelevantly.

"I didn't realize how hard this was going to be," he said, sitting down. His head bowed, he clasped his big hands between his splayed knees and stared at the floor. "There are a lot of things I want to tell you. I just can't find the right words."

She didn't speak. Her eyes were still on the blood-dotted tissue. She felt his dark eyes on her, searching, studying, assessing her.

"If I'd…known about your past…" he tried again.

Her head came up. Her eyes were as dead as stone. "You just didn't like me. It's all right. I didn't like you, either. And you couldn't have known. I came here to hide the past, not to talk about it. But I guess you were right about secrets. I'll have to find another place to go, that's all.''

He cursed under his breath. "Don't go! You're safe in Jacobsville," he continued, his voice growing stronger and more confident as he spoke. "There won't be any more suspicious reporters, no more movie deals, no more persecution. I can make sure that nobody touches you as long as you're here. I can't…protect you anywhere else," he added impatiently.

Oh, that was just great, she thought furiously. Pity. Guilt. Shame. Now he was going to go to the opposite extreme. He was going to watch over her like a protective father wolf. Well, he could think again. She scooped up one of her crutches and slammed the tip on the floor. "I don't need protection from you or anybody else. I'm leaving on the morning bus. And as for you, Mr. Caldwell, you can get out of here and leave me alone!" she raged at him.

It was the first spark of resistance he'd seen in her since he arrived. The explosion lightened his mood. She wasn't acting like a victim anymore. That was real independence in her tone, in the whole look of her. She was healing already with the retelling of that painful episode in her life.

The hesitation in him was suddenly gone. So was the somber face. Both eyebrows went up and a faint light touched his black eyes. "Or what?"

She hesitated. "What do you mean, or what?"

"If I don't get out, what do you plan to do?" he asked pleasantly.

She thought about that for a minute. "Call Ed."

He glanced at his watch. "Karla's bringing him coffee about now. Wouldn't it be a shame to spoil his break?"

She moved restlessly in the chair, still holding on to the crutch.

He smiled slowly, for the first time since he'd arrived. "Nothing more to say? Have you run out of threats already?"

Her eyes narrowed with bad temper. She didn't know what to say, or what to do. This was completely unexpected.

He studied the look of her in the pretty blue-patterned housedress she was wearing, barefoot. She was pretty, too. "I like that dress. I like your hair that color, too."

She looked at him as if she feared for his sanity. Something suddenly occurred to her. "If you didn't come rushing over here to put me on the bus and see that I left town, why are you here?"

He nodded slowly. "I was wondering when you'd get around to that." He leaned forward, just as another car pulled up outside the house.

"Ed," she guessed.

He grimaced. "I guess he rushed over to save you," he said with resignation.

She glared at him. "He was worried about me."

He went toward the door. "He wasn't the only one," he muttered, almost to himself. He opened the door before Ed could knock. "She's all in one piece," he assured his cousin, standing aside to let him into the room.

Ed was worried, confused, and obviously puzzled when he saw that she wasn't crying. "Are you all right?" he asked her.

She nodded.

Ed looked at her and then at Matt, curious, but too polite to start asking questions.

"I assume that you're staying in town now?" Matt asked her a little stiffly. "You still have a job, if you want it. No pressure. It's your decision."

She wasn't sure what to do next. She didn't want to leave Jacobsville for another town of strange people.

"Stay," Ed said gently.

She forced a smile. "I guess I could," she began. "For a while."

Matt didn't let his relief show. In a way he was glad Ed had shown up to save him from what he was about to say to her.

"You won't regret it," Ed promised her, and she smiled at him warmly.

The smile set Matt off again. He was jealous, and furious that he *was* jealous. He ran a hand through his hair again and glowered with frustration at both of them. "Oh, hell, I'm going back to work," he said shortly. "When you people get through playing games on my time, you might go to the office and earn your damned paychecks!''

He went out the door still muttering to himself, slammed into the Jaguar, and roared away.

Ed and Leslie stared at each other.

"He went to see my mother," she told him.

"And?"

"He didn't say a lot, except...except that there won't be any more reporters asking questions."

"What about Carolyn?" he asked.

"He didn't say a word about her," she murmured, having just remembered that Ed said Carolyn had gone to Houston with him. She grimaced. "I guess she'll rush home and tell the whole town about me."

"I wouldn't like to see what Matt would do about it, if she did. If he asked you to stay, it's because he plans to protect you."

"I suppose he does, but it's a shock, considering the way he was before he went out of town. Honestly, I don't know what's going on. He's like a stranger!"

"I've never heard him actually apologize," he said. "But he usually finds ways to get his point across, without saying the words."

"Maybe that was what he was doing," she replied, thinking back over his odd behavior. "He doesn't want me to leave town."

"That seems to be the case." He smiled at her. "How about it? You've still got a job if you want it, and Matt's taken you off the endangered list. You're safe here. Want to stay?"

She thought about that for a minute, about Matt's odd statement that she was safe in Jacobsville and she wouldn't be hounded anymore. It was like a dream come true after six years of running and hiding. She nodded slowly. "Oh, yes," she said earnestly. "Yes, I want to stay!"

"Then I suggest you put on your shoes and grab a jacket, and I'll drive you back to work, while we still have jobs."

"I can't go to work like this," she protested.

"Why not?" he wanted to know.

"It isn't a proper dress to wear on the job," she said, rising.

He scowled. "Did Matt say that?"

"I'm not giving him the chance to," she said. "From now on, I'm going to be the soul of conservatism at work. He won't get any excuses to take potshots at me."

"If you say so," he said with a regretful thought for the pretty, feminine dress that he'd never seen her wear in public. So much for hoping that Matt might have coaxed her out of her repressive way of dressing. But it was early days yet.

Chapter Ten

For the first few days after her return to work, Leslie was uneasy every time she saw Matt coming. She shared that apprehension with two of the other secretaries, one of whom actually ripped her skirt climbing over the fence around the flower garden near the front of the building in a desperate attempt to escape him.

The incident sent Leslie into gales of helpless laughter as she told Karla Smith about it. Matt came by her office just as they were discussing it and stood transfixed at a sound he'd never heard coming from Leslie since he'd known her. She looked up and saw him, and made a valiant attempt to stop laughing.

"What's so funny?" he asked pleasantly.

Karla choked and ran for the ladies' room, leaving Leslie to cope with the question.

"Did you say something to the secretaries the other day to upset them?" she asked him right out.

He shifted. "I may have said a word or two that I shouldn't have," was all he'd admit.

"Well, Daisy Joiner just plowed through a fence avoiding you, and half her petticoat's still...out... there!" She collapsed against her desk, tears rolling down her cheeks.

She was more animated than he'd ever seen her. It lifted his heart. Not that he was going to admit it.

He gave her a harsh mock glare and pulled a cigar case out of his shirt pocket. "Lily-livered cowards," he muttered as he took out a cigar, flicked off the end with a tool from his slacks pocket, and snapped open his lighter with a flair. "What we need around here are secretaries with guts!" he said loudly, and flicked the lighter with his thumb.

Two streams of water hit the flame at the same time from different directions.

"Oh, for God's sake!" Matt roared as giggling, scurrying feet retreated down the hall.

"What were you saying about secretaries with guts?" she asked with twinkling gray eyes.

He looked at his drenched lighter and his damp cigar, and threw the whole mess into the trash can by Leslie's desk. "I quit," he muttered.

Leslie couldn't help the twinkle in her eyes. "I

believe that was the whole object of the thing,'' she pointed out, ''to make you quit smoking?''

He grimaced. ''I guess it was.'' He studied her intently. ''You're settling back in nicely,'' he remarked. ''Do you have everything you need?''

''Yes,'' she replied.

He hesitated, as if he wanted to say something else and couldn't decide what. His dark eyes swept over her face, as if he were comparing her dark hair and glasses to the blond camouflage she'd worn when she first came to work for him.

''I guess I look different,'' she said a little self-consciously, because the scrutiny made her nervous. His face gave nothing away.

He smiled gently. ''I like it,'' he told her.

''Did you need to see Ed?'' she asked, because he still hadn't said why he was in Ed's office.

He shrugged. ''It's nothing urgent,'' he murmured. ''I met with the planning and zoning committee last night. I thought he might like to know how I came out.''

''I could buzz him.''

He nodded, still smiling. ''Why don't you do that?''

She did. Ed came out of his office at once, still uncertain about Matt's reactions.

''Got a minute?'' Matt asked him.

''Sure. Come on in.'' Ed stood aside to let the taller man stride into his office. He glanced back toward Leslie with a puzzled, questioning expression. She only smiled.

He nodded and closed the door, leaving Leslie to go back to work. She couldn't quite figure out Matt's new attitude toward her. There was nothing predatory about him lately. Ever since his return from Houston and the explosive meeting at her apartment, he was friendly and polite, even a little affectionate, but he didn't come near her now. He seemed to have the idea that any physical contact upset her, so he was being Big Brother Matt instead.

She should have been grateful. After all, he'd said often enough that marriage wasn't in his vocabulary. An affair, obviously, was out of the question now that he knew her past. Presumably affection was the only thing he had to offer her. It was a little disappointing, because Leslie had learned in their one early encounter that Matt's touch was delightful. She wished that she could tell him how exciting it was to her. It had been the only tenderness she'd ever had from a man in any physical respect, and she was very curious about that part of relationships. Not with just anyone, of course.

Only with Matt.

Her hands stilled on the keyboard as she heard footsteps approaching. The door opened and Carolyn came in, svelte in a beige dress that made the most of her figure, her hair perfectly coiffed.

"They said he let you come back to work here. I couldn't believe it, after what that reporter told him," the older woman began hotly. She gave Leslie a haughty, contemptuous stare. "That disguise won't do you any good, you know," she added, pausing to dig in her purse. She drew out a worn page from an old tabloid and tossed it onto Leslie's desk. It was the photo they'd used of her on the stretcher, with the caption, Teenager, Lover, Shot By Jealous Mother In Love Triangle.

Leslie just sat and looked at it, thinking how the past never really went away. She sighed wistfully. She was never going to be free of it.

"Don't you have anything to say?" Carolyn taunted.

Leslie looked up at her. "My mother is in prison. My life was destroyed. The man responsible for it all was a drug dealer." She searched Carolyn's cold eyes. "You can't imagine it, can you? You've always been wealthy, protected, safe. How could you understand the trauma of being a very innocent seventeen-year-old and having four grown men strip you naked in a drug-crazed frenzy and try to rape you in your own home?"

Amazingly Carolyn went pale. She hesitated, frowning. Her eyes went to the tabloid and she shifted uneasily. Her hand went out to retrieve the page just as the door to Ed's office opened and Matt came through it.

His face, when he saw Carolyn with the tearsheet in her hand, became dangerous.

Carolyn jerked it back, crumpled it, and threw it

in the trash can. "You don't need to say anything," she said in a choked tone. "I'm not very proud of myself right now." She moved away from Leslie without looking at her. "I'm going to Europe for a few months. See you when I get back, Matt."

"You'd better hope you don't," he said in a voice like steel.

She made an awkward movement, but she didn't turn. She squared her shoulders and kept walking.

Matt paused beside the desk, retrieved the page and handed it to Ed. "Burn that," he said tautly.

"With pleasure," Ed replied. He gave Leslie a sympathetic glance before he went back into his office and closed the door.

"I thought she came to make trouble," she told Matt with evident surprise in her expression. Carolyn's abrupt about-face had puzzled her.

"She only knew what I mumbled the night I got drunk," he said curtly. "I never meant to tell her the rest of it. She's not as bad as she seems," he added. "I've known her most of my life, and I like her. She got it into her head that we should get married and saw you as a rival. I straightened all that out. At least, I thought I had."

"Thanks."

"She'll come back a different woman," he continued. "I'm sure she'll apologize."

"It's not necessary," she said. "Nobody knew the true story. I was too afraid to tell it."

He stuck his hands into his pockets and studied

her. His face was lined, his eyes had dark circles under them. He looked worn. "I would have spared you this if I could have," he gritted.

He seemed really upset about it. "You can't stop other people from thinking what they like. It's all right. I'll just have to get used to it."

"Like hell you will. The next person who comes in here with a damned tabloid page is going out right through the window!"

She smiled faintly. "Thank you. But it's not necessary. I can take care of myself."

"Judging by Carolyn's face, you did a fair job of it with her," he mused.

"I guess she's not really so bad." She glanced at him and away. "She was only jealous. It was silly. You never had designs on me."

There was a tense silence. "And what makes you think so?"

"I'm not in her league," she said simply. "She's beautiful and rich and comes from a good family."

He moved a step closer, watching her face lift. She didn't look apprehensive, so he moved again. "Not frightened?" he murmured.

"Of you?" She smiled gently. "Of course not."

He seemed surprised, curious, even puzzled.

"In fact, I like bears," she said with a deliberate grin.

That expression went right through him. He smiled. He beamed. Suddenly he caught the back of her chair with his hand and swiveled her around so that her face was within an inch of his.

"Sticks and stones, Miss Murry," he whispered softly, with a lazy grin, and brought his lips down very softly on hers.

She caught her breath.

His head lifted and his dark, quiet eyes met hers and held them while he tried to decide whether or not she was frightened. He saw the pulse throbbing at her neck and heard the faint unsteadiness of her breath. She was unsettled. But that wasn't fear. He knew enough about women to be sure of it.

He chuckled softly, and there was pure calculation in the way he studied her. "Any more smart remarks?" he taunted in a sensual whisper.

She hesitated. He wasn't aggressive or demanding or mocking. She searched his eyes, looking for clues to this new, odd behavior.

He traced her mouth with his forefinger. "Well?"

She smiled hesitantly. All her uncertainties were obvious, but she wasn't afraid of him. Her heart was going wild. But it wasn't with fear. And he knew it.

He bent and kissed her again with subdued tenderness.

"You taste like cigar smoke," she whispered impishly.

"I probably do, but I'm not giving up cigars completely, regardless of the water pistols," he whispered. "So you might as well get used to the taste of them."

She searched his dark eyes with quiet curiosity.

He put his thumb over her soft lips and smiled down at her. "I've been invited to a party at the Ballengers' next month. You'll be out of your cast by then. How about buying a pretty dress and coming with me?" He bent and brushed his lips over her forehead. "They're having a live Latin band. We can dance some more."

She wasn't hearing him. His lips were making her heart beat faster. She was smiling as she lifted her face to those soft kisses, like a flower reaching up to the sun. He realized that and smiled against her cheek.

"This isn't businesslike," she whispered.

He lifted his head and looked around. The office was empty and nobody was walking down the hall. He glanced back down at her with one lifted eyebrow.

She laughed shyly.

The teasing light in his eyes went into eclipse at the response that smile provoked in him. He framed her soft face in his big hands and bent again. This time the kiss wasn't light, or brief.

When she moaned, he drew back at once. His eyes were glittery with strong emotion. He let go of her face and stood up, looking down at her solemnly. He winced, as if he remembered previous encounters when he hadn't been careful with her, when he'd been deliberately cruel.

She read the guilt in his face and frowned. She

was totally unversed in the byplay between men and women, well past the years when those things were learned in a normal way.

"I didn't mean to do that," he said quietly. "I'm sorry."

"It's all right," she stammered.

He drew in a long, slow breath. "You have nothing to be afraid of now. I hope you know that."

"I'm not frightened," she replied.

His face hardened as he looked at her. One hand clenched in his pocket. The other clenched at his side. She happened to look down and she drew in her breath at the sight of it.

"You're hurt!" she exclaimed, reaching out to touch the abrasions that had crusted over, along with the swollen bruises that still remained there.

"I'll heal," he said curtly. "Maybe he will, too, eventually."

"He?" she queried.

"Yes. That yellow-backed reporter who came down here looking for you." His face tautened. "I took Houston apart looking for him. When I finally found him, I delivered him to his boss. There won't be any more problems from that direction, ever. In fact, he'll be writing obituaries for the rest of his miserable life."

"He could take you to court..."

"He's welcome, after my attorneys get through with him," he returned flatly. "He'll be answering charges until he's an old man. Considering the dif-

ference in our ages, I'll probably be dead by then.''
He paused to think about that. "I'll make sure the
money's left in my estate to keep him in court until
every penny runs out!'' he added after a minute. "He
won't even be safe when I'm six feet under!''

She didn't know whether to laugh or cry. He was
livid, almost vibrating with temper.

"But you know what hurts the most?'' he added,
looking down into her worried eyes. "What he did
still wasn't as bad as what I did to you. I won't ever
forgive myself for that. Not if I live to be a hundred.''

That was surprising. She toyed with her keyboard
and didn't look at him. "I thought...you might
blame me, when you knew the whole story,'' she
said.

"For what?'' he asked huskily.

She moved her shoulders restlessly. "The papers
said it was my fault, that I invited it.''

"Dear God!'' He knelt beside her and made her
look at him. "Your mother told me the whole story,''
he said. "She cried like a baby when she got it all
out.'' He paused, touching her face gently. "Know
what she said? That she'd gladly spend the rest of
her life where she is, if you could only forgive her
for what she did to you.''

She felt the tears overflowing. She started to wipe
them, but he pulled her face to his and kissed them
away so tenderly that they came in a veritable flood.

"No,'' he whispered. "You mustn't cry. It's all

right. I won't let anything hurt you ever again. I promise.''

But she couldn't stop. ''Oh, Matt…!'' she sobbed.

All his protective instincts bristled. ''Come here to me,'' he said gently. He stood up and lifted her into his arms, cast and all, and carried her down the deserted hall to his office.

His secretary saw him coming and opened the door for him, grimacing at Leslie's red, wet face.

''Coffee or brandy?'' she asked Matt.

''Coffee. Make it about thirty minutes, will you? And hold my calls.''

''Yes, sir.''

She closed the door and Matt sat down on the burgundy couch with Leslie in his lap, cradling her while she wept.

He tucked a handkerchief into her hand and rocked her in his arms, whispering to her until the sobs lessened.

''I'm going to replace the furniture in here,'' he murmured. ''Maybe the paneling, too.''

''Why?''

''It must hold some painful memories for you,'' he said. ''I know it does for me.''

His voice was bitter. She recalled fainting, and coming to on this very couch. She looked up at him without malice or accusation. Her eyes were red and swollen, and full of curiosity.

He traced her cheek with tender fingers and smiled at her. ''You've had a rough time of it, haven't you?'' he asked quietly. "Will it do any good to tell you that a man wouldn't normally treat a woman, especially an innocent woman, the way those animals treated you?"

"I know that," she replied. "It's just that the publicity made me out to be little more than a call girl. I'm not like that. But it's what people thought I was. So I ran, and ran, and hid...if it hadn't been for Ed and his father, and my friend Jessica, I don't know what I would have done. I don't have any family left."

"You have your mother," he assured her. "She'd like to see you. If you're willing, I'll drive you up there, anytime you like."

She hesitated. "You do know that she's in prison for murder?" she asked.

"I know it."

"You're well-known here," she began.

"Oh, good Lord, are you trying to save me?" he asked with an exasperated sigh. "Woman, I don't give two hoots in hell for gossip. While they're talking about me, they're leaving some other person alone." He took the handkerchief and wiped her cheeks. "But for the record, most reporters keep out of my way." He pursed his lips. "I can guarantee there's one in Houston who'll run the next time he sees me coming."

It amazed her that he'd gone to that much trouble defending her. She lay looking at him with eyes like a cat's, wide and soft and curious.

They had an odd effect on him. He felt his body react to it and caught his breath. He started to move her before she realized that he was aroused.

The abrupt rejection startled her. All at once she was sitting beside him on the couch, looking stunned.

He got up quickly and moved away, turning his back to her. "How would you like some coffee?" he asked gruffly.

She shifted a little, staring at him with open curiosity. "I...I would, thank you."

He went to the intercom, not to the door, and told his secretary to bring it in. He kept his back to Leslie, and to the door, even when Edna came in with the coffee service and placed it on the low coffee table in front of the sofa.

"Thanks, Edna," he said.

"Sure thing, boss." She winked at Leslie and smiled reassuringly, closing the door quietly behind her.

Leslie poured coffee into the cups, glancing at him warily. "Don't you want your coffee?"

"Not just yet," he murmured, trying to cool down.

"It smells nice."

"Yes, it does, but I've already had a little too much stimulation for the moment, without adding caffeine to the problem."

She didn't understand. He felt her eyes on his stiff back and with a helpless laugh, he turned around. To his amazement, and his amusement, she didn't notice anything wrong with him.

He went back to the couch and sat down, shaking his head as he let her hand him a cupful of fresh coffee.

"Is something wrong?" she asked.

"Not a thing in this world, baby doll," he drawled. "Except that Edna just saved you from absolute ruin and you don't even know it."

Leslie stared into Matt's dancing eyes with obvious confusion.

"Never mind," he chuckled, sipping his coffee. "One day when we know each other better, I'll tell you all about it."

She sipped her coffee and smiled absently. "You're very different since you came back from Houston."

"I've had a bad knock." He put his cup down, but his eyes stayed on it. "I can't remember ever being grossly unfair to anyone before, much less an employee. It's hard for me, remembering some of the things I said and did to you." He grimaced, still not looking straight at her. "It hurt my pride that you'd let Ed get close, but you kept backing away from me. I never stopped to wonder why." He laughed hollowly. "I've had women throw themselves at me most of my adult life, even before I made my first million." He glanced at her. "But I couldn't get near you, except once, on the dance floor." His eyes narrowed. "And that night, when you let me touch you."

She remembered, too, the feel of his eyes and his

hands and his mouth on her. Her breath caught audibly.

He winced. "It was the first time, wasn't it?"

She averted her eyes.

"I even managed to soil that one, beautiful memory." He looked down at his hands. "I've done so much damage, Leslie. I don't know how to start over, to begin again."

"Neither do I," she confessed. "What happened to me in Houston was a pretty bad experience, even if I'd been older and more mature when it happened. As it was, I gave up trying to go on dates afterward, because I connected anything physical with that one sordid incident. I couldn't bear it when men wanted to kiss me good-night. I backed away and they thought I was some sort of freak." Her eyes closed and she shuddered.

"Tell me about the doctor."

She hesitated. "He only knew what he'd been told, I guess. But he made me feel like trash." She wrapped both arms around her chest and leaned forward. "He cleaned the wound and bandaged my leg. He said that they could send me back to the hospital from jail for the rest."

Matt muttered something vicious.

"I didn't go to jail, of course, my mother did. The leg was horribly painful. I had no medical insurance and Jessica's parents were simple people, very poor. None of us could have afforded orthopedic surgery. I was able to see a doctor at the local clinic, and he put a cast on it, assuming that it had already been set properly. He didn't do X rays because I couldn't afford any.''

"You're lucky the damage could even be repaired," he said, his eyes downcast as he wondered at the bad luck she'd had not only with the trauma of the incident itself, but with its painful aftermath.

"I had a limp when it healed, but I walked fairly well." She sighed. "Then I fell off a horse." She shook her head.

"I wouldn't have had that happen for the world," he said, meeting her eyes. "I was furious, not just that you'd backed away from me, but that I'd caused you to hurt yourself. Then at the dance, it was even worse, when I realized that all those quick steps had caused you such pain."

"It was a good sort of pain," she told him, "because it led to corrective surgery. I'm really grateful about that."

"I'm sorry it came about in the way it did." He smiled at her new look. "Glasses suit you. They make your eyes look bigger."

"I always wore them until the reporter started trying to sell an idea for a television movie about what happened. I dyed my hair and got contacts, dressed like a dowager, did everything I could to change my appearance. But Jacobsville was my last chance. I thought if I could be found here, I could be tracked anywhere." She smoothed her skirt over the cast.

"You won't be bothered by that anymore," he

said. "But I'd like to let my attorneys talk to your mother. I know," he said, when she lifted her head and gave him a worried look, "it would mean resurrecting a lot of unpleasant memories, but we might be able to get her sentence reduced or even get her a new trial. There were extenuating circumstances. Even a good public defender isn't as good as an experienced criminal lawyer."

"Did you ask her that?"

He nodded. "She wouldn't even discuss it. She said you'd had enough grief because of her."

She lowered her eyes back to her skirt. "Maybe we both have. But I hate it that she may spend the rest of her life in prison."

"So do I." He touched her hair. "She really is blond, isn't she?"

"Yes. My father had dark hair, like mine, and gray eyes, too. Hers are blue. I always wished mine were that color."

"I like your eyes just the way they are." He touched the wire rims of her frames. "Glasses and all."

"You don't have any problem seeing, do you?" she wondered.

He chuckled. "I have trouble seeing what's right under my nose, apparently."

"You're farsighted?" she asked, misunderstanding him.

He touched her soft mouth with his forefinger and the smile faded. "No. I mistake gold for tinsel."

His finger made her feel nervous. She drew back. His hand fell at once and he smiled at her surprise.

"No more aggression. I promise."

Her fascinated eyes met his. "Does that mean that you won't ever kiss me again?" she asked boldly.

"Oh, I will," he replied, delighted. He leaned forward. "But you'll have to do all the chasing from now on."

Chapter Eleven

Leslie searched his dark eyes slowly and then she began to smile. "Me, chase you?" she asked.

He pursed his lips. "Sure. Men get tired of the chase from time to time. I think I'd like having you pursue me."

Mental pictures of her in a suit and Matt in a dress dissolved her in mirth. But the reversed relationship made her feel warm inside, as if she wasn't completely encased in ice. The prospect of Matt in her arms was exhilarating, even with her past. "Okay, but I draw the line at taking you to football games," she added, trying to keep things casual between them, just for the time being.

He grinned back. "No problem. We can always

watch them on TV.'' The light in her eyes made him
light-headed. ''Feeling better now?'' he asked softly.

She nodded. ''I guess you can get used to anything
when you have to,'' she said philosophically.

''I could write you a book on that,'' he said bitterly, and she remembered his past—his young life
marked with such sadness.

''I'm sure you could,'' she agreed.

He leaned forward with the coffee cup still in his
hands. He had nice hands, she thought absently, lean
and strong and beautifully shaped. She remembered
their touch on her body with delight.

''We'll take this whole thing one step at a time,''
he said quietly. ''There won't be any pressure, and I
won't run roughshod over you. We'll go at your
pace.''

She was a little reluctant. That one step at a time
could lead anywhere, and she didn't like the idea of
taking chances. He wasn't a marrying man and she
wasn't the type for affairs. She did wonder what he
ultimately had in mind for them, but she wasn't confident enough of this new relationship to ask. It was
nice to have him like this, gentle and concerned and
caring. She hadn't had much tenderness in her life,
and she was greedy for it.

He glanced suddenly at the thin gold watch on his
wrist and grimaced. ''I should have been in Fort
Worth an hour ago for a meeting with some stock
producers.'' He glanced at her ruefully. ''Just look

at what you do to me," he murmured. "I can't even think straight anymore."

She smiled gently. "Good for me."

He chuckled, finished his coffee and put down the cup. "Better late than never, I suppose." He leaned down and kissed her, very softly. His eyes held a new, warm light that made her feel funny all over. "Stay out of trouble while I'm gone."

Her eyebrows rose. "Oh, that's cute."

He nodded. "You never put a foot wrong, did you?"

"Only by being stupid and gullible."

His dark eyes went even darker. "What happened wasn't your fault. That's the first idea we have to correct."

"I was madly infatuated for the first time in my life," she said honestly. "I might have inadvertently given him the idea...."

He put his thumb against her soft lips. "Leslie, what sort of decent adult man would accept even blatant signals from a teenager?"

It was a good question. It made her see what had happened from a different perspective.

He gave her mouth a long scrutiny before he abruptly removed his thumb and ruffled her short dark hair playfully. "Think about that. You might also consider that people on drugs very often don't know what they're doing anyway. You were in the wrong place at the wrong time."

She readjusted her glasses as they slipped further on her nose. "I suppose so."

"I'll be in Fort Worth overnight, but maybe we can go out to dinner tomorrow night?" he asked speculatively.

She indicated the cast. "I can see me now, clumping around in a pretty dress."

He chuckled. "I don't mind if you don't."

She'd never been on a real date before, except nights out with Ed, who was more like a brother than a boyfriend. Her eyes brightened. "I'd love to go out with you, if you mean it."

"I mean it, all right."

"Then, yes."

He grinned at her. "Okay."

She couldn't look away from his dark, soft eyes. It felt like electricity flowing between them. It was exciting to share that sort of intimate look. She colored. He arched an eyebrow and gave her a wicked smile.

"Not now," he said in a deep, husky tone that made her blush even more, and turned toward the door.

He opened it. "Edna, I'll be back tomorrow," he told his secretary.

"Yes, sir."

He didn't look back. The outer door opened and closed. Leslie got up with an effort and moved to the office door. "Do you want me to clean up in here?" she asked Edna.

The older woman just smiled. "Heavens, no. You go on back to work, Miss Murry. How's that leg feeling?"

"Awkward," she said, glowering at it. "But it's going to be nice not to limp anymore," she added truthfully. "I'm very grateful to Mr. Caldwell for having it seen to."

"He's a good man," his secretary said with a smile. "And a good boss. He has moods, but most people do."

"Yes."

Leslie clumped her way back down the hall to her office. Ed came out when he heard her rustling paper and lifted both eyebrows. "Feeling better?" he asked.

She nodded. "I'm a watering pot lately. I don't know why."

"Nobody ever had a better reason," he ventured. He smiled gently. "Matt's not so bad, is he?"

She shook her head. "He's not what I thought he was at first."

"He'll grow on you," he said. He reached for a file on his desk, brought it out and perched himself on the edge of her desk. "I need you to answer these. Feel up to some dictation?"

She nodded. "You bet!"

Matt came back late the next morning and went straight to Leslie when he arrived at the office. "Call Karla Smith and ask if she'll substitute for you," he said abruptly. "You and I are going to take the afternoon off."

"We are?" she asked, pleasantly surprised. "What are we going to do?"

"Now there's a leading question," he said, chuckling. He pressed the intercom on her phone and told Ed he was swiping his secretary and then moved back while Leslie got Karla on the phone and asked her to come down to Ed's office.

It didn't take much time to arrange everything. Minutes later, she was seated beside Matt in the Jaguar flying down the highway just at the legal speed limit.

"Where are we going?" she asked excitedly.

He grinned, glancing sideways at the picture she made in that pretty blue-and-green swirl-patterned dress that left her arms bare. He liked her hair short and dark. He even liked her glasses.

"I've got a surprise for you," he said. "I hope you're going to like it," he added a little tautly.

"Don't tell me. You're taking me to see all the big snakes at the zoo," she said jokingly.

"Do you like snakes?" he asked unexpectedly.

"Not really. But that would be a surprise I wouldn't quite like," she added.

"No snakes."

"Good."

He slid into the passing lane and passed several other cars on the four-lane.

"This is the road to Houston," she said, noting a road sign.

"So it is."

She toyed with her seat belt. "Matt, I don't really like Houston."

"I know that." He glanced at her. "We're going to the prison to see your mother."

Her intake of breath was audible. Her hands clenched on her skirt.

He reached a lean hand over and gently pressed both of hers. "Remember what Ed says? Never back away from a problem," he said softly. "Always meet it head-on. You and your mother haven't seen each other in over five years. Don't you think it's time to lay rest to all the ghosts?"

She was uneasy and couldn't hide it. "The last time I saw her was in court, when the verdict was read. She wouldn't even look at me."

"She was ashamed, Leslie."

That was surprising. Her eyes met his under a frown. "Ashamed?"

"She wasn't taking huge amounts of drugs, but she was certainly addicted. She'd had something before she went back to the apartment and found you with her lover. The drugs disoriented her. She told me that she doesn't even remember how the pistol got into her hand, the next thing she knew, her lover was dead and you were bleeding on the floor. She barely remembers the police taking her away." His lips flattened. "What she does remember is coming back to her senses in jail and being told what she did. No, she didn't look at you during the trial or afterward. It wasn't that she blamed you. She blamed herself for being so gullible and letting herself be taken in by a smooth-talking, lying drug dealer who pretended to love her in return for a place to live.''

She didn't like the memories. She and her mother had never been really close, but when she looked back, she remembered that she'd been standoffish and difficult, especially after the death of her father.

His hand contracted on both of hers. ''I'm going to be right with you every step of the way,'' he said firmly. ''Whatever happens, it won't make any difference to me. I only want to try to make things easier for you.''

''She might not want to see me,'' she ventured.

''She wants to,'' he said grimly. ''Very badly. She realizes that she might not have much time left.''

She bit her lower lip. ''I never realized she had heart trouble.''

''She probably didn't, until she started consuming massive quantities of drugs. The human body can only take so much abuse until it starts rebelling.'' He glanced at her. ''She's all right for now. She just has to take it easy. But I still think we can do something for her.''

''A new trial would put a lot of stress on her.''

''It would,'' he agreed. ''But perhaps it isn't the sort of stress that would be damaging. At the end of that road, God willing, she might get out on parole.''

Leslie only nodded. The difficult part lay yet ahead of her; a reunion that she wasn't even sure she wanted. But Matt seemed determined to bring it about.

It was complicated to get into a prison, Leslie learned at once. There were all sorts of checkpoints and safety measures designed to protect visitors. Leslie shivered a little as they walked down the long hall to the room where visitors were allowed to see inmates. For her, the thought of losing her freedom was akin to fears of a lingering death. She wondered if it was that bad for her mother.

There was a long row of chairs at little cubicles, separated from the prisoners' side by thick glass. There was a small opening in the glass, which was covered with mesh wiring so that people could talk back and forth. Matt spoke to a guard and gestured Leslie toward one of the cubicles, settling her in the straight-backed chair there. Through the glass, she could see a closed door across the long room.

As she watched, aware of Matt's strong, warm hand on her shoulder, the door opened and a thin, drawn blond woman with very short hair was ushered into the room by a guard. She went forward to the cubicle where Leslie was sitting and lifted her eyes to the tense face through the glass. Her pale blue eyes were full of sadness and uncertainty. Her thin hands trembled.

"Hello, Leslie," she said slowly.

Leslie just sat there for a moment with her heart beating half to death. The thin, drawn woman with the heavily lined face and dull blue eyes was only a shadow of the mother she remembered. Those thin hands were so wasted that the blue veins on their backs stood out prominently.

Marie smiled with faint self-contempt. "I knew this would be a mistake," she said huskily. "I'm so sorry…" She started to get up.

"Wait," Leslie croaked. She grimaced. She didn't know what to say. The years had made this woman a stranger.

Matt moved behind her, both hands on her shoulders now, supporting her, giving her strength.

"Take your time," he said gently. "It's all right."

Marie gave a little start as she noticed that Matt was touching Leslie with some familiarity, and Leslie wasn't stiff or protesting. Her eyes connected with his dark ones and he smiled.

Marie smiled back hesitantly. It changed her lined, worn face and made her seem younger. She looked into her daughter's eyes and her own softened. "I like your boss," she said.

Leslie smiled back. "I like him, too," she confessed.

There was a hesitation. "I don't know where to start," she began huskily. "I've rehearsed it and rehearsed it and I simply can't find the words." Her pale eyes searched Leslie's face, as if she was trying to recall it from the past. She winced as she compared it with the terror-stricken face she'd seen that night so long ago. "I've made a lot of mistakes, Leslie. My biggest one was putting my own needs ahead of everybody else's. It was always what *I* wanted, what *I* needed. Even when I started doing drugs, all I thought about was what would make me happy." She shook her head. "Selfishness carries a high price tag. I'm so sorry that you had to pay such a high price for mine. I couldn't even bear to look at you at the trial, after the tabloids came out. I was so ashamed of what I'd subjected you to. I thought of you, all alone, trying to hold your head up with half the state knowing such intimate things about our lives..." She drew in a slow, unsteady breath and she seemed to slump. "I can't even ask you to forgive me. But I did want to see you, even if it's just this once, to tell you how much I regret it all."

The sight of her pinched face hurt Leslie, who hadn't realized her mother even felt remorse. There had been no communication between them. She knew now that Matt had been telling the truth about her mother's silence. Marie was too ashamed to face her, even now. It eased the wound a little. "I didn't know about the drugs," Leslie blurted out abruptly.

Her tone brought Marie's eyes up, and for the first time, there was hope in them. "I never used them around you," she said gently. "But it started a long time ago, about the time your father...died." The light in her eyes seemed to dim. "You blamed me for his death, and you were right. He couldn't live up to being what I wanted him to be. He couldn't give me the things I thought I deserved.'' She looked down at the table in front of her. ''He was a good, kind man. I should have appreciated him. It wasn't until he died that I realized how much he meant to me. And it was too late.'' She laughed hollowly. ''From then on, everything went downhill. I didn't care anymore, about myself or you, and I went onto harder drugs. That's how I met Mike. I guess you figured out that he was my supplier.''

''Matt did,'' Leslie corrected.

Marie lifted her eyes to look at Matt, who was still standing behind Leslie. ''Don't let them hurt her anymore,'' she pleaded gently. ''Don't let that reporter make her run anymore. She's had enough.''

''So have you,'' Leslie said unexpectedly, painfully touched by Marie's concern. ''Matt says…that he thinks his attorneys might be able to get you a new trial.''

Marie started. Her eyes lit up, and then abruptly shifted. ''No!'' she said gruffly. ''I have to pay for what I did.''

''Yes,'' Leslie said. ''But what you did…'' She hesitated. ''What you did was out of shock and outrage, don't you see? It wasn't premeditated. I don't know much about the law, but I do know that intent is everything. You didn't plan to kill Mike.''

The older woman's sad eyes met Leslie's through the glass. ''That's generous of you, Leslie,'' she said quietly. "Very generous, considering the notoriety and grief I caused you."

"We've both paid a price," she agreed.

"You're wearing a cast," her mother said suddenly. "Why?"

"I fell off a horse," Leslie said and felt Matt's hands contract on her shoulders, as if he was remembering why. She reached up and smoothed her hand over one of his. "It was a lucky fall, because Matt got an orthopedic surgeon to operate on my leg and put it right."

"Do you know how her leg was hurt?" the other woman asked Matt with a sad little smile.

"Yes," he replied. His voice sounded strained. The tender, caressing action of Leslie's soft fingers on his hand was arousing him. It was the first time she'd touched him voluntarily, and his head was reeling.

"That's another thing I've had on my conscience for years," the smaller woman told her daughter. "I'm glad you had the operation."

"I'm sorry for the position you're in," Leslie said with genuine sympathy. "I would have come to see you years ago, but I thought...I thought you hated me," she added huskily, "for what happened to Mike."

"Oh, Leslie!" Marie put her face in her hands and her shoulders shook. She wept harshly, while her daughter sat staring at her uncomfortably. After a minute, she wiped the tears from her red, swollen eyes. "No, I didn't hate you! I never blamed you!" Marie said brokenly. "How could I hate you for something that was never your fault? I wasn't a good mother. I put you at risk the minute I started using drugs. I failed you terribly. By letting Mike move in, I set you up for what he and his friends did to you. My poor baby," she choked. "You were so very young, so innocent, and to have men treat you...that way—" She broke off. "That's why I couldn't ask you to come, why I couldn't write or phone. I thought you hated *me!*"

Leslie's fingers clenched around Matt's on her shoulder, drawing strength from his very presence. She knew she could never have faced this without him. "I didn't hate you," she said slowly. "I'm sorry we couldn't talk to each other, at the trial. I...did blame you for Dad," she confessed. "But I was so young when it happened, and you and I had never been particularly close. If we had..."

"You can't change what was," her mother said with a wistful smile. "But it's worth all this if you can forgive me." Her long fingers moved restlessly on the receiver. Her pained eyes met Leslie's. "It means everything if you can forgive me!"

Leslie felt a lump in her throat as she looked at her mother and realized the change in her. "Of course I can." She bit her lip. "Are you all right? Is your health all right?"

"I have a weak heart, probably damaged by all the drugs I took," Marie said without emphasis. "I take medicine for it, and I'm doing fine. I'll be all right, Leslie." She searched the younger woman's eyes intently. "I hope you're going to be all right, too, now that you aren't being stalked by that reporter anymore. Thank you for coming to see me."

"I'm glad I did," Leslie said, and meant it sincerely. "I'll write, and I'll come to see you when I can. Meanwhile, Matt's lawyers may be able to do something for you. Let them try."

There was a hesitation while the other woman exchanged a worried look with Matt.

Both his hands pressed on Leslie's shoulders. "I'll take care of her," he told Marie, and knew that she understood what he was saying. Nobody would bother Leslie again, as long as there was a breath in his body. He had power and he would use it on her daughter's behalf. She relaxed.

"All right, then," she replied. "Thank you for trying to help me, even if nothing comes of it."

Matt smiled at her. "Miracles happen every day," he said, and he was looking at Leslie's small hand caressing his.

"You hold on to him," the older woman told Leslie fervently. "If I'd had a man like that to care about me, I wouldn't be in this mess today."

Leslie flushed. Her mother spoke as if she had a chance of holding on to Matt, and that was absurd.

He might feel guilt and sympathy, even regret, but her mother seemed to be mistaking his concern for love. It wasn't.

Matt leaned close to Leslie and spoke. "It's rather the other way around," Matt said surprisingly, and he didn't smile. "Women like Leslie don't grow on trees."

Marie smiled broadly. "No, they don't. She's very special. Take care of yourself, Leslie. I…I do love you, even if it doesn't seem like it."

Leslie's eyes stung with threatening tears. "I love you, too, Mama," she said in a gruff, uneasy tone. She could barely speak for the emotion she felt.

The other woman couldn't speak at all. Her eyes were bright and her smile trembled. She only nodded. After one long look at her daughter, she got up and went to the door.

Leslie sat there for a minute, watching until her mother was completely out of sight. Matt's big hands contracted on her shoulders.

"Let's go, sweetheart," he said gently, and pressed a handkerchief into her hands as he shepherded her out the door.

That tenderness in him was a lethal weapon, she thought. It was almost painful to experience, especially when she knew that it wasn't going to last. He was kind, and right now he was trying to make amends. But she'd better not go reading anything into his actions. She had to take one day at a time and just live for the present.

She was quiet all the way to the parking lot. Matt smoked a cigar on the way, one hand in his pocket, his eyes narrow and introspective as he strode along beside Leslie until they reached the car. He pushed a button on his electronic controller and the locks popped up.

"Thank you for bringing me here," Leslie said at the passenger door, her eyes full of gratitude as they lifted to his. "I'm really glad I came, even if I didn't want to at first."

He stayed her hand as she went to open the door and moved closer, so that she was standing between his long, muscular body and the door. His dark eyes searched hers intently.

His gaze fell to her soft mouth and the intensity of the look parted her lips. Her pulse raced like mad. Her reaction to his closeness had always been intense, but she could almost feel his mouth on her body as she looked up at him. It was frightening to feel such wanton impulses.

His eyes lifted and he saw that expression in her soft, dazed gray eyes. The muscles in his jaw moved and he seemed to be holding his breath.

Around them, the parking lot was deserted. There was nothing audible except the sound of traffic and the frantic throb of Leslie's pulse as she stared into Matt's dark, glittery eyes.

He moved a step closer, deliberately positioning his body so that one long, powerful leg brushed between her good leg and the bulky cast on the other one.

"Matt?" she whispered shakily.

His eyes narrowed. His free hand went to her face and spread against her flushed cheek. His thumb nudged at her chin, lifting it. His leg moved against her thighs and she gasped.

There was arrogance not only in the way he touched her, but in the way he looked at her. She was completely vulnerable when he approached her like this, and he must surely know it, with his experience of women.

"So many women put on an act," he murmured conversationally. "They pretend to be standoffish, they tease, they provoke, they exaggerate their responses. With you, it's all genuine. I can look at you and see everything you're thinking. You don't try to hide it or explain it. It's all right there in the open."

Her lips parted. It was getting very hard to breathe. She didn't know what to say.

His head bent just a little, so that she could feel his breath on her mouth. "You can't imagine the pleasure it gives me to see you like this. I feel ten feet tall."

"Why?" she whispered unsteadily.

His mouth hovered over hers, lightly brushing, teasing. "Because every time I touch you, you offer yourself up like a virgin sacrifice. I remember the taste of your breasts in my mouth, the soft little cries that pulsed out of you when I pressed you down into the mattress under my body." He moved against her, slowly and deliberately, letting her feel his instant response. "I want to take your clothes off and ease inside your body on crisp, white sheets…" he whispered as his hard mouth went down roughly on her soft lips.

She made a husky little cry as she pictured what he was saying to her, pictured it, ached for it. Of all the outrageous, shocking things to say to a woman…!

Her nails bit into his arms as she lifted herself against his arousal and pushed up at his mouth to tempt it into violence. The sudden whip of passion was unexpected, overwhelming. She moaned brokenly and her legs trembled.

He groaned harshly. For a few seconds, his mouth devoured her own. He had to drag himself away from her, and when he did, his whole body seemed to vibrate. There was a flush high on his cheekbones, and his eyes glittered.

She loved the expression on his face. She loved the tremor of the arms propped on either side of her head. Her chin lifted and her eyes grew misty with pleasure.

"Do you like making me this way?" he asked gruffly.

"Yes," she said, something wild and impulsive rising in her like a quick tide. She looked at the pulse in his throat, the quick rhythmic movement of his shirt under the suit he was wearing. Her eyes dropped boldly down his body to the visible effect of passion on him.

His intake of breath was audible as he watched her eyes linger on him, there. His whole body shook convulsively, as if with a fever.

Her eyes went back to his. It was intimate, to look at him this way. She could feel his passion, taste it.

Her hands went to his chest and rested against his warm muscles through the shirt, feeling the soft cushion of hair under it. He wasn't trying to stop her, and she remembered what he'd said to her in his office, that she was going to have to make all the running. Well, why not? She had to find out sooner or later what the limits of her capability were. Now seemed as good a time as any, despite their surroundings. Shyly, involuntarily, her nervous hands slid down to his belt and hesitated.

His jaw clenched. He was helpless. Did she know? Her hands slowly moved over the belt and down barely an inch before they hesitated again. His heavy brows drew together in a ferocious scowl as he fought for control.

He seemed to turn to stone. There was not a trace

of emotion on his lean, hard face, but his eyes were glittering wildly.

"Go ahead if you want to. But if you touch me there," he said in a choked, harsh tone, "I will back you into this car, push your skirt up, and take you right here in the parking lot without a second's hesitation. And I won't give a damn if the entire staff of the prison comes out to watch!"

Chapter Twelve

The terse threat brought Leslie to her senses. She went scarlet as her hands jerked back from his body.

"Oh, good Lord!" she said, horrified at what she'd been doing.

Matt closed his eyes and leaned his forehead against hers. It was damp with sweat and he shuddered with helpless reaction even as he laughed at her embarrassment.

She could barely get her own breath, and her body felt swollen all over. "I'm sorry, Matt, I don't know what got into me!"

The raging desire she'd kindled was getting the best of him. He'd wanted her for such a long time. He hadn't even thought of other women. "Leslie,

I'm fairly vulnerable, and you're starting something both of us know you can't finish," he added huskily.

"I'm…not sure that I can't," she said, surprising both of them. She felt the damp warmth of his body close to hers and marveled at his vulnerability.

His eyes opened. He lifted his head slowly and looked down at her, his breath on her mouth. "If you have a single instinct for self-preservation left, you'd better get in the car, Leslie."

"Okay," she agreed breathlessly, her heart in her eyes as she looked at him with faint wonder.

She got in on the passenger side and fastened her seat belt. He came around to the driver's side and got into the car.

Her hands were curling in on the soft material of her purse and she looked everywhere except at him. She couldn't believe what she'd done.

"Don't make such heavy weather of it," he said gently. "I did say that you'd have to do the chasing, after all."

She cleared her throat. "I think I took it a little too literally."

He chuckled. The sound was deep and pleasant as the powerful car ate up the miles toward Jacobsville. "You have definite potential, Miss Murry," he mused, glancing at her with indulgent affection. "I think we're making progress."

She stared at her purse. "Slow progress."

"That's the best kind." He changed gears and passed a slow-moving old pickup truck. "I'll drop you by your house to change. We're going out on the town tonight, cast and all.''

She smiled shyly. "I can't dance.''

"There's plenty of time for dancing when you're back on your feet," he said firmly. "I'm going to take care of you from now on. No more risks.''

He made her feel like treasure. She didn't realize she'd spoken aloud until she heard him chuckle.

"That's what you are,'' he said. "My treasure. I'm going to have a hard time sharing you even with other people." He glanced at her. "You're sure there's nothing between you and Ed?''

"Only friendship,'' she assured him.

"Good.''

He turned on the radio and he looked more relaxed than she'd ever seen him. It was like a beginning. She had no idea where their relationship would go, but she was too weak to stop now.

They went out to eat, and Matt was the soul of courtesy. He opened doors for her, pulled out chairs for her, did all the little things that once denoted a gentleman and proved to her forcefully that he wasn't a completely modern man. She loved it. Old World courtesy was delicious.

They went to restaurants in Jacobsville and Victoria and Houston in the weeks that followed, and Matt even phoned her late at night, just to talk. He sent her flowers at the boardinghouse, prompting teasing remarks and secret smiles from other residents. He was Leslie's fellow, in the eyes of Jacobsville, and she began to feel as if her dreams might actually come true—except for the one problem that had never been addressed. How was she going to react when Matt finally made love to her completely? Would she be able to go through with intimacy like that, with her past?

It haunted her, because while Matt had been affectionate and kind and tender with her, it never went beyond soft, brief kisses in his car or at her door. He never attempted to take things to a deeper level, and she was too shy from their encounter at the prison parking lot to be so bold again.

The cast came off just before the Ballengers' party to which all of Jacobsville was invited. Leslie looked at her unnaturally pale leg with fascination as Lou Coltrain coaxed her into putting her weight on it for the first time without the supporting cast.

She did, worried that it wouldn't take her weight, while Matt stood grim-faced next to Lou and worried with her.

But when she felt the strength of the bone, she gasped. "It's all right!" she exclaimed. "Matt, look, I can stand on it!"

"Of course you can," Lou chuckled. "Dr. Santos is the best, the very best, in orthopedics."

"I'll be able to dance again," she said.

Matt moved forward and took her hand in his, lifting it to his mouth. "*We'll* be able to dance again," he corrected, holding her eyes with his.

Lou had to stifle amusement at the way they looked together, the tall dark rancher and the small brunette, like two halves of a whole. That would be some marriage, she thought privately, but she kept her thoughts to herself.

Later, Matt came to pick her up at her apartment. She was wearing the long silver dress with the spaghetti straps, and this time without a bra under it. She felt absolutely vampish with her contacts back in and her hair clean and shining. She'd gained a little weight in the past few weeks, and her figure was all she'd ever hoped it would be. Best of all, she could walk without limping.

"Nice," he murmured, smiling as they settled themselves into the car. "But we're not going to overdo things, are we?"

"Whatever you say, boss," she drawled.

He chuckled as he cranked the car. "That's a good start to the evening."

"I have something even better planned for later," she said demurely.

His heart jumped and his fingers jerked on the steering wheel. "Is that a threat or a promise?"

She glanced at him shyly. "That depends on you."

He didn't speak for a minute. "Leslie, you can only go so far with a man before things get out of hand," he began slowly. "You don't know much about relationships, because you haven't dated. I want you to understand how it is with me. I haven't touched another woman since I met you. That makes me more vulnerable than I would be normally.'' His eyes touched her profile and averted to the highway. ''I can't make light love to you anymore,'' he said finally, his voice harsh. ''The strain is more than I can bear.''

Her breath caught. She smoothed at an imaginary spot on her gown. ''You want us to...to go on like we are.''

''I do not,'' he said gruffly. ''But I'm not going to put any pressure on you. I meant what I said about letting you make the moves.''

She turned the small purse over in her hands, watching the silver sequins on it glitter in the light. ''You've been very patient.''

''Because I was very careless of you in those first weeks we knew each other,'' he said flatly. ''I'm trying to show you that sex isn't the basis of our relationship.''

She smiled. ''I knew that already,'' she replied. ''You've taken wonderful care of me.''

He shrugged. ''Penance.''

She grinned, because it wasn't. He'd shown her in a hundred nonverbal ways how he felt about her. Even the other women in the office had remarked on it.

He glanced at her. ''No comment?''

"Oh, I'm sorry, I was just thinking about something."

"About what?" he asked conversationally.

She traced a sequin on the purse. "Can you teach me how to seduce you?"

The car went off the road and barely missed a ditch before he righted it, pulled onto the shoulder and flipped the key to shut off the engine.

He gaped at her. "What did you say?"

She looked up at him in the dimly lit interior where moonlight reflected into the car. "I want to seduce you."

"Maybe I have a fever," he murmured.

She smiled. She laughed. He made her feel as if she could do anything. Her whole body felt warm and uninhibited. She leaned back in her seat and moved sinuously in the seat, liking the way the silky fabric felt against her bare breasts. She felt reckless.

His gaze fell to the fabric against which her hard nipples were distinctly outlined. He watched her body move and knew that she was already aroused, which aroused him at once.

He leaned over, his mouth catching hers as his lean hand slipped under the fabric and moved lazily against her taut breasts.

She moaned and arched toward his fingers, pulling them back when he would have removed them. Her mouth opened under his as she gave in to the need to experience him in a new way, in a new intimacy.

"This is dangerous." He bit off the words against her mouth.

"It feels wonderful," she whispered back, pressing his hand to her soft skin. "I want to feel you like this. I want to touch you under your shirt..."

He hadn't realized how quickly he could get a tie and a shirt out of the way. He pulled her across the console and against him, watching her pert breasts bury themselves in the thick hair that covered his chest. He moved her deliberately against it and watched her eyes grow languid and misty as she experienced him.

His mouth opened hers in a sensual kiss that was as explicit as lovemaking. She felt his tongue, his lips, his teeth, and all the while, his chest moved lazily against her bare breasts. His hand went to the base of her spine and moved her upon the raging arousal she'd kindled. He groaned harshly, and she knew that he wouldn't draw back tonight. The strange thing, the wonderful thing, was that she wasn't afraid.

A minute later, he forced his head up and looked at her, lying yielding and breathless against him. He touched her breasts possessively before he lifted his eyes to search hers. "You aren't afraid of me like this," he said huskily.

She drew in a shaking breath. "No. I'm not."

His eyes narrowed as he persisted. "You want me."

She nodded. She touched his lips with fingers that

trembled. "I want you very much. I like the way you feel when you want me," she whispered daringly, the surprise of it in her expression as she moved restlessly against him. "It excites me to feel it."

He groaned out loud and closed his eyes. "For God's sake, honey, don't say things like that to me!"

Her fingers moved down to his chest and pressed there. "Why not? I want to know if I can be intimate with you. I have to know," she said hesitantly. "I've never been able to want a man before. And I've never felt anything like this!" She looked up into his open, curious eyes. "Matt, can we…go somewhere?" she whispered.

"And make love?" he asked in a tone that suggested he thought she was unbalanced.

Her expression softened. "Yes."

He couldn't. His brain told him he couldn't. But his stupid body was screaming at him that he certainly could! "Leslie, sweetheart, it's too soon…"

"No, it isn't," she said huskily, tracing the hair on his chest with cool fingers. "I know you don't want anything permanent, and that's okay. But I…"

The matter-of-fact statement surprised him. "What do you mean, I don't want anything permanent?"

"I mean, you aren't a marrying man."

He looked puzzled. He smiled slowly. "Leslie, you're a virgin," he said softly.

"I know that's a drawback, but we all have to start somewhere. You can teach me how," she said stubbornly. "I can learn."

"No!" he said softly. "It's not that at all." His eyes seemed to flicker and then burn like black coals. "Leslie, I don't play around with virgins."

Her mind wasn't getting this at all. She felt dazed by her own desire. "You don't?"

"No, I don't," he said firmly.

"Well, if you'll cooperate, I won't be one for much longer," she pointed out. "So there goes your last argument, Matt." She pressed deliberately closer to him, as aware as he was that his body was amazingly capable.

He actually flushed. He pushed away from her and moved her back into her own seat firmly, pulling up the straps of her dress with hands that fumbled a little. He looked as if she'd hit him in the head with something hard.

Puzzled, she fiddled with her seat belt as he snapped his own into place.

He looked formidably upset. He started the car with subdued violence and put it in gear, his expression hard and stoic.

As the Jaguar shot forward, she slanted a glance at him. It puzzled her that he'd backed away from her. Surely he wasn't insulted by her offer? Or maybe he was.

"Are you offended?" she asked, suddenly self-conscious and embarrassed.

"Heavens, no!" he exclaimed.

"Okay." She let out a relieved sigh. She glanced

at him. He wouldn't look at her. "Are you sure you aren't?"

He nodded.

She wrapped her arms around her chest and stared out the windshield at the darkened landscape, trying to decide why he was acting so strangely. He certainly wasn't the man she thought she knew. She'd been certain that he wanted her, too. Now she wasn't.

The Jaguar purred along and they rode in silence. He didn't speak or look at her. He seemed to be deep in thought and she wondered if she'd ruined their budding relationship for good with her wanton tendencies.

It wasn't until he turned the car down a dirt road a few miles from the ranch that she realized he wasn't going toward the Ballengers' home.

"Where are we?" she asked when he turned down an even narrower dirt road that led to a lake. Signposts pointed to various cabins, one of which had Caldwell on it. He pulled into the yard of a little wood cabin in the woods, facing the lake, and cut off the engine.

"This is where I come to get away from business," he told her bluntly. "I've never brought a woman here."

"You haven't?"

His eyes narrowed on her flushed face. "You said you wanted to find out if you could function intimately. All right. We have a place where we won't be disturbed, and I'm willing. More than willing. So there's no reason to be embarrassed," he said quietly. "I want you every bit as badly as you want me. I have something to use. There won't be any risk. But you have to be sure this is what you really want. Once I take your virginity, I can't give it back. There's only one first time."

She stared at him. Her whole body felt hot at the way he was looking at her. She remembered the feel of his mouth on her breasts and her lips parted hungrily. But it was more than just hunger. He knew it.

She lifted her face to his and brushed a breathless little kiss against his firm chin. "I wouldn't let any other man touch me," she said quietly. "And I think you know it."

"Yes. I know it." He knew something else as well; he knew that it was going to be a beginning, not an affair or a one-night stand. He was going to be her first man, but she was going to be his last woman. She was all he wanted in the world.

He got out and led her up the steps on to the wide porch where there was a swing and three rocking chairs. He unlocked the door, ushered her inside and locked it again. Taking her hand in his, he led her to the bedroom in back. There was a huge king-size bed in the room. It was covered by a thick comforter in shades of beige and red.

For the first time since she'd been so brazen with him, reality hit her like a cold cloth. She stood just inside the doorway, her eyes riveted on that bed, as erotic pictures of Matt without clothing danced in her thoughts.

He turned to her, backing her up against the closed door. He sensed her nervousness, her sudden uncertainty.

"Are you afraid?" he asked somberly.

"I'm sorry, I guess I am," she said with a forced smile.

His lean hands framed her face and he bent and kissed her eyelids. "This may be your first time. It isn't mine. By the time we end up on that bed, you'll be ready for me, and fear is the very last thing you're going to feel."

He bent to her mouth then and began to kiss her. The caresses were tender and slow, not arousing. If anything, they comforted. She felt her fear of him, of the unknown, melt away like ice in the hot sun. After a few seconds, she relaxed and gave in to his gentle ardor.

At first it was just pleasant. Then she felt him move closer and his body reacted at once to hers.

He caught his breath as he felt the sudden surge of pleasure.

Her hands smoothed up his hard thighs, savoring the muscular warmth of them while his mouth captured hers and took possession of it a little roughly, because she was intensifying the desire that was already consuming him.

His body began to move on her, slow and caressing, arousing and tantalizing. Her breasts felt heavy.

Her nipples were taut, and the friction of the silky cloth against them intensified the sensations he was kindling in her body, the desire she was already feeling.

His knee edged between both her legs in the silky dress and the slow movement of his hips made her body clench.

His hands went between them, working deftly on the tiny straps of her dress while he kissed her. It wasn't until she felt the rough hair of his chest against her bare breasts that she realized both of them were uncovered from the waist up.

He drew away a little and looked down at her firm, pretty little breasts while he traced them with his fingers.

"I'd like to keep you under lock and key," he murmured gruffly. "My own pretty little treasure," he added as his head bent.

She watched his mouth take her, felt the pleasure of warm lips on her body. She liked the sight of his mouth over her nipple, that dark, wavy hair falling unruly onto his broad forehead while his heavy eyebrows met and his eyes closed under the delicious whip of passion. She held his head to her body, smoothing the hair at his nape, feeling it cool and clean under her fingers.

When he finally lifted his head, she was leaning back against the door for support. Her eyes were misty with desire, her body trembled faintly with the force of it. She looked at him hungrily, with all the barriers down at last. Other men might repulse her, but she wanted Matt. She loved the feel of his hands and his eyes and his mouth on her body. She wanted to lie under him and feel the delicious pressure of his body against and over and inside her own. She wanted it so badly that she moaned softly.

"No second thoughts?" he asked gently.

"Oh, no! No second thoughts, Matt," she whispered, adoring him with her eyes.

With a slow, secret smile, he began to divest her of the dress and the remaining piece of clothing, leaving her standing before him with her body unveiled, taut with passion.

She was shy, but his hands soon made a jumble of her embarrassment. She felt her body jerk rhythmically as he suckled her breasts. It was so sweet. It was paradise.

When he eased her down onto the huge bed, she lay back against the pillows, totally yielding, and watched his evening clothes come off little by little. He watched her while he undressed, laughing softly, a sensual predatory note in his deep voice. She moved helplessly on the coverlet, her entire being aflame with sensations she'd never known. She could barely wait. She felt as if she was throbbing all over, burning with some unknown fire that threatened to consume her, an ache that was almost painful.

Her eyes widened when the last piece of fabric came away from his powerful body and her breath caught.

He liked that expression. He turned away just for a minute, long enough to extricate a packet from his wallet. He sat down beside her, opened it, and taught her matter-of-factly what to do with it. She fumbled a little, her eyes incredibly wide and fascinated and a little frightened.

"I won't hurt you," he said gently, searching her eyes. "Women have been doing this for hundreds of thousands of years. You're going to like it, Leslie. I promise you are."

She lay back, watching him with wide gray eyes full of curiosity as he slid alongside her.

His dark head bent to her body and she lay under him like a creamy, blushing sacrifice, learning the different ways she responded to his touch. He laughed when she arched up and moaned. He liked the way she opened to him, the way her breath rasped when his mouth slid tenderly over her belly and the soft, inner skin of her thighs. He made a sensual meal of her there on the pretty, soft comforter, while the sound of rain came closer outside the window, the moonlit night clouding over as a storm moved above the cabin.

She hadn't known that physical pleasure could be so devastating. She watched him touch and taste her, with eyes equally fascinated and aroused by some of the things he did to her.

Her shocked exclamation pulled an amused laugh from him. "Am I shocking you? Don't you read books and watch movies?" he asked as he poised just above her.

"It isn't...the same," she choked, arching as his body began to tease hers, her long legs shifting eagerly out of his way as he moved down against her.

Her hands were clenched beside her head, and he watched her eyes dilate as his hips shifted tenderly and she felt him against her in a shattering new intimacy. She gasped, looking straight into his dark eyes. "I...never dreamed...!"

"No words on earth could describe how this feels," he murmured, his breath rasping as he hesitated and then moved down again, tenderly. "You're beautiful, Leslie. Your body is exquisite, soft and warm and enticing. I love the way your skin feels under my mouth." His breath caught as he moved closer and felt her body protest at the invasion. He paused to search over her flushed, drawn face. "I'm becoming your lover," he whispered huskily, drawing his body against hers sensuously to deepen his possession. "I'm going inside you. Now."

His face became rigid with control, solemn as he met her eyes and pushed again, harder, and watched her flinch. "I know. It's going to hurt a little, in spite of everything," he said softly. "But not for long. Do you still want me?"

"More than anything...in the world!" she choked, lifting her hips toward his in a sensual invitation. "It's all right." She swallowed. Impulsively she looked down and her mouth fell open. She couldn't have imagined watching, even a day before. "Matt...!" she gasped.

Her eyes came back up to his. His face looked as if every muscle in it was clenched. "It feels like my first time, too," he said a little roughly. His hands slid under her head, cradling it as he shifted slightly and then pushed once more.

Her pretty body lifted off the bed. It seemed to ripple as he moved intimately into closer contact. "I never thought...we could talk...while we did something so intimate," she whispered back, gasping when he moved again and pleasure shot through her. "Yes...oh, yes, please do...that!" she pleaded huskily, clutching at his shoulders.

"Here, like this?" he asked urgently, and moved again.

Her tiny cry was affirmation enough. He eased down on her, his eyes looking straight into hers as he began a rhythm that combined tension with exquisite pleasure and fleeting, burning pain.

His eyes dilated as he felt the barrier. He shivered. His body clenched. He'd never had an innocent woman. Leslie was totally out of his experience. He hadn't thought about how it would feel until now. Primitive thoughts claimed his mind, ancestral memories perhaps that spoke of an ancient age when this would have been a rite of passage.

She was feeling something very similar as her body yielded to the domination of his. The discomfort paled beside the feelings that were consuming her. Glimpses of unbelievable pleasure were mingling with the stinging pain. Past it, she knew, lay ecstasy.

He kissed her hungrily as his lean, fit body moved on her in the silence of the cabin. Suddenly rain pounded hard outside the curtained window, slamming into the roof, the ground, the trees. The wind howled around the corner. There was a storm in him, too, as he lay stretched tight with desire, trying to hold back long enough to let Leslie share what he knew he would feel.

"I've never been so hungry," he bit off against her mouth. His hands contracted under her head, tangling in her hair. His body shuddered. "I'm going to have to hurt you. I can't wait any longer. It's getting away from me. I have to have you…now!"

Her legs moved sensuously against his, loving the faint abrasion of the hair that covered his. "Yes!" she said huskily, her eyes full of wonder. "I want it. I want…it with you."

One lean hand went to her upper thigh. His lips flattened. He looked straight into her eyes as his hand suddenly pinned her hips and he thrust down fiercely.

She cried out, grimacing, writhing as she felt him deep in her body, past a stinging pain that engulfed her.

He stilled, holding her in place while he gave her body time to adjust, his eyes blazing with primitive triumph. His gaze reflected pride and pleasure and possession.

"Yes," he said roughly. "You're part of me and I'm part of you. Now you belong to me, completely."

Her eyes mirrored her shocked fascination. She moved a little and felt him move with her. She swallowed, and then swallowed again, her breath coming in soft jerks as she adjusted to her first intimacy. She loved him. The feel of him was pure delight. She was a woman. She could be a woman. The past was dying already and she was whole and sensuous and fully capable. Her smile was brilliant with joyful self-discovery.

She pulled his head down to hers and kissed him hungrily. The pain had receded and now she felt a new sensation as his hips moved. There were tiny little spasms of pleasure. Her breath came raggedly as she positioned herself to hold on to them. Her nails bit into the hard muscle of his upper arms.

His dark eyes were full of indulgent amusement as he felt her movements. She hesitated once, shy. "Don't stop," he whispered. "I'll do whatever you want me to do."

Her lips parted. It wasn't the answer she'd expected.

He bent and kissed her eyelids again, his breath growing more ragged by the minute. "Find a position that gives you what you need," he coaxed. "I won't take my pleasure until you've had yours."

"Oh, Matt," she moaned, unbearably touched by a generosity that she hadn't expected.

He laughed through his desire, kissing her face tenderly. "My own treasure," he whispered. "I wish I could make it last for hours. I want you to blush when you're sixty, remembering this first time. I want it to be perfect for you."

The pleasure was building. It was fierce now, and she was no longer in control of her own body. It lifted up to Matt's and demanded pleasure. She was totally at the mercy of her awakened passion, blind with the need for fulfillment. She became aware of a new sort of tension that was lifting her fiercely to meet every quick, downward motion of his lean hips, that stretched her under his powerful body, that made her pulse leap with delicious throbs of wild delight.

He watched her body move and ripple, watched the expression on her face, in her wide, blind eyes, and smiled. "Yes," he murmured to himself. "Now you understand, don't you? You can't fight it, or deny it, or control it…" He stopped abruptly.

"No! Please, don't…stop!" Her choked cry was followed by frantic, clinging hands that pulled at him.

He eased down again, watching as she shivered. "I'm not going to stop," he whispered softly. "Trust me. I only want to make it as good as it can be for you."

"It feels…wonderful," she said hoarsely. "Every time you move, it's like…like electric shocks of pleasure."

"And we've barely started, baby," he whispered.

He shifted his hips, intensifying her cries. She was completely yielded to him, open to him, wanton. He'd never dreamed that it would be like this. His head began to spin with the delight his body was taking from hers.

She curled her long legs around his powerful ones and lifted herself, gasping when it brought a sharp stab of pleasure.

His hand swept down her body. His face hardened as he began to increase the pressure and the rhythm. She clung to him, her mouth in his throat, on his chest, his chin, wherever she could reach, while he gave in to his fierce hunger and threw away his control.

She'd never dreamed how it would be. She couldn't get close enough, or hold on tight enough. She felt him in every cell of her body. She was ardent, inciting him, matching his quick, hard movements, her back lifting to promote an even closer contact.

She whispered things to him, secret, erotic things that drove him to sensual urgency. She was moaning. She could hear her frantic voice pleading, hear the sound their movements made on the box springs, feel the power and heat of him as her body opened for him and clenched with tension that begged for release.

She whispered his name and then groaned it, and then repeated it in a mad, hoarse little sound until the little throbs of pleasure became one long, aching,

endless spasm of ecstasy that made her blind and
deaf under the fierce, demanding thrust of his body.
She cried out and shivered in the grip of it, her voice
throbbing like her body. She felt herself go off the
edge of the world into space, into a red heat that
washed over every cell in her body.

When she was able to think again, she felt his
body shake violently, heard the harsh groan at her
ear as he, too, found ecstasy.

He shuddered one last time and then his warm
strong body relaxed and she felt it push hers deeper
into the mattress. His mouth was at her throat, pressing hungrily. His lips moved all over her face, touching and lifting in a fever of tenderness.

Her dazed eyes opened and looked up into his. He
was damp with sweat, as she was. His dark eyes
smiled with incredible gentleness into hers.

She arched helplessly and moaned as the pleasure
washed over her again.

"More?" he whispered, and his hips moved obligingly, so that the sweet stabs of delight came again
and again and again.

She sobbed helplessly afterward, clinging to him
as she lay against his relaxed body.

His hand smoothed over her damp hair. He seemed
to understand her shattered response, as she didn't.

"I don't know why I'm bawling my head off,"
she choked, "when it was the closest to heaven I've
ever been."

"There are half a dozen technical names for it,"

he murmured drowsily. "It's letdown blues. You go so high that it hurts to come down."

"I went high," she murmured with a smile. "I walked on the moon."

He chuckled. "So did I."

"Was…was it all right?" she asked suddenly.

He rolled her over on her back and looked down into her curious face. "You were the best lover I've ever had," he said, and he wasn't teasing. "And you will be, from now on, the only woman I ever have."

"Oh, that sounds serious," she murmured.

"Doesn't it, though?" His dark eyes went over her like an artist's brush committing beauty to canvas. He touched her soft breasts with a breathlessly tender caress. "I won't be able to stop, you know," he added conversationally.

"Stop?"

"This," he replied. "It's addictive. Now that I've had you, I'll want you all the time. I'll go green every time any other man so much as looks at you."

It sounded as if he was trying to tell her something, and she couldn't decide what it was. She searched his dark eyes intently.

He smiled with indulgent affection. "Do you want the words?"

"Which words?" she whispered.

He brushed his lips over hers with incredible, breathless tenderness. "Marry me, Leslie."

Chapter Thirteen

Her gasp was audible. It was more than she'd dared hope for when she came in here with him. He chuckled at her expression.

"Did you think I was going to ask you to come out to the ranch and live in sin with me?" he teased with twinkling eyes. His hand swept down over her body possessively. "This isn't enough. Not nearly enough."

She hesitated. "Are you sure that you want something, well, permanent?"

His eyes narrowed. "Leslie, if I'd been a little more reckless, you'd have something permanent. I wanted very badly to make you pregnant."

Her face brightened. "Did you, really? I thought about it, too, just at the end."

He smoothed back her hair and found himself fighting the temptation to start all over again with nothing between them.

"We'll have children," he promised her. "But first we'll build a life together, a secure life that they'll fall into very naturally."

She was fascinated by the expression on his face. It was only just dawning on her that he felt more than a fleeting desire for her body. He was talking about a life together, children together. She knew very little about true relationships, but she was learning all the time.

"Heavy thoughts?" he teased.

"Yes." She smoothed her fingers over his lean cheek.

"Care to share them?" he murmured.

"I was thinking how sweet it is to be loved," she whispered softly.

He lifted an eyebrow. "Physically loved?"

"Well, that, too," she replied.

He smiled quizzically. "Too?"

"You'd never have taken me to bed unless you loved me," she said simply, but with conviction. "You have these strange old-world hang-ups about innocence."

"Strange, my foot!"

She smiled up at him complacently. "Not that I don't like them," she assured him. The smile faded as she searched his dark eyes. "It was perfect. Just perfect. And I'm glad I waited for you. I love you, Matt.''

His chest rose and fell heavily. "Even after the way I've treated you?"

"You didn't know the truth," she said. "And even if you were unfair at first, you made all sorts of restitution. I won't have a limp anymore," she added, wide-eyed. "And you gave me a good job and looked out for me..."

He bent and kissed her hungrily. "Don't try to make it sound better than it was. I've been an ogre with you. I'm only sorry that I can't go back and start over again."

"None of us can do that," she said. "But we have a second chance, both of us. That's something to be thankful for."

"From now on," he promised her solemnly, "everything is going to be just the way you want it. The past has been hard for me to overcome. I've distrusted women for so long, but with you I've been able to forget what my mother did. I'll cherish you as long as I live."

"And I'll cherish you," she replied quietly. "I thought I would never know what it was to be loved."

He frowned a little, drawing her palm to his lips. "I never thought I would, either. I was never in love before."

She sighed tenderly. "Neither was I. And I never dreamed it would be so sweet."

"I imagine it's going to get better year after year," he ventured, toying with her fingers.

Her free hand slid up into his dark hair. "Matt?"

"What?"

"Can we do that again?"

He pursed his lips. "Are you sure that you can?" he asked pointedly.

She shifted on the coverlet and grimaced with the movement. "Well, maybe not. Oh, dear."

He actually laughed, bending to wrap her up against him and kiss her with rough affection. "Come here, walking wounded. We'll have a nice nap and then we'll go home and make wedding plans." He smoothed down her wild hair. "We'll have a nice cozy wedding and a honeymoon anywhere you want to go."

"I don't mind if we don't go anywhere, as long as I'm with you," she said honestly.

He sighed. "My thoughts exactly." He glanced down at her. "You could have had a conventional wedding night, you know."

She smoothed her hand over his hair-roughened chest. "I didn't know that you'd want to marry me. But just the same, I had to know if I could function intimately with you. I wasn't sure, you see."

"I am," he said with a wicked grin.

She laughed heartily. "Yes, so am I, now, but it was important that I knew the truth before things went any further between us. I knew it was difficult for you to hold back, and I couldn't bear the thought of letting you go. Not that I expected you to want to marry me,'' she added ruefully.

"I wanted to marry you the first time I kissed you,'' he confessed. "Not to mention the first time I danced with you. It was magic.''

"For me, too.''

"But you had this strange aversion to me and I couldn't understand why. I was a beast to you. Even Ed said it wasn't like me to treat employees that badly. He read me the riot act and I let him.''

"Ed's nice.''

"He is. But I'm glad you weren't in love with him. At first, I couldn't be sure of the competition.''

"Ed was a brotherly sort. He still is.'' She kissed his chest. "But I love you.''

"I love you, too.''

She laid her cheek against the place she'd kissed and closed her eyes. "If the lawyers can help my mother, maybe she'll be out for the first christening.''

"At least for the second,'' he agreed, and smiled as his arms closed warm and protective around her, drawing her closer. It was the safest she'd ever been in her life, in those warm, strong arms in the darkness. The nightmares seemed to fade into the shadows of reality that they'd become. She would walk in the light, now, unafraid. The past was over, truly over. She knew that it would never torment her again.

Matt and Leslie were married in the local Presbyterian church, and the pews were full all the way to the back. Leslie thought that every single inhabitant of Jacobsville had shown up for the wedding, and she wasn't far wrong. Matt Caldwell had been the town's foremost bachelor for so long that curiosity brought people for miles around. All the Hart boys showed up, including the state attorney general, as well as the Ballengers, the Tremaynes, the Jacobs, the Coltrains, the Deverells, the Regans and the Burkes. The turnout read like the local social register.

Leslie wore a white designer gown with a long train and oceans of veiling and lace. The women in the office served as maids and matrons of honor, and Luke Craig acted as Matt's best man. There were flower girls and a concert pianist. The local press was invited, but no out of town reporters. Nobody wrote about Leslie's tragic past, either. It was a beautiful ceremony and the reception was uproarious.

Matt had pushed back her veil at the altar with the look of a man who'd inherited heaven. He smiled as he bent to kiss her, and his eyes were soft with love, as were her own.

They held hands all through the noisy reception on the lawn at Matt's ranch, where barbecue was the order of the day.

Leslie had already changed clothes and was walking among the guests when she came upon Carolyn Engles unexpectedly.

The beautiful blonde came right up to her with a genuine smile and a present in her hands.

"I got this for you, in Paris," Carolyn said with visible hesitation and self-consciousness. "It's sort of a peace offering and an apology, all in one."

"You didn't have to do this," Leslie stammered.

"I did." She nodded toward the silver-wrapped present. "Open it."

Leslie pulled off the paper with helpless excitement, puzzled and touched by the other woman's gesture. She opened the velvet box inside and her breath caught. It was a beautiful little crystal swan, tiny and perfect.

"I thought it was a nice analogy," Carolyn murmured. "You've turned out to be a lovely swan, and nobody's going to hurt you when you go swimming around in the Jacobsville pond."

Impulsively Leslie hugged the older woman, who laughed nervously and actually blushed.

"I'm sorry for what I did that day," Carolyn said huskily. "Really sorry. I had no idea…"

"I don't hold grudges," Leslie said gently.

"I know that." She shrugged. "I was infatuated with Matt and he couldn't see me for dust. I went a little crazy, but I'm myself again now. I want you both to be very happy."

"I hope the same for you," Leslie said with a smile.

Matt saw them together and frowned. He came up beside Leslie and placed an arm around her protectively.

"Carolyn brought this to me from Paris," Leslie

said excitedly, showing him the tiny thing. "Isn't it beautiful?"

Matt was obviously puzzled as he exchanged looks with Carolyn.

"I'm not as bad as you think I am," Carolyn told him. "I really do hope you'll be happy. Both of you."

Matt's eyes smiled. "Thank you."

Carolyn smiled back ruefully. "I told Leslie how sorry I was for the way I behaved. I really am, Matt."

"We all have periods of lunacy," Matt replied. "Otherwise, nobody in his right mind would ever get into the cattle business."

Carolyn laughed delightedly. "So they say. I have to go. I just wanted to bring Leslie the peace offering. You'll both be on my guest list for the charity ball, by the way."

"We'll come, and thank you," Matt returned.

Carolyn nodded, smiled and moved away toward where the guests' cars were parked.

Matt pulled his new wife closer. "Surprises are breaking out like measles."

"I noticed." She linked her arms around his neck and reached up to kiss him tenderly. "When everybody goes home, we can lock ourselves in the bedroom and play doctor."

He chuckled delightedly. "Can we, now? Who gets to go first?"

"Wait and see!"

He turned her back toward their guests with a grin that went from ear to ear. "Lucky me," he said, and he wasn't joking.

They woke the next morning in a tangle of arms and legs as the sun peered in through the gauzy curtains. Matt's ardor had been inexhaustible, and Leslie had discovered a whole new world of sensation.

She rolled over onto her back and stretched, uninhibited by her nudity. Matt propped himself on an elbow and looked at her with eyes full of love and possession.

"I never realized that marriage would have so many fringe benefits," she murmured. She stretched again. "I don't know if I have enough strength to walk after last night."

"If you don't, I'll carry you," he said with a loving smile. He reached over to kiss her lazily. "Come on, treasure. We'll have a nice shower and then we'll go and find some breakfast."

She kissed him back. "I love you."

"Same here."

"You aren't sorry you married me, are you?" she asked impulsively. "I mean, the past never really goes away. Someday some other reporter may dig it all back up again."

"It won't matter," he said. "Everybody's got a skeleton or two. And no, I'm not sorry I married you. It was the first sensible thing I've done in years. Not to mention," he added with a sensual touch of his mouth to her body, "the most pleasurable."

She laughed. "For me, too." Her arms pulled him down to her and she kissed him heartily.

Her mother did get a new trial, and her sentence was shortened. She went back to serve the rest of her time with a light heart, looking forward to the day when she could get to know her daughter all over again.

As for Leslie, she and Matt grew closer with every passing day and became known locally as "the love-birds," because they were so rarely seen apart.

Matt's prediction about her mother's release came true as well. Three years after the birth of their son, Leslie gave birth to a daughter who had Matt's dark hair and, he mused, a temper to match his own. He had to fight tears when the baby was placed in his arms. He loved his son, but he'd wanted a little girl who looked like his own treasure, Leslie. Now, he told her, his life was complete. She echoed that sentiment with all her heart. The past had truly been laid to rest. She and Matt had years of happiness ahead of them.

Most of Jacobsville showed up for the baby's christening, including a small blond woman who was enjoying her first days of freedom. Leslie's mother had pride of place in the front pew. Leslie looked from Matt to her mother, from their three-year-old son to the baby in her arms. Her gray eyes, when they lifted to Matt's soft, dark ones, were radiant with joy. Dreams came true, she thought. Dreams came true.

*　*　*　*　*

0606/049/MB037 V2

Perfect for the
beach, these
BRAND NEW
sizzling reads
will get your
pulse racing
and the
temperature
rising!

PLAYING GAMES by Dianne Drake
On air she's the sexy, sassy radio shrink – off air she's
mild-mannered Roxy Rose. Both have only one desire –
the sexy handyman next door.

**UNDERCOVER WITH THE MOB
by Elizabeth Bevarly**
Jack Miller isn't the type you bring home to mum,
which is exactly why Natalie should stay clear of him.
But her attraction to him is undeniable, as is her need
to uncover his story.

WHAT PHOEBE WANTS by Cindi Myers
Men think Phoebe is a pushover, but now she's refusing to take
orders from anyone – especially hunky Jeff Fisher. Because
now it's all about what Phoebe wants.

On sale 2nd June 2006

*Available at WHSmith, Tesco, ASDA, Borders, Eason, Sainsbury's
and all good paperback bookshops*

www.millsandboon.co.uk

0606/055/MB035 V2

It's a world of Gucci and gossip and suddenly everyone is talking about the steamy antics at the Cannes Film Festival.

HOLLYWOOD LIFE OR ROYAL WIFE? by Fiona Hood-Stewart

When scandal threatens to engulf Hollywood sensation Victoria Woodward, Prince Rodolfo sweeps her off to his Mediterranean kingdom. But despite her dreams of a royal wedding, it seems Rodolfo's princess must be chosen for her blue blood, not her red carpet reputation…

MARRIAGE SCANDAL, SHOWBIZ BABY! by Sharon Kendrick

The world's most glamorous couple, Jennifer Warren and Matteo D'Arezzo, are on the red carpet at their latest premiere – despite having just split up! Only, watching their steamy movie together sparks unstoppable passion…with life-changing consequences.

SEX, LIES AND A SECURITY TAPE by Jackie Braun

Rumour has it former film star Colin McKinnon's got serious political ambition. No wonder he can't afford to be seen with infamous Tempest Herriman. Too bad he's been caught on CCTV in flagrante with the wild child!

On sale 19th May 2006

Available at WHSmith, Tesco, ASDA, Borders, Eason, Sainsbury's and all good paperback bookshops

www.millsandboon.co.uk

Part basset, part beagle, all Cupid… can a matchmaking hound fetch a new love for his owner?

For Nina Askew, turning forty means freedom – from the ex-husband, from their stuffy suburban home. Freedom to have her own apartment in the city, freedom to focus on what *she* wants for a change. And what she wants is a bouncy puppy to cheer her up. Instead she gets…Fred.

Overweight, smelly and obviously suffering from some kind of doggy depression, Fred is light-years from perky. But for all his faults, he does manage to put Nina face-to-face with Alex Moore, her gorgeous younger neighbour…

On sale 5th May 2006
Don't miss out!

Available at WHSmith, Tesco, ASDA, Borders, Eason, Sainsbury's and all good paperback bookshops

www.millsandboon.co.uk

0606/121/MB036 V2

From No. 1 New York Times
bestselling author Nora Roberts

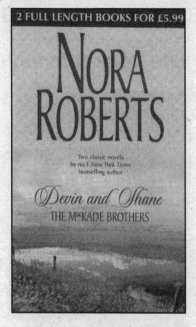

The sinfully sexy MacKade brothers
are back!
Nora Roberts's reader favourites are
once again breaking the hearts of
women everywhere.

On sale 2nd June 2006

*Available at WH Smith, Tesco, ASDA, Borders, Eason, Sainsbury's
and all good paperback bookshops*

www.silhouette.co.uk

SPECIAL EDITION™

Life, love & family

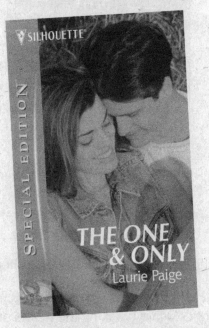

6 brand-new titles every month

find out more at **www.silhouette.co.uk**

*Available at most branches of WHSmith, Tesco,
ASDA, Borders, Eason, Sainsbury's,
and most bookshops.*

GEN/23/RTL6 V

0506/23a V2

▼ SILHOUETTE®

SPECIAL EDITION™

THE ULTIMATE TEXAS BACHELOR
by Cathy Gillen Thacker

The McCabes

After his reality TV romance finishes, Brad McCabe swears off all women. But Lainey Carrington could be just the woman to change his mind. Although she's at his ranch under false pretences...

THE SUGAR HOUSE by Christine Flynn

Going Home

Emmy Larkin believed that Jack Travers' father had betrayed her father. But successful, handsome Jack wanted to make things right when confronted by this lovely, fiercely independent woman...

WANTED: ONE FATHER
by Penny Richards

Single dad Max Murdock needed a quiet place to write and a baby-sitter for his baby girl. Zoe Barlow could help with both. It was a perfect match, but were irresistible Zoe and her three impish boys the perfect family?

Don't miss out!
On sale from 19th May 2006

Available at WHSmith, Tesco, ASDA, Borders, Eason, Sainsbury's and most bookshops

www.silhouette.co.uk

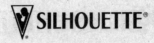

▼ SILHOUETTE®

SPECIAL EDITION™

ALL HE EVER WANTED
by Allison Leigh

Montana

When young Erik fell down a mine shaft, he was saved by brave and beautiful Faith Taylor. Faith was amazed by the feelings Erik's handsome father, Cameron, awoke. But was Cam ready to find a new happiness?

PLAYING WITH FIRE by Arlene James

Lucky in Love

Struggling hairstylist Valerie Blunt had a lot on her mind —well, mainly the infuriatingly attractive Fire Marshal Ian Keene. Ian set Valerie alight whenever he was near...

BECAUSE A HUSBAND IS FOREVER
by Marie Ferrarella

The Cameo

Talk show host Dakota Delaney agreed to allow bodyguard Ian Russell to shadow her. But she hadn't counted on the constant battling or that he would want to take hold of her safety—and her heart.

Don't miss out!
On sale from 19th May 2006

Available at WHSmith, Tesco, ASDA, Borders, Eason, Sainsbury's and most bookshops

www.silhouette.co.uk

SILHOUETTE®

Desire™

**Passionate, dramatic
love stories**

4 brand-new titles every month

find out more at **www.silhouette.co.uk**

*Available at most branches of WHSmith, Tesco,
ASDA, Borders, Eason, Sainsbury's,
and most bookshops.*

GEN/51/RTL6 V2

0506/51 V2

SILHOUETTE®
Desire™ 2 in 1

A MAN APART by Joan Hohl

Notorious charmer Justin Grainger wasn't planning on settling down, but a week of unbridled passion with sexy Hannah Deturk just wasn't enough. He was going to have to rethink his plans and incorporate a baby, too!

HOT TO THE TOUCH by Jennifer Greene

Fox Lockwood was suffering and no doctor could cure him. Enter Phoebe Schneider – a masseuse specialising in soothing infants. But Fox was a fully grown adult male, who wanted their relationship to take a more personal turn…

RULES OF ATTRACTION by Susan Crosby

Behind Closed Doors

PI Quinn Gerard was following a suspect, but the sexy bombshell turned out to be her twin sister, Claire. Could Quinn convince Claire to bend the rules and give in to their mutual attraction?

SCANDALOUS PASSION by Emilie Rose

Phoebe Drew feared intimate photos of her and her first love, Carter Jones, would affect her grandfather. So she went to Carter for help in finding them. But digging up the past also uncovered long-hidden passion.

THE RUGGED LONER by Bronwyn Jameson

Princes of the Outback

Australian widower Tomas Carlisle was stunned to learn that he had to father a child to inherit a cattle empire. Making a deal with friend Angelina Mori seemed the perfect solution – until their passion escalated.

AT YOUR SERVICE by Amy Jo Cousins

Runaway heiress Grace Haley donned an apron and posed as a waitress. She found herself sparring with her gorgeous new boss Christopher Tyler, wondering how he would react if he knew her secret.

On sale from 19th May 2006

Visit our website at www.silhouette.co.uk

Modern
r o m a n c e™

...international affairs – seduction and passion guaranteed

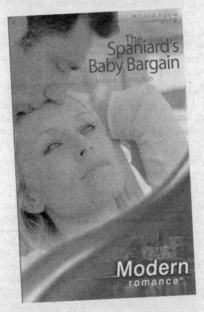

8 brand-new titles each month

Take a break and find out more about
Modern Romance™ on our website
www.millsandboon.co.uk

*Available at most branches of WH Smith,
Tesco, Martins, Borders, Eason, Sainsbury's,
and all good paperback bookshops.*

GEN/01/RTL8 V2

MILLS & BOON®

Live the emotion

Modern
romance™

PRINCE OF THE DESERT *by Penny Jordan*

Gwynneth had vowed that she would never become a
slave to passion. But one hot night of love-making with a
stranger from the desert has left her fevered and unsure.
Little does Gwynneth know that she shared a bed with
Sheikh Tariq bin Salud…

FOR PLEASURE…OR MARRIAGE? *by Julia James*

Tycoon Markos Makarios thinks he has the perfect
woman in Vanessa: she's beautiful, passionate, adoring,
living only to please him. Until he has to warn her
not to think of marriage; a mistress is only for pleasure,
after all…

THE ITALIAN'S PRICE *by Diana Hamilton*

Cesare Saracino wants revenge – no one steals from
his family! But the woman he tracks down is not the
thief – it's her identical twin, Milly Lee. Milly struggles
to masquerade as her sexy sister, but she's powerless to
refuse Cesare's advances…

THE JET-SET SEDUCTION *by Sandra Field*

From the moment Slade Carruthers lays eyes on
Clea Chardin he knows he must have her. But Clea
has a reputation, and Slade isn't a man to share his
spoils. If Clea wants to come to his bed, she will come
on his terms…

On sale 2nd June 2006

*Available at WHSmith, Tesco, ASDA, Borders, Eason,
Sainsbury's and most bookshops*

www.millsandboon.co.uk

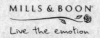

MILLS & BOON

Live the emotion

Modern
romance™

HIS PRIVATE MISTRESS by Chantelle Shaw

Rafael Santini and Eden Lawrence's passionate relationship
ended in betrayal and deceit. Only now Rafael is
determined to make her his mistress once more. Eden
may be older and wiser, but she is still unable to resist the
only man she has ever loved...

BERTOLUZZI'S HEIRESS BRIDE by Catherine Spencer

Falling in love is not on Natalie Cavanaugh's agenda
– particularly not with notorious Demetrio Bertoluzzi...
Natalie finds herself drawn to him like a moth to the
flame. But to surrender her innocence to this allegedly
dangerous man could be her undoing...

CAPTIVE IN HIS BED by Sandra Marton

When Matthew Knight accepts the case of missing
Mia Palmieri, the only way to unearth the truth is to
kidnap her! But, while Mia is held prisoner in Matthew's
luxury hideaway, she can't resist his hard muscled
handsomeness...

KEPT BY THE TYCOON by Lee Wilkinson

Madeleine Knight gave Rafe Lombard her heart, but when
she learnt secrets of his past she knew he would never
be hers – so she ran. Rafe is determined to prove that no
woman leaves him without his say-so and wants Madeleine
back by his side...

On sale 2nd June 2006

Available at WHSmith, Tesco, ASDA, Borders, Eason,
Sainsbury's and most bookshops

www.millsandboon.co.uk

0506/01b V2

***Through days of hard work
and troubles shared, three women
will discover that what was lost
can be found again...***

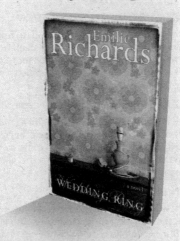

Tessa MacCrae has reluctantly agreed to spend
the summer helping her mother and grandmother clean
out the family home. They've never been close, but
Tessa hopes that time away will help her avoid facing the
tragedy of her daughter's death and the toll it's
exacting on her marriage.

At first, the summer is filled with all-too-familiar
emotional storms. But with the passing weeks each of
their lives begins to change. And for the first time,
Tessa can look past the years of resentment.

**'This much-loved family saga of insecurity and
tragic loss is compulsive.'**
—*The Bookseller*

19th May 2006

M027/BH/PB

"*I was fifteen when my mother finally told me the truth about my father. She didn't mean to. She meant to keep it a secret forever. If she'd succeeded it might have saved us all.*"

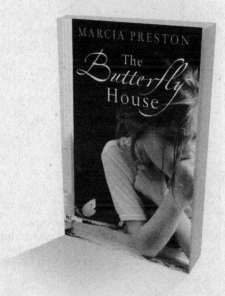

MARCIA PRESTON

The Butterfly House

When a hauntingly familiar stranger knocks on Roberta Dutreau's door, she is compelled to begin a journey of self-discovery leading back to her childhood. But is she ready to know the truth about what happened to her, her best friend Cynthia and their mothers that tragic night ten years ago?

16th June 2006

MIRA